INTRODUCTION TO STATISTICAL MECHANICS

INTERNATIONAL SERIES IN PURE AND APPLIED PHYSICS

G. P. HARNWELL, *Consulting Editor*

BRILLOUIN—WAVE PROPAGATION IN PERIODIC STRUCTURES
CADY—PIEZOELECTRICITY
CLARK—APPLIED X-RAYS
CURTIS—ELECTRICAL MEASUREMENTS
EDWARDS—ANALYTIC AND VECTOR MECHANICS
FINKELNBURG—ATOMIC PHYSICS
GURNEY—INTRODUCTION TO STATISTICAL MECHANICS
HARDY AND PERRIN—THE PRINCIPLES OF OPTICS
HARNWELL—ELECTRICITY AND ELECTROMAGNETISM
HARNWELL AND LIVINGOOD—EXPERIMENTAL ATOMIC PHYSICS
HOUSTON—PRINCIPLES OF MATHEMATICAL PHYSICS
HOUSTON—PRINCIPLES OF QUANTUM MECHANICS
HUGHES AND DuBRIDGE—PHOTOELECTRIC PHENOMENA
HUND—HIGH-FREQUENCY MEASUREMENTS
INGERSOLL, ZOBEL, AND INGERSOLL—HEAT CONDUCTION
KEMBLE—THE FUNDAMENTAL PRINCIPLES OF QUANTUM
      MECHANICS
KENNARD—KINETIC THEORY OF GASES
KOLLER—THE PHYSICS OF ELECTRON TUBES
MORSE—VIBRATION AND SOUND
MUSKAT—PHYSICAL PRINCIPLES OF OIL PRODUCTION
PAULING AND GOUDSMIT—THE STRUCTURE OF LINE SPECTRA
RICHTMYER AND KENNARD—INTRODUCTION TO MODERN PHYSICS
RUARK AND UREY—ATOMS, MOLECULES, AND QUANTA
SCHIFF—QUANTUM MECHANICS
SEITZ—THE MODERN THEORY OF SOLIDS
SLATER—INTRODUCTION TO CHEMICALS PHYSICS
      MICROWAVE TRANSMISSION
SLATER AND FRANK—ELECTROMAGNETISM
                INTRODUCTION TO THEORETICAL PHYSICS
                MECHANICS
SMYTHE—STATIC AND DYNAMIC ELECTRICITY
STRATTON—ELECTROMAGNETIC THEORY
WHITE—INTRODUCTION TO ATOMIC SPECTRA

Dr. Lee A. DuBridge was Consulting Editor of the series from 1939 to 1946.

INTRODUCTION TO STATISTICAL MECHANICS

By RONALD W. GURNEY

RESEARCH PROFESSOR, INSTITUTE FOR
FLUID DYNAMICS AND APPLIED
MATHEMATICS, UNIVERSITY
OF MARYLAND

FIRST EDITION
SECOND IMPRESSION

New York   Toronto   London
McGRAW-HILL BOOK COMPANY, INC.
1949

INTRODUCTION TO STATISTICAL MECHANICS

PREFACE

Among students of physics and chemistry there seems to be a widespread belief that statistical mechanics is necessarily a difficult and abstruse subject that cannot be presented in a form attractive to the experimentalist. In recent years several of the author's friends have challenged him to write a book to show that such a point of view is mistaken.

In a book with this modest objective the reader will not wish to be involved at the outset in an intricate discussion of the abstract principles on which the theory is supposed to rest. Rather he will be willing, at first, to make one or two assumptions in order to obtain as quickly as possible an insight into the methods by which problems are solved.

It has been supposed that later in the book the reader will be glad to look more closely into the fundamental concepts. Consequently the book falls roughly into two parts. The first seven chapters may be regarded as Part 1. The remaining chapters, which may be considered as Part 2, include not only more applications but also theoretical material that was omitted from Part 1 in order to make it more easily readable. Thus, in the last five chapters of the book some attention has been paid to classical mechanics and its use of phase space; the interaction between particles has been given detailed consideration; and so have the Fermi-Dirac statistics.

In Chapter 7, in the discussion of liquid and solid solutions, there has been included a treatment of alloys, especially the alloys of iron, which should be of interest to students of metallurgy. The author originally wrote much of this chapter in connection with some research on solutions for which he received a grant from the Commonwealth Fund. This work will be published in due course, but in the meantime he is glad to take this early opportunity of expressing his gratitude to the directors of the Commonwealth Fund.

It is a pleasure to express thanks to various friends who have given helpful criticisms and suggestions, especially to Dr. A. F. Devonshire of Bristol University, England, and to Dr. W. Band of the Institute for the Study of Metals in the University of Chicago.

R. W. GURNEY

THE JOHNS HOPKINS UNIVERSITY
BALTIMORE, MD.
March 1949

v

CONTENTS

PAGE

PREFACE v

CHAPTER

1. Groups of Particles—The Number of Different Ways in Which the Energy
   Can Be Shared—The Most Probable Distribution—The Concept of Temperature.. 1

2. The Use of Undetermined Multipliers—An Absolute Scale of Temperature—
   The Partition Function—Bose-Einstein Statistics—A Monatomic Gas..... 35

3. The Distribution of Particles through Alternative Sets of Energy Levels—
   Conditions for Equilibrium—A Saturated Vapor—Order and Disorder in
   Crystals... 68

4. The Partition Function and Properties of Monatomic and Diatomic Gases—
   Localized and Unlocalized Particles.................................. 88

5. The Relation between Statistical Mechanics and Thermodynamics........ 101

6. Conditions of Equilibrium for a Partially Dissociated Diatomic Gas—For a
   Saturated Vapor—For Alternative Modifications of a Solid.............. 115

7. Substitutional and Interstitial Solutions—Solubility—Lowering of the Freezing Point—Substances Which Are Not Miscible in All Proportions—A Solute
   Which Is Completely Dissociated—Solutions in the High and Low Temperature Modifications of a Solid Solvent—Solutions in Alpha and Gamma Iron—
   Equilibrium between Cementite and Gamma Iron—Adsorption........... 128

8. The Total Energy Shared by Interacting Particles—Quantization of the
   Total Energy—A Group of Samples................................. 172

9. Classical Mechanics—Phase Space—Imperfect Gases—The Condensation
   of a Vapor.. 186

10. Vibration of Molecules and of Crystal Lattices—The Density of States—
    Evaluation of the Partition Function of a Solid....................... 205

11. The Rotation of Diatomic Molecules—Vapor Pressure Constants and Chemi-
    cal Constants—Orthohydrogen and Parahydrogen...................... 224

12. Particles in Electric and Magnetic Fields—Order and Disorder in Crystals—
    Fermi-Dirac Statistics—Free Electrons in a Metal—Bose-Einstein Statis-
    tics—Atomic Nuclei... 238

APPENDIX.. 257

NAME INDEX... 263

SUBJECT INDEX... 265

CHAPTER 1

Groups of Particles—The Number of Different Ways in Which the Energy Can Be Shared—The Most Probable Distribution—The Concept of Temperature

1. Particles and Their Energies. Before studying a compound or mixture, it is natural to discuss one of the chemical elements. Although any pure substance ordinarily consists of a mixture of isotopes, we may at first disregard this fact and may say that we are interested in a group of particles that are all alike—all of the same species. We may add that we are interested in particles that are confined in a certain volume. We study a gas or vapor when the particles are confined in a vessel of volume v, through which the particles are free to move. In a homogeneous solid each particle is closely surrounded by similar particles; each particle vibrates in a little volume whose boundaries are determined by the positions of the neighboring particles. This volume may be the order of 10^{-23} cubic centimeter, whereas, in the case of a gas, the available volume may be several cubic centimeters or more.

The basic principle of the quantum theory is that when a particle is confined in a certain volume, no matter whether the volume is large or small, the energy of the particle can take only certain discrete values; the energy of the particle is *quantized*. This is true whether the said volume is several cubic centimeters or a minute fraction of a cubic centimeter.

In everyday life we are accustomed to seeing bodies falling to the ground and to seeing water falling to a lower level. Using the same language, we speak of a particle "falling to a state of lower energy" or "falling to a lower level" when it loses energy. The state of the smallest allowed energy is called the "lowest energy level" or the "ground level." For any particle the energy of this lowest level will be denoted by ϵ_0. The first allowed energy higher than the ground level will be denoted by ϵ_1, the next higher level by ϵ_2, and so on. On a diagram, taking a vertical scale to represent the energy of a particle, these various levels (the allowed energies) may be represented by a set of horizontal lines, one above the other at the correct intervals. This book will contain many such diagrams; see, for example, Fig. 12.

1

The temperature of a substance depends on the amount of thermal energy that the particles share. In the middle of the nineteenth century, from thermodynamic considerations, Lord Kelvin introduced the idea of an "absolute zero of temperature," below which the temperature of matter cannot fall. In 1854 the idea was new; now, however, from the point of view of quantum theory the concept seems quite natural. At the absolute zero of temperature everything will be in its lowest quantized state; no particles will be in states of higher energy. In order to raise the temperature of a substance, we have to put additional energy into it; that is to say, we raise particles to higher energy levels. It is not the business of statistical mechanics to say what are the *values* of these allowed energies; that information must be supplied by quantum theory. Given a set of energy levels, it is the aim of statistical mechanics to say how the particles will be distributed among the various energy levels at any temperature. In each problem, then, we start with a number of quantized states for the particles of the substance, and we seek to predict the properties and behavior of the substance by describing how these states are populated by the particles.

In a gas the molecules are continually exchanging energy by collision. Sometimes a molecule receives energy and at other times it loses energy. The total energy may be shared among the individual particles in an enormous number of different ways. The same is true of the particles of a solid. Even for a group of a dozen particles the number of different ways is very large. To make the principles clear it will be convenient to study in detail a "solid" consisting of a still smaller group of particles. We shall begin by considering a group of *three* similar particles, which will share a certain amount of thermal energy.

2. The Sharing of Energy among Particles. Suppose that we have one particle vibrating about a certain point A, another similar particle vibrating about a neighboring point B, and a third similar particle vibrating about a neighboring point C. Let us suppose that each of these particles is a linear harmonic oscillator. We choose this type of vibration because a linear oscillator, as is well known, has an unusually simple set of energy levels, namely, a set of allowed energies with equal intervals between them. Such a set of levels may be represented by a set of horizontal lines with uniform spacing; we number the levels, starting from the bottom, as in Figs. 1 to 3. The spacing between the levels may be relatively narrow or relatively wide, depending on the mass of the particle and on the forces acting on it. Let the interval between any two successive levels be denoted by u; this will be a convenient unit of energy to use.

To study the sharing of energy among a small group of particles, suppose then that at the three points A, B, and C we have similar particles, each having a set of energy levels with the same uniform spacing. At the absolute zero of temperature each of the three particles would be permanently in its lowest level. But we will give to the group a certain amount of thermal energy and then ask how the particles will share this energy among themselves, supposing that there is a continual free interchange of energy among them. Sometimes one particle will have the whole of the thermal energy; sometimes it will have none; at other times it will have a large or a small share.

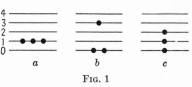

FIG. 1

Let us discuss first the situation where the total thermal energy shared by the group of particles is equivalent to $3u$. One way in which this amount of energy may be distributed among the group is, of course, that each of the three particles is in the level 1, as indicated by the three dots in Fig. 1a. The other two possible distributions are shown in Figs. 1b and 1c; in each case the total energy is the same.

As we suppose that the group of particles can neither lose energy nor gain energy, the distribution of the energy cannot take any form except those shown in Fig. 1. But it will be continually passing through these three forms owing to the internal exchange of energy among the three particles. Suppose now that a long time has elapsed. During this time the various levels will not have been equally populated on the average; the total length of time during which a level has been occupied will not be the same for the different levels.

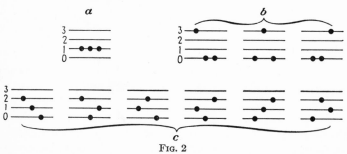

FIG. 2

We must recognize that the distributions shown in Fig. 1 can arise in various ways. For example, in Fig. 1b the particle that is in the level 3 may either be the particle vibrating about the point A, or that vibrating about the point B, or that vibrating about the point C; these three states of the group are indicated by dots in Fig. 2b. If the three oscillators are precisely similar, there is no reason why one of the three states of Fig. 2b should occur more often than either of the other two.

Turning next to the distribution shown in Fig. 1c, we see that this can arise in the six different ways shown in Fig. 2c. For example, when the particle in level 2 is the particle at the point A, the particle in level 1 may be either the particle at the point B or the one at C. Finally, there remains the distribution shown in Fig. 1a. This can arise in only one way, namely, when each of the particles is in the level 1.

From Fig. 2 we see that there are altogether 10 different ways in which the energy $3u$ may be shared among the three particles. If there is no reason why any of these ten should be favored with respect to the others, we must treat them as being equally probable. It is a simple matter to see what will be the result of this assumption of equal a priori probabilities for the 10 states. If by experiments we could at intervals observe the

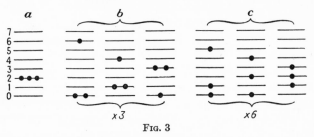

Fig. 3

state of the group, we should expect to find each of the 10 occurring with almost equal frequency. The greater the number of observations, the more nearly equal should the observed frequency of occurrence be. We wish to find the relative degrees to which each of the energy levels will be populated on the average. In Fig. 2 we have only to add up the number of dots in each level. In the lowest level we find 12; in the next higher level we find 9; in the next 6; and in the next 3; thus the lowest level is the most populated, and in each of the higher levels the population is less than in the next level below.

3. For comparison, we can now ask what happens if we apply the same ideas to the group of three particles when they are sharing twice as much energy, that is to say, $6u$. This amount of energy is sufficient to place each of the three particles into the level 2, as depicted in Fig. 3a. Each particle will spend part of the time in the level 2, part of the time in the lower levels, 0 and 1, and part of the time in the higher levels, 3, 4, and so on. A student approaching the subject for the first time may suppose that the particles will tend to spend *most* of the time in the neighborhood of level 2, with the result that both level 0 and level 4 will be less populated than level 2. It is important to understand clearly why this is not the case.

Figure 3 shows the various ways in which the six units of energy can be shared among the group of three particles. When we ask in how many ways each of these distributions can arise, the answers are the same as for Fig. 1, namely: (a) when all the particles are in the same level, this can arise in one way; (*b*) when two of the particles are in the same level, this can arise in three different ways; (*c*) when each particle is in a different level, this can arise in six ways. Thus, from Fig. 3, we have altogether

$$1 + (3 \times 3) + (3 \times 6) = 28$$

We find that there are 28 different ways in which the energy $6u$ can be shared among the group of three particles. If we take each of these as equally probable, we may suppose that, when a long time has elapsed, the group will have spent very nearly $\frac{1}{28}$ of this time in each of these 28 states. The relative population of the different levels during this time may be found, as before, by counting the number of particles in the diagram, provided that the number in each level of Fig. 3*b* is multiplied by the factor 3 and the number in each level of Fig. 3*c* is multiplied by the factor 6. Doing this, we find 21 in the lowest level, 18 in the next higher level, 15 in the next, and so on. Again we find that the lowest level is the most populated, and the population of the states above falls off progressively. Thus the

Fig. 4

average population of the levels may be visualized as having the definite shape or form shown in Fig. 4, where at each level is drawn a horizontal line whose length is proportional to the average number of particles in this level during the time that has elapsed. When we speak of "the shape or form of the population," we refer to the relative numbers of particles found on the average in each level. Here we have found again that the lowest level is the most populated and that in the higher quantum states the number of particles falls off steadily.

This is always so. No matter how many particles we consider or how much energy they share, the lowest state is always the most populated. One can see from Fig. 3 how it comes about that the lowest levels are favored. In Fig. 3 one particle can be in a high level only if *both* the other particles are in low levels. In Fig. 3 there is not sufficient energy to bring two particles at the same time into levels 4, 5, and 6. But among the 28 states there are 18 in which one particle is in level 4, 5, or 6; this situation is reached because *both* the other particles occupy low levels. When we are dealing with a large group of particles, we can make the corresponding statement: a minority of the particles can be in high levels only if a *majority* of the particles occupy low levels, and of these low levels the lowest is the most populated.

We arrived at Fig. 4 by asking how the group of three particles would be likely to behave over a certain period of time. The same conclusion can be reached by an alternative procedure, using a device that was introduced in the nineteenth century. Suppose that, instead of *one* group of three oscillators, we have many such groups of three; all groups are to be alike and all independent of each other. Each group of particles is usually called a "system," while the whole collection of similar groups is called an "ensemble of systems." Let us apply this idea to the problem of Fig. 3. We suppose that we have many groups of three oscillators, each group possessing energy $6u$. We have to make some assumption about the 28 different ways in which this energy $6u$ can be shared. If, as before, we assume equal a priori probabilities for each of the 28 states, we may imagine that we set up an ensemble such that each of the 28 states is equally likely to be represented. Instead of asking what the average population of the various levels has been over a certain period of time, we can ask what the relative population of the levels in the entire ensemble is likely to be at any moment. The final result will be the same as before; proceeding from Fig. 3 we find the relative population of the levels depicted in Fig. 4. The properties of the ensemble are determined by the properties that we have assigned to the individual systems of which it is composed. The usefulness of the device lies in the fact that it enables us to fix our attention on a population that shows no wide fluctuations and whose form, we assume, gives the average to be expected for a single group of particles.[1]

4. To enumerate all the distributions for a group containing more than three or four particles is too long a task. But before going on to consider a very large number of particles, we may briefly consider a group of 20 oscillators, similar to those discussed above. At 20 different points, $A, B, C, D \ldots$, let there be one of these oscillators, and let them share, for example, an amount of energy equivalent to $20u$, where u is again the energy interval between successive levels. We may take the 20 circles of Fig. 5a to represent schematically the positions of these 20 particles. Let the two circles marked "3" represent two particles each of which is at the moment in its level 3, while the four circles marked "2" represent four particles each of which is at the moment in its level 2, and so on. The distribution corresponding to Fig. 5a is depicted in Fig. 5b; the reader may verify that Figs. 5a and 5b correspond to the sharing of a total energy $20u$. Figure 5a depicts *one* of the numerous arrangements corresponding to Fig. 5b, which itself depicts only *one* of the many distributions whereby $20u$ may be shared among the 20 particles. One example of the other possible distributions is shown in Fig. 5c.

Returning to Fig. 5a, we see that if any two circles with different labels are interchanged, this will give another arrangement having the distribu-

[1] Ensembles of more interesting types will be considered in Chapters 8 to 10. The physical basis of the whole procedure is, however, open to question. "It is assumed that the observable properties of the system considered are the same as the average properties of a virtual assembly of equal but unconnected systems. The only justification of this hypothesis is that it gives useful results. Einstein, in his classical papers on statistical mechanics, was aware of this difficulty, and based his theory on the consideration of a single system, taking averages over time," Max Born and H. S. Green, *Proc. Roy. Soc. A.*, **192**, 166 (1948).

The term *system* is used by most authors to denote a group of particles. R. H. Fowler, on the other hand, used the term to refer to a molecule or other particle that is a member of the group under investigation. "Statistical Mechanics," 2d ed., Cambridge, 1936.

tion of the energy shown in Fig. 5b. In this way we can, in fact, obtain more than 100 million different arrangements, all having that distribution shown in Fig. 5b; for we can calculate from formula (1), which will be given in Sec. 7, that the distribution of Fig. 5b can arise in more than 10^8 different ways. The same is true of Fig. 5c.

The proposal was made in Sec. 1 that the energy of the lowest allowed state of a particle should be denoted by ϵ_0, the next by ϵ_1, and so on. Let us consider a group of n particles sharing a total energy E. At any moment let the number of particles that are in the ground state ϵ_0 be denoted

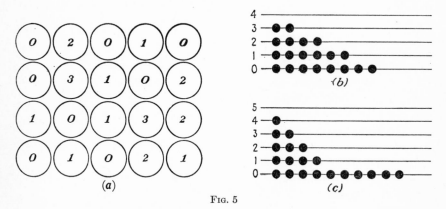

FIG. 5

by n_0, while the number of particles in the state ϵ_2 is denoted by n_2, and the number in the rth state by n_r. The total energy shared by the particles is

$$E = n_0\epsilon_0 + n_1\epsilon_1 + n_2\epsilon_2 + \cdots = \Sigma n_r\epsilon_r$$

If we specify a set of values for n_0, n_1, $n_2 \ldots$ consistent with E, we have thereby specified one possible way in which the total energy E may be distributed among the n particles. In the problem of Fig. 5 we have seen that the diagrams of Figs. 5b and 5c depict two of the many possible distributions, while Fig. 5a represents one of the many arrangements corresponding to the distribution of Fig. 5b. In general, let w denote the number of ways in which a given distribution can arise. We have said that the value of w is greater than 10^8 for the distribution of Fig. 5b, while the value of w was 6 for the distribution of Fig. 3c.

When a group of n particles is sharing a total energy E, let Z_E denote the total number of possible states. It will be recalled that in the problem of Fig. 3 the value of Z_E was 28. The reader may verify the fact that if more energy is added to this group of particles, the value of Z increases rapidly. This result is quite general; if more energy is added to any group of particles, additional distributions become possible, and thus the value of Z is increased. On the other hand, at the absolute zero of temperature, when all particles are in the lowest energy state, Z has its smallest value, namely, unity. In general, the value of Z for any group of particles is the sum of the various values of w belonging to the different possible distributions. In the problem of Fig. 5 the value of Z will be greater than 10^{10}.

Let us consider some of the possible distributions not shown in Fig. 5. For 20 particles sharing energy equivalent to $20u$, one of the possible distributions will be that where each of the 20 particles is in its level ϵ_1. This state of the group (analogous to Figs. 2a and 3a) can arise in only one way. If we suppose that the various distributions are adopted in any random order, the chance of finding every one of the 20 particles simultaneously in its level ϵ_1 is negligibly small in comparison with 10^8. Clearly, in evaluating the resultant average population of the levels, it will make no appreciable difference whether this particular distribution is included with the others or not. The contribution that it makes to the final result is negligible. In Fig. 3, where we had altogether only 28 different states for the group, none of these 28 could safely be omitted. But here, in view of the fact that there are several distributions each of which can arise in more than 10^8 different ways, this is no longer true. We reach then the important distinction between those distributions which must be taken into account and those which may safely be neglected. In drawing this distinction, we are, of course, not abandoning the basic principle according to which each of the possible states of the group must be treated as equally probable.

At the same time it is useful to ask whether these "distributions which can be safely neglected" have a form or shape by which they can be recognized. For this purpose, let us consider the resultant average population of the levels for the 20 particles of Fig. 5. If this is computed, as was done in Fig. 4, we find a shape somewhat resembling that of Fig. 4, in that, on the average, each quantum state would be less populated than those below and more populated than those above. In the problem of Fig. 4 this graded shape emerged only as the result of averaging and was not present in any of the component distributions depicted in Fig. 3. But from Fig. 5 we see that, in the case of a larger group of particles, this graded character is already present in some of the component distributions. In drawing Fig. 5 two examples were intentionally chosen in which each populated level contains fewer particles than any level below and more particles than any level above.

Among the distributions not depicted in Fig. 5 there are, of course, distributions of very different shapes. We have already mentioned one of these, namely, where the lowest level is completely empty and all 20 particles are in the next level above. This, as has been pointed out, can occur in only one way; that is to say, for this distribution $w = 1$. There are other distributions with only one or two particles in the lowest level; these can occur in a few different ways. A more detailed study shows that in any large group of particles the distributions which can occur in the greatest number of ways are the *graded* distributions, in which each energy state is less populated than those below and more populated than those above.

Let us discuss once more the group of three particles to which Fig. 1 refers and let us consider the group when it happens to be in the state represented by Fig. 1*b*. We suppose that, as a result of interchange of energy between the particles, the group will soon leave the distribution corresponding to Fig. 1*b*; when it does so, there are seven possibilities. The group may either go to one of the six states corresponding to Fig. 1*c* or it may go to the single state corresponding to Fig. 1*a*. If there is no factor that restricts the transition, it is clear that we are more likely to find that the group has gone from *b* to *c* in Fig. 1 than that it has gone from *b* to *a*. This example illustrates in its simplest form the tendency for any group of particles to move spontaneously in the direction of the distribution that has the greatest value of w. Let us, for example, return to the group of particles to which Fig. 5 refers, and let us suppose that at a certain moment the 20 particles have a distribution for which $w = 380$. By a slight redistribution of the energy the particles can adopt a distribution for which $w = 29,070$ or alternatively can adopt the distribution (mentioned above) for which $w = 1$. Unless there is some factor that severely restricts the transition, the group is much more likely to adopt the distribution for which w has the larger value; having done so, it is likely to proceed to a distribution that has a value of w greater than 10^5, and so on, until it reaches the distributions with w greater than 10^8. In drawing this conclusion, we have not assumed an agency that drives the particles in any direction; we have supposed only that the outcome shall be due to the free operation of chance. In any group of particles there is always a finite but small probability of adopting distributions with small values of w; but if such an excursion occurs, it is likely to last for only a very short interval of time.[1]

In practice, the quantity of matter that we deal with usually amounts to at least a few grams and contains more than 10^{22} particles. In such a large group of particles, although exactly the same basic principles are used, the character of the population differs profoundly from the small groups we have discussed. In Sec. 5 we shall describe the changes that will be encountered when we consider progressively larger groups of particles. In the problem of Fig. 5 we have already noticed two features that were not present in the problem of Fig. 3. On the one hand, we have noted the presence of distributions having the character that we have

[1] See the reference to R. C. Tolman, "The Principles of Statistical Mechanics," in footnote 1, p. 53.

called "graded"; and on the other hand, we have noted the presence of distributions occurring so seldom that they need not be taken into account at all.

5. Larger Groups of Particles. When we consider a larger group of particles, we find that *both these tendencies are accentuated.* We find many distributions in which the population of the lower levels (at least) has this graded character; and we find that these are the only distributions for which the value of w is large enough to affect the final result; they are the only distributions that will occur frequently, and consequently the only ones that will need to be taken into account in deriving the average resultant distribution. All distributions in which the population of the lower levels is ungraded will make a negligible contribution. The graded distributions will include, as in the problem of Fig. 5, many different shapes. When we speak of "the shape of a distribution," we refer, of course, to the set of values of n_1/n_0, n_2/n_0, n_3/n_0, and so on. We need to take into account only those for which $n_0 > n_1 > n_2 > \cdots$ throughout the well-populated levels.

When we go on to consider a still larger group of particles sharing a large amount of energy E, we find that we are able to make a still narrower restriction—distributions that approximate very closely *to a particular shape* are the only distributions for which w is large; these are the only distributions which occur frequently and which, consequently, are instrumental in determining the resultant distribution. All distributions that differ appreciably from this particular shape will occur seldom and will therefore make a negligible contribution to the resultant shape of the population.

We have said that the shape of a population, or of a distribution, is defined when values are assigned to the ratios n_1/n_0, n_2/n_0, and so on. Now when the value of n_1 is, say, as large as 10^{19}, it is clear that there is very little difference between the value of n_1/n_0 and the value of $(n_1 + 1,000,000)/n_0$, for example; in fact, the difference is not more than one part in 10^{13}. In discussing the shape of a population, we would regard this as a negligible difference. The same applies to the values of the ratios n_2/n_0, n_3/n_0 ... when the values of n_2, n_3 ... are sufficiently large. Our meaning will be clear, then, when we say that in such a case there is an enormous number of distributions of practically the same shape.

In dealing with the small number of particles of Figs. 3 and 5, when we suppose that the various possible distributions will be adopted by the particles in any random order, the result is that the values of n_1/n_0, n_2/n_0, and so on fluctuate violently from one moment to the next. But in a very large group of particles, as soon as the group has come to equilibrium and the population has adopted its optimum shape, the values of the ratios n_1/n_0, n_2/n_0 ... are practically constant, showing only minor fluctuations that we can neglect.

It should be stressed that, in dealing with a very large group of particles, we have supposed that the behavior of each particle is in no way different from that of the particles in the problem of Fig. 3. The difference in the final result is due entirely to the fact that many particles are sharing the total energy. Let us briefly review the stages that have been outlined. (1) Figure 4 was the resultant average distribution derived from Fig. 3, but not one of the component distributions of Fig. 3 could be said to resemble the resultant distribution derived from them. (2) In the next problem, Fig. 5 depicted two component distributions that at any rate showed some resemblance to each other and to the final average distribution that would be arrived at as the resultant of all the component distributions; that is, they had the character that we have called graded. (3) For a still larger group of particles we should find several distributions showing a closer resemblance to each other and to the resultant average distribution. (4) When we come to a still larger group of particles sharing a certain energy E, the necessity of deriving a resultant average distribution from the component distributions will have disappeared. For now all the component distributions that occur frequently have practically the same shape. Of course, the resultant average distribution likewise has this shape. Momentarily the particles might by chance adopt a distribution of appreciably different shape, but the probability for this is so small that it may be neglected. For a very large group of particles, then, the problem is quite straightforward—as soon as the group of n particles has settled down to equilibrium, we can speak of *the* shape of the population appropriate to the energy E, and the problem reduces to finding the values of n_1/n_0, n_2/n_0, n_3/n_0 . . . that describe this shape of the population.

6. In Fig. 3, where we were considering a group of three particles, we saw that some of the distributions could arise in six different ways, namely, those arrangements where each particle is in a different level. If we imagine that the levels are initially empty and that we have to assign the three particles to the various levels, starting, say, with the highest level, we have three choices for the first particle—it may be either the particle at point A, the particle at B, or the particle at C. When this particle has been allocated, there remain two choices for the particle to go into the second level. When this second particle has been allocated, the remaining particle must go into the other level. The total number of ways in which the three particles may be arranged, each in a different level, is consequently $3 \times 2 \times 1$, that is, 6.

In general, if we have n particles distributed each in a different level, we have n choices for the first particle, $(n - 1)$ choices for the second, $(n - 2)$ choices for the third, and so on, until we reach the last particle. The number of ways is thus given by the product of the n factors

$$n(n - 1)(n - 2) \cdots 3 \cdot 2 \cdot 1$$

which is known as "factorial n" and is denoted by $n!$.

Let us now compare Fig. 6a with Fig. 6b. In both diagrams we have seven particles. Starting with the particle in the highest level, we have 7 choices for the first particle, 6 choices for the second, and so on. In Fig. 6a, where each particle is in a different level, the total number of possible arrangements is obviously 7! Consider now Fig. 6b, again starting with the particle in the highest level. We have 7 choices for the first, 6 choices for the second, and 5 for the third; after that, all the remaining particles go, without choice, into a single level. The number of possible arrangements is thus given by the product $7 \times 6 \times 5$. This product differs from $7!$ in that the factors $4 \times 3 \times 2 \times 1$ are missing. Thus for Fig. $6b$, the number of possible arrangements w is conveniently written in the form

$$w = \frac{7!}{4!}$$

Consider next the nine particles in Fig. $6c$. If we start again with the particle in the highest level, we have 9 choices for the first and 8 for the second. Of the remaining particles, 3 are to be put together into one level and 4 together into another level. By

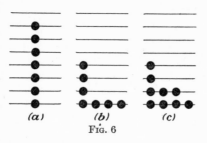

(a)   (b)   (c)

Fig. 6

extension of the reasoning used in the previous example, both the factors $3!$ and $4!$ have to be put into the denominator, leading to the value

$$w = \frac{9!}{3! \times 4!}$$

7. The general problem is equivalent to the familiar problem of the number of different ways in which n objects may be arranged in p piles, placing n_0 in the first pile, n_1 in the second pile, and so on; for we have n particles distributed as follows: n_0 together in one level, n_1 particles together in another level, n_2 in another, and so on. As in the above examples, the numerator is to be simply $n!$, while the denominator must contain a factorial from each quantum state that contains any particles; thus

$$w = \frac{n!}{n_0! \, n_1! \, n_2! \, \cdots \, n_r! \, \cdots} \tag{1}$$

It will be noticed that if each factor in the denominator were unity, the value of w would reduce to $n!$, which, as we have seen, is the correct value when the n particles are arranged each in a different level. If any quantum state is empty, it makes no contribution to the denominator.

The expression (1) can be derived from a slightly different point of view. Hitherto we have fixed attention on the process of allocating the n particles to the various energy levels, and we regarded the n that occurs in the numerator of (1) as denoting the total number of particles in the solid. We can equally well start from the fact that in the solid we have n sites that have to be assigned to the n particles; then the meaning of (1) is that n_0 of these sites, chosen at random, are to be assigned to particles that are, at the moment, in their lowest level; while n_1 other sites, chosen at random, are to be assigned to particles that are, at the moment, in the level 1; and so on, until all the sites are filled. (Figure $5a$ is an illustration of this process.) In this way we reach, of course, the same result as before, but we regard the n that occurs in the numerator of (1) as denoting the total number of sites to be assigned.

We must now make use of (1) to find the optimum shape for the population, namely, that which gives to (1) its maximum value consistent with a total energy E. Our intention is to suppose that, if initially the population does not have its optimum form, a spontaneous redistribution of energy among the particles will take place and will continue until the optimum form has been adopted, that is, until w has reached the maximum value consistent with the total energy E.

When the n particles share a certain amount of energy E, there are a large number of different arrangements consistent with this value for the total energy. We need a method of testing which of these distributions have the optimum shape or form. For this purpose we use the fact that, when w has its maximum value, any slight redistribution of the energy among the particles will leave the value of w unchanged.

If y is any function of x and if the value of y passes through a maximum for a certain value of x, at this point any small increase or decrease in the value of x is, of course, accompanied by no appreciable change in the value of y. In (1) the value of w depends on a large number of variables n_0, n_1, n_r ...; when w has the maximum value consistent with a certain value of the total energy E, small alterations in *any or all* of the variables n_0, n_1 ... leave the value of w unchanged, so long as these alterations are chosen so that the total energy E is constant and the total number of particles n is constant.

8. Two Numerical Illustrations. Two examples will illustrate how w changes or does not change when a small rearrangement of the particles is made. For this purpose, a set of energy levels with uniform spacing, like those already used above, is convenient. If we move a particle from any level to a higher level, we thereby increase the total energy E. If we move a particle to a lower level, we thereby diminish the total energy E. If, taking two particles from any level, we shift one to a lower level and at the same time shift the other to a higher level, we leave the total energy E unchanged if the three levels are equally spaced; the amount of energy liberated on moving one particle down is exactly sufficient to raise the other particle to the level above. We may ask then whether this process of shifting two particles has brought about a change in the value of w.

As a numerical example, let us take a set of levels with uniform spacing and populate them with any arbitrary numbers of particles, putting, say, 2002 particles into the lowest level, 1002 particles into the next level, 102 particles into level 2, and so on, as in Fig. 7a. For the moment we are not interested in the numbers of particles (n_3, n_4, and so on) put into the higher levels. The value of w will be

$$w = \frac{n!}{2002! \times 1002! \times 102! \times n_3! \times n_4! \times \cdots}$$

We can now test this distribution by making a slight rearrangement of the particles, as indicated by the arrows in Fig. 7a. We take two particles from level 1 and put one of them into the level below and one into the level above. If we leave the values of n_3, n_4 ... undisturbed, the value of E remains the same. The new value of w is given by

$$w^* = \frac{n!}{2003! \times 1000! \times 103! \times n_3! \times n_4! \times \cdots}$$

Thus the ratio of w^* to the original w is given by

$$\frac{w^*}{w} = \frac{2002! \times 1002! \times 102!}{2003! \times 1000! \times 103!} \tag{2}$$

Now 2003! differs from 2002! only in that it possesses the extra factor 2003, and in 103! there will be the extra factor 103. Likewise, if we compare 1000! with 1002!, we see that the first two factors 1002 and 1001 are missing. We can now find whether the slight rearrangement of the particles has caused a large or a small alteration in the value of w. From (2) we obtain the result

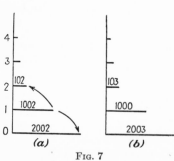

Fig. 7

$$\frac{w^*}{w} = \frac{1002 \times 1001}{2003 \times 103} = \frac{1,003,001}{206,309} \tag{3}$$

We find that by shifting only one particle to a higher level and one to a lower level, keeping the total energy constant, we have increased the value of w nearly five times. The reader will see that if the process is repeated, by shifting another pair of particles in the same way, keeping the total energy E constant, we shall obtain a similar increase, so that w reaches thereby a value nearly 25 times its original value. Evidently, as far as these three levels are concerned, the distribution of the particles that we happened to choose was very far from being the optimum distribution for the given amount of energy E. We conclude that there are relatively too many particles in the middle level, since removal of particles from this level increases the value of w.

Consider then a distribution with relatively fewer particles in this level; let us try 722 particles instead of 1002. If at the same time we take $n_0 = 2142$ in the lowest level, and $n_2 = 242$ in the level above, the reader may verify that we shall have in these three levels the same number of particles sharing the same amount of energy as in the previous example. If now we test this distribution by shifting two particles, as before, we go from the distribution 2142, 722, 242 to the distribution 2143, 720, 243, and the value of w thereby changes in the ratio

$$\frac{w^*}{w} = \frac{2142! \times 722! \times 242!}{2143! \times 720! \times 243!} = \frac{722 \times 721}{2143 \times 243} \tag{4}$$

$$= \frac{520{,}562}{520{,}749} \tag{5}$$

We see that this time there is very little change in the value of w. This means that as far as these three levels are concerned, the population of the levels must be very near the optimum for the given amount of energy. The reader will find that whatever rearrangement of the particles is made, keeping the total energy constant, a greater value of w for the population of these three levels cannot be obtained.

9. The Condition That Gives w Its Greatest Value. Writing n_0, n_1, and n_2 in place of 242, 722, and 2142 in equation (4), we obtain the general result for such a rearrangement

$$\frac{w^*}{w} = \frac{n_1(n_1 - 1)}{(n_0 + 1)(n_2 + 1)} \tag{6}$$

Now in practice, as already pointed out, we usually deal with at least 10^{20} particles and are not interested in levels containing less than about 10^{15} particles. Under these circumstances, there will be in (6) no appreciable difference between the value of $n_1/(n_0 + 1)$ and n_1/n_0, nor between the value of $(n_1 - 1)/(n_2 + 1)$ and n_1/n_2. Thus for any large group of particles equation (6) reduces to

$$\frac{w^*}{w} = \frac{n_1^2}{n_0 n_2} \tag{7}$$

If this slight rearrangement of the particles has caused no change in w, the value of w^*/w will be unity, that is,

$$n_1^2 = n_0 n_2 \tag{8}$$

A rearrangement of the particles could equally have been carried out in the reverse direction. Instead of shifting two particles *from* the middle level, two particles could have been added to this level, one of which had been taken from the level below and the other from the level above. In place of (6) we should have the expression

$$\frac{w^*}{w} = \frac{n_0 n_2}{(n_1 + 1)(n_1 + 2)} \tag{9}$$

which reduces to $n_0 n_2/n_1^2$ when the numbers are very large and so leads again to the condition (8). In either case we find from (8) the very simple requirement that

$$\frac{n_2}{n_1} = \frac{n_1}{n_0} \tag{10}$$

Between the numbers of particles in levels 2 and 1 there must be the same ratio as between the numbers of particles in levels 1 and 0. In the numerical example, if the three numbers 242, 722, and 2142 are examined, it will be found that they satisfy this condition almost exactly; that is why the shifting of two particles was found to leave the value of w practically unchanged.

Instead of fixing attention on n_0, n_1, and n_2, we could have fixed attention on n_1, n_2, and n_3, or on any three equally spaced energy levels and could have subjected their population to the same examination, with the same result. In order that w shall have its maximum value, we find then that the numbers of particles in successive levels must have the relation

$$\frac{n_0}{n_1} = \frac{n_1}{n_2} = \frac{n_2}{n_3} = \cdots \qquad (11)$$

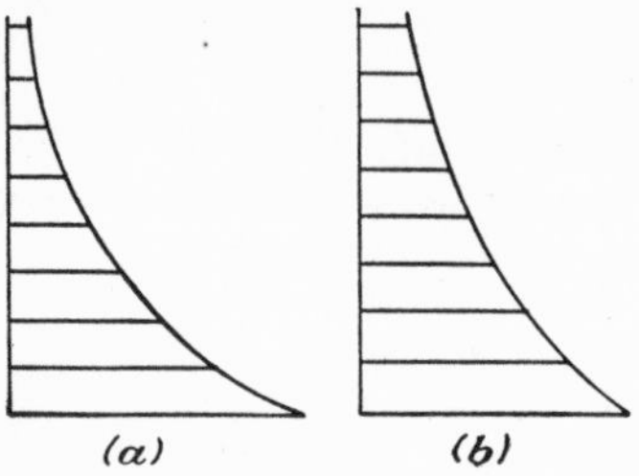

10. The Most Probable Distribution of the Energy.

In the foregoing paragraphs, taking a set of equally spaced energy levels, we have been asking how these levels must be populated so that the value of w shall be a maximum. We have found the important and remarkably simple result that the numbers n_0, n_1, n_2, n_3 ... must lie in a geometrical progression. In accordance with Sec. 3 this progression will be one in which the lowest level is the most populated.

(a)   (b)

FIG. 8

In Fig. 8a (and 8b) the spacing of the horizontal lines is uniform, and the lines have been drawn so that their lengths are in a geometrical progression. This diagram, rather than Fig. 4, depicts the form of a large population if the ordinates are the energy ϵ and the abscissas are the number of particles in the levels.

In Fig. 8 the curve that would pass through the ends of these lines is, of course, an exponential curve. If then we choose to express the population of these levels as a function of the energy ϵ, this will be an exponential function $e^{-\mu\epsilon}$, where μ is a positive constant determined by the value of E, the energy that is shared by the group of particles.

Let ϵ_0, ϵ_1, ϵ_2 ... denote the energies of successive levels and let us take the lowest level as the zero of energy from which to measure the energies of the other levels, that is, we write

$$\epsilon_0 = 0$$

Then

$$n_1 = n_0 e^{-\mu\epsilon_1} \qquad n_2 = n_0 e^{-\mu\epsilon_2} \qquad (12)$$

and in general

$$n_r = n_0 e^{-\mu\epsilon_r} \qquad (13)$$

Figure 8a is intended to represent the n particles when the average energy per particle has a certain value E/n. In Fig. 8b the lengths of the horizontal lines are likewise in a geometrical progression. The curve that would pass through the ends of these lines is exponential with a smaller value of μ than in Fig. 8a. Since the number of particles falls off more slowly as we go to higher levels, this diagram evidently corresponds to a larger value of E/n than in Fig. 8a. Conversely, a smaller value of E/n requires a larger value of μ, which will confine the majority of the particles to the lowest levels. In drawing a pair of diagrams like Figs. 8a and 8b the length of the base line must be adjusted so that the sum of all the lines corresponds to the total number of particles.

In Secs. 15 and 25 we shall discuss the population of a set of levels with any arbitrary non-uniform spacing between the levels. We shall again find that, in order for w to have its maximum value, the population of the levels must be in accordance with (13). This expression is thus of general application. It was stated in Sec. 5 that when we are considering a large group of particles sharing a total energy E, all distributions could be neglected except those which approximate very closely to a particular shape. The shape that we had in mind was that of (13), namely, exponential with that particular value of μ which is appropriate to the value of E/n. We must now ask whether it is true that all distributions that have a shape differing appreciably from this will occur so seldom that they may be disregarded.

11. The expression (13) gives the form that will have the greatest value of w, which we shall denote by w_{max}. By shifting particles to other levels, we may readily obtain distributions, having the same E, with values of w in the neighborhood of $\frac{1}{2}w_{max}$, for example, or in the neighborhood of $\frac{1}{4}w_{max}$, and so on. Since these values of w are not small compared with w_{max}, spontaneous rearrangements of these kinds will occur frequently. To examine these, let us denote by n_0, n_1, and n_2 three numbers that are in an exact geometrical progression and denote by n_0, n_1, and n_2 any set of three numbers obtained from the former by shifting particles, at constant E, in the manner used in Sec. 9.

The reader may easily verify the fact that if he chooses any three numbers in a geometrical progression, for example, 2000, 200, and 20, w has its maximum value consistent with the total energy possessed by these particles; and that the shifting of particles from or to the middle level, keeping the total energy constant, causes w to fall below the value w_{max}. In the numerical example, it is easily calculated from (1) that if five particles are shifted from the middle level to each of the other two levels, leading to the distribution 2005, 190, 25, the resulting value of w is already less than $\frac{1}{2}w_{max}$. Similarly, if five particles are shifted to the middle level from each of the other two levels, leading to 1995, 210, 15, the value of w likewise falls to less than $\frac{1}{2}w_{max}$.

In Fig. 8 a set of horizontal lines was used to represent the values of n_0, n_1, n_2 .... In the same way, we can use a set of vertical lines to represent the successive values of w obtained by shifting particles in the manner described. Starting from the optimum values n_0, n_1, and n_2, let p be the number of particles shifted to the middle level ϵ_1 from each of the other two levels. A *negative* value of p then denotes a number of particles shifted *from* the middle level ϵ_1 to each of the other two levels. Taking p as abscissas and choosing a vertical scale for w, let the length of the longest vertical line, standing at $p = 0$, be drawn equal to the value of w_{max}. On the right-hand side, the vertical lines, counting from the center, represent the values of w that would result when one, two, three ... p ... particles are shifted to the level ϵ_1 from each of the other levels.

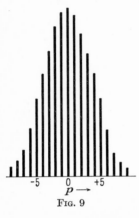

On the left-hand side the lengths of the vertical lines likewise represent the values of w obtained by progressively shifting particles from the level ϵ_1 to each of the other levels. To provide a rough illustration of the numerical example $(n_0 = 2000, n_1 = 200, n_2 = 20)$, the fifth line on either side of Fig. 9 has been drawn less than half the length of the central line. The group of particles in this numerical example is, however, too small to be of much interest. Instead of three levels populated by 2000, 200, and 20 particles, we would be more interested in the population $n_0 = 10^{20}$, $n_1 = 10^{19}$, and $n_2 = 10^{18}$. In such a case the vertical lines will be so numerous that we draw instead the bounding curve,[1] as in Fig. 10.

-5   0   +5
$p \longrightarrow$
Fig. 9

12. The Total Number of Different States. Let us suppose that in a particular case the diagram of Fig. 9 has been completed and let us consider the sum of the lengths of all the vertical lines, asking what this sum represents. It is evidently equal to the total number of different states that can be obtained by shifting particles in the manner described, keeping $(n_0 + n_1 + n_2)$ constant and keeping E constant. Some insight into the behavior of a large group of particles may be obtained by the use of such diagrams as Figs. 9 and 10, if we take for the sake of illustration an exceptionally simple set of levels. Suppose that a particle has a set of levels consisting only of three equally spaced energy states ϵ_0, ϵ_1, and ϵ_2, like the three that we discussed in Sec. 11; and let us consider a group of n such particles sharing a total energy E. If Fig. 9 is completed for this group, it will contain a vertical line for every possible distribution of the energy E. The sum of the lengths of the vertical lines of Fig. 9 will evidently represent the total number of different ways in which the energy E can be shared by the n similar particles. This is the quantity for which the notation Z_E was proposed in Sec. 4. Thus in this simple

---

[1] It will be shown in Sec. 19 that for a large group of particles the significant part of the curve is symmetrical and has the form

$$w = w_{max}e^{-\alpha p^2}$$

case we have at once a graphical representation of the quantity that we denote by Z_E, or simply by Z. This number is evidently a much larger number than w_{max}, since the value of w_{max} corresponds to the length of the central vertical line in Fig. 9 while the value of Z corresponds to the sum of the lengths of all the vertical lines.

For a large group of particles, when the bounding line is drawn as in Fig. 10, the area under the curve is numerically equal to the sum of the lengths of all the vertical lines, since within definite limits there will be a vertical line for each integral value of p. With w as ordinate and p as abscissa, the area under the curve will be numerically equal to Z. In the simplified solid the n particles occupy n different sites, each particle being in one of the allowed energy states; and Z is the number of different ways in which the particles can be allocated to the n sites consistent with their sharing a total energy E. For any value of E there is a definite set of possible distributions; if additional energy is given to the group of particles, new possible distributions are added to the list and the value of Z increases; in Fig. 10 the curve is raised and the area under the curve becomes larger. Conversely, if a body loses energy the value of Z is diminished; in Fig. 10 the curve falls and the area under the curve becomes smaller.

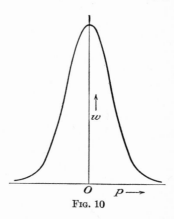

FIG. 10

We have been discussing a group of particles that are all of the same kind. Let us now briefly consider a mixture. For example, when two colorless liquids have been mixed, if the stirring has been insufficient, we may be able to detect a lack of uniformity by a refractive index measurement or by some other means. By a uniform solution at a uniform temperature we mean one in which we cannot detect a lack of uniformity by any known means. This, of course, does not mean that on a molecular scale two such solutions will be identical at any time; the solute and solvent particles will occupy different positions in the solution but this difference cannot be detected on a macroscopic scale.

Consider next a solid at the absolute zero of temperature. If two or more isotopes are present, these various species of particles can be distributed among the n lattice sites in a very large number of different ways. It is only when the particles are strictly all alike that we may assert that, at the absolute zero, there is only one possible state for the crystal. It will be convenient to use the symbols w and Z in the widest sense to refer to the number of states available to the group of particles. When the group contains one species only and when the environment of each particle is similar, as, for example, in a perfect crystal, we arrive at this number through the use of (1) by considering only the number of different ways in which the total energy E may be shared among the n similar particles. In Secs. 13 to 64 we shall continue to discuss homogeneous groups of particles, each of which contains *only one* species.

13. Two Groups of Particles in Thermal Contact. To illustrate the part that the quantity Z plays in determining the behavior of matter, let us consider an important problem. Suppose that two bodies, say, a piece of silver and a piece of copper, are placed in contact. When contact is made, unless the two bodies happen to be already at the same temperature, they are not in equilibrium. A certain flow of heat will take place from one body to the other until finally they come to equilibrium with each other. Our aim must be to say what the conditions for equilibrium are. In general, let the first body contain n_A particles populating a set of energy levels and sharing a total energy E_A, while the second body consists of n_B particles of a different kind, populating a different set of energy levels and sharing a total energy E_B. While the values of n_A and n_B are fixed in advance, we suppose that the values of E_A and E_B can change as soon as the bodies are placed in contact with each other, even though the whole energy $(E_A + E_B)$ is to remain constant.

Let Z_A be the total number of states available to n_A particles when they share energy E_A, and let Z_B be the total number of states available to the n_B particles when they share energy E_B. Now the Z_A different ways in which the energy E_A may be distributed among the n_A particles is quite *independent* of the Z_B different ways in which the energy E_B may be distributed among the n_B particles. In other words, any one of the Z_A different states can be combined with any one of the Z_B states. Consequently, the product $Z_A Z_B$ gives the total number of different states available to the pair of bodies when they have energies E_A and E_B, respectively.

To this pair of bodies we must apply the same principles that we have used for a single body. If changes can take place that will allow the product $Z_A Z_B$ to adopt values greater than its initial value, these changes will occur spontaneously and will continue until finally $Z_A Z_B$ attains its maximum value consistent with the total energy $(E_A + E_B)$.

From what was said in Sec. 12, it follows that if an amount of energy is transferred from A to B, the value of Z_A necessarily falls while the value of Z_B rises. If, then, a spontaneous flow of heat from A to B takes place when the bodies are placed in thermal contact with each other, this must be because the factor by which Z_B is increased is greater than the factor by which Z_A is diminished. With further transfer of heat, however, the rate of increase of $Z_A Z_B$ is not maintained, and finally a state is reached when the effect of a further increase in Z_B is fully compensated by the diminution of Z_A. There is then no longer any reason why the flow of heat should continue; equilibrium has been attained. To solve this problem, we shall need to investigate, for any group of particles, the rate of change of Z with E; we shall return to this question in Sec. 17.

14. In studying (1), we have been asking how the value of w depends on the factors occurring in the denominator of this expression. In Figs. 7 and 9 we discussed the smallest rearrangement that leaves the total energy unchanged—a rearrangement involving only two particles—because from a series of such unit rearrangements we can build up any arbitrary rearrangement involving any number of particles and any number of levels. If the energy E is unchanged in each component step of the series, it will of course be unchanged in the whole. Conversely, if we are confronted with any arbitrary rearrangement for constant E, this can be analyzed into a set of rearrangements of the kind we have discussed, each involving two particles only.

In this process of shifting two particles, the resultant change in E was zero because the amount gained in moving one particle to a lower level was canceled by the equal amount lost in shifting the other particle to a higher level. Although the fact has not been stressed, we have been making a similar demand for w. We have been demanding that the change in the value of w due to moving one particle to a higher level shall be canceled by an equal and opposite change in the value of w due to moving the other particle down to a lower level. It was only in this way that we were able to obtain w^* equal to w.

We can now begin to consider a set of levels with arbitrary non-uniform spacing.[1] Let us discuss the shifting of *one* particle from any level that initially contains n_j particles to any other level that initially contains n_k particles. Before the shift we have

$$w = \frac{n!}{n_0! \, n_1! \cdots n_j! \, n_k! \cdots}$$

[1] As soon as we leave the artificially simple set of levels that we have been discussing, we must decide upon the notation to be used in cases where two or more levels almost coincide in energy, that is, where two or more of the allowed energies are so close together that the difference in energy may be regarded as insignificant. In numbering the whole set of levels, starting from the bottom, 0, 1, 2, 3 ... r ..., two procedures may be adopted when we come to states that coincide in energy. One is to assign a number, or a letter such as r, to each of the coincident energy states; the other is to assign a number or letter to the coincident group of states, calling them "a multiple level." In the latter case, if the rth level, for example, has been called a multiple level, n_r would have to mean the number of particles in this whole group of energy states that coincide in energy and the expression for n_r would have to take this into account. This procedure is inconvenient except in special cases where it is preferable (see Sec. 71). There is no reason why a number or letter should not be assigned to each energy state, and we shall assume that this has been done.

and afterwards we shall have

$$w^* = \frac{n!}{n_0! \, n_1! \cdots (n_j - 1)! \, (n_k + 1)! \cdots}$$

Thus in this case

$$\frac{w^*}{w} = \frac{n_j! \, n_k!}{(n_j - 1)! \, (n_k + 1)!}$$

$$= \frac{n_j}{(n_k + 1)}$$

We may write

$$\frac{w^*}{w} = \frac{n_j}{n_k} \tag{14}$$

when n_k is very large compared with unity. This result is correct whether the level to which the particle has been shifted lies above or below its original level. Thus when *one* particle is moved from any level (the initial level) to any other level (the final level) we obtain the simple rule

$$\frac{w^*}{w} = \frac{\text{the number of particles in the initial level}}{\text{the number of particles in the final level}} \tag{15}$$

Thus if the initial level is the more populated, the value of w will be increased, and vice versa. In practice, in a graded distribution this means that when a particle is moved to a state of higher energy, w is increased, since the lower level is the more highly populated. Conversely, when one particle is moved to a lower level, the value of w decreases.

It follows from (14) that if two particles are thus shifted, either simultaneously or successively, the value of w^*/w will be $(n_j/n_k)^2$. If q particles are shifted between the same two levels, we shall have

$$\frac{w^*}{w} = \left(\frac{n_j}{n_k}\right)^q \tag{16}$$

provided that the value of q is sufficiently small.[1] Since the expressions (14), (15), and (16) concern only two levels, they are correct no matter what are the other allowed energies in the set of levels.

In the special case of equally spaced levels ϵ_i, ϵ_j, and ϵ_k, the expression (16) leads at once to (11). It is sufficient and necessary that the factor $(n_j/n_k)^q$ be accompanied by and be compensated by its reciprocal, if the value of w is to remain unchanged. If the same number of particles—q particles—is shifted from the level ϵ_j to the level ϵ_i, this will contribute the factor $(n_j/n_i)^q$, that is to say, $(n_i/n_j)^{-q}$, and at the same time this will maintain the total energy E constant. In order that the second factor

---

[1] From what is said below in Sec. 20, it appears that "sufficiently small" means small compared with $\sqrt{n_j}$ or $\sqrt{n_k}$, whichever is the smaller.

shall be the reciprocal of the first, the numbers n_i, n_j, and n_k must conform to (13). Thus the rule (15) obviously provides the simplest and shortest derivation of (7), (8), and (11). When one particle is raised from the level ϵ_1 to the level ϵ_2, the value of w will be increased in the ratio n_1/n_2; when another particle is taken from the level ϵ_1 to the level ϵ_0, the value of w will be changed to the ratio n_1/n_0. If the two processes together are to leave the value of w unchanged, the value of n_1/n_2 must be equal to the reciprocal of n_1/n_0; that is to say, the values of n_0, n_1, and n_2 must be in a geometrical progression or an exponential function of the energy.

15. Although the expression (13) was derived only for a set of levels with uniform spacing, it may easily be shown that the same exponential form gives to w its maximum value for any arbitrary set of levels. In a set of levels, consider any three energy states ϵ_i, ϵ_j, and ϵ_k; and for brevity let $(\epsilon_j - \epsilon_i)$ be denoted by a and let $(\epsilon_k - \epsilon_j)$ be denoted by b, as in Fig. 11. We shall consider a rearrangement of the particles in which the total energy remains almost unchanged. If, for example, the quantities a and b are roughly in the ratio of 5 to 3, we can shift eight particles from the middle level, taking three of them to the lower level and the other five particles to the upper level. This will leave the total energy

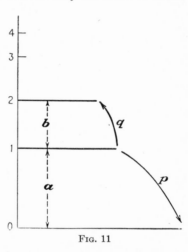

Fig. 11

almost unchanged. In general, we can shift $(p + q)$ particles from the middle level, taking p particles to the lower level and the remaining q particles to the upper level. The total energy will remain almost unchanged if the integers p and q have approximately the relation

$$ap = bq \tag{17}$$

Any arbitrary rearrangement, involving many particles and any number of levels, may be built up by supposing that several small rearrangements are made simultaneously or successively; if the slight gain in total energy resulting from some of these is compensated by the slight loss in energy from others, the whole rearrangement will leave the total energy nearly unchanged. In order to find the form of the population that will give w its maximum value—the distribution that can arise in the greatest number of ways—it is necessary to consider only the shifting of $(p + q)$ particles where the condition of (17) is fulfilled.

Taking $(p + q)$ particles from the middle level, we place p in the level below and q in the level above. In accordance with (16) the latter step changes w by the factor $(n_j/n_k)^q$ while the former step changes w by the factor $(n_j/n_i)^p$. For the complete process we have then

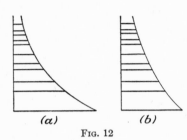

$$\frac{w^*}{w} = \frac{n_j^{(p+q)}}{n_i^p n_k^q} \qquad (18)$$

We wish to know how these levels must be populated so that the value of w shall remain unchanged. We shall show that the required distribution is again a simple exponential distribution

(a)   (b)

Fig. 12

$$n_r = A e^{-\mu \epsilon_r} \qquad (19)$$

In other words, it makes no difference whether the spacing of the energy levels is uniform or non-uniform. From (19) we have

$$n_i = A e^{-\mu \epsilon_i} \qquad n_j = A e^{-\mu (\epsilon_i + a)} \qquad n_k = A e^{-\mu(\epsilon_i + a + b)}$$

Substituting in (18), we have $\dfrac{w^*}{w} = \dfrac{e^{-\mu(\epsilon_i + a)(p+q)}}{e^{-\mu p \epsilon_i} \, e^{-\mu q(\epsilon_i + a + b)}}$ $\qquad (20)$

This will be equal to unity if

$$(\epsilon_i + a)(p + q) = p\epsilon_i + q(\epsilon_i + a + b) \qquad (21)$$

in other words, if

$$ap = bq$$

But this, by (17), is merely the condition that the total energy remains unchanged. Hence (19) ensures that w remains unchanged.

We should obtain the same result if we considered a similar rearrangement involving any number of levels. For non-uniform spacing we reach then the same conclusion that we reached for levels with uniform spacing; that is, the shape of the population the particles will spontaneously adopt is exponential, of the simple form

$$n_r = A e^{-\mu \epsilon_r}$$

If we take the lowest level as the zero of energy, writing $\epsilon_0 = 0$, we have as before

$$n_r = n_0 e^{-\mu \epsilon_r} \qquad (22)$$

Figure 12 may now replace Fig. 8 to depict a typical population, and we may again make the observation that a smaller value of μ implies a larger value of E/n, and vice versa. We shall find later that for many substances at room temperature it is almost true that μ is inversely proportional to E/n.

16. Changes in the value of w. Consider any two levels of ϵ_j and ϵ_k differing in energy by an amount η, the former being the lower of the two levels. If the population is in accordance with (22), we have

$$\frac{n_j}{n_k} = \frac{n_0 e^{-\mu \epsilon_j}}{n_0 e^{-\mu \epsilon_k}} = e^{\mu(\epsilon_k - \epsilon_j)}$$

$$= e^{\mu \eta} \tag{23}$$

Thus if two levels (not necessarily successive levels of the set) differ in energy by an amount η, the population of the lower level will be greater than that of the upper level in the ratio $e^{\mu \eta}$. If the same set of levels contains two other levels ϵ_r and ϵ_s that happen to differ by the same amount η, the ratio n_r/n_s will again be equal to $e^{\mu \eta}$. We shall see that this has important consequences if we now consider an amount of heat flowing into the body or out of the body. When heat is added to a group of particles, particles are raised to higher levels. We know from the rule (15) that each particle raised will result in an increase in w. We can now make the suggestion that, under certain circumstances, the total change in w will depend only on the amount of heat added and not at all on the particular energy levels from which and to which particles have been raised.

Consider, for example, the two pairs of levels ϵ_j and ϵ_k, ϵ_r and ϵ_s in the set of levels that has just been mentioned. In order to add an amount of energy η to the group of particles, we can either raise a particle from ϵ_j to ϵ_k, or alternatively from ϵ_r to ϵ_s. The former step would increase w by the factor n_j/n_k; the latter step would increase w by the factor n_r/n_s. In general, if the population is *not* exponential, the values of these factors are *different*. On the other hand, if the population is exponential, the values of n_j/n_k and n_r/n_s are the same and the change in w will be the same whichever pair of levels is affected.

Furthermore, it does not matter how many particles are moved in order to effect the addition of a given quantity of heat. We can move either a few particles through large energy differences or more particles through smaller energy differences. Suppose, for example, that the same set of levels contains two levels that happen to differ in energy by q times $(\epsilon_k - \epsilon_j)$, that is to say, by an amount $q\eta$, where q is an integer. In order to add an amount of energy $q\eta$ to the group of particles, we can either shift one particle through this energy difference, or alternatively we can shift q particles from the level ϵ_j to the level ϵ_k. According to (16), the latter process would change w by the factor $(n_j/n_k)^q$. If the population is exponential, this factor is $(e^{\mu \eta})^q$; but this is the same as $e^{\mu q \eta}$, which would be obtained by the alternative process of shifting one particle through an energy interval $q\eta$. We see then that an exponential population has the property that, when energy is added or removed, the change in w depends only on the amount of energy and not on the number of particles shifted or on the particular energy levels between which they are shifted.

In an exponential population, (23) combined with (14) gives

$$\ln w^* - \ln w = \mu \eta \tag{24}$$

For an amount of heat δQ, which consists of various amounts of energy given by

$$\delta Q = \eta_1 + \eta_2 + \eta_3 + \eta_4 + \cdots \tag{25}$$

we shall have

$$\ln w^* - \ln w = \mu\eta_1 + \mu\eta_2 + \mu\eta_3 + \cdots \tag{26}$$

Thus for any exponential population we obtain the important expression

$$\delta \ln w = \mu \, \delta Q \tag{27}$$

When some particles are raised to higher levels and other particles are taken down to lower levels, there is at the same time a gain and a loss of energy—a gain and a loss that may or may not cancel each other. Thus the value of δQ in (27) may be positive, negative, or zero. The more nearly complete the cancellation is, the smaller, according to (27), will be the change in w. Thus (27) is seen to embody the fundamental condition that a group of particles adopts the state that can arise in the greatest number of ways. In Sec. 8 we started from the condition that, when a rearrangement of the particles among their energy levels leaves the total energy E unaltered, there should be no change in w; for this purpose we have to suppose that the group of particles is thermally isolated. But the condition

$$\delta \ln w = \mu \, \delta Q$$

is wider, since it covers all values of δQ, positive and negative as well as zero.

We have derived (27) only for the simple case of a single group of particles populating a fixed set of energy levels. In some cases the addition of an amount of heat δQ to a group of particles will cause a change in spacing of the energy levels. We shall find later that (27) continues to hold in these cases and to cover all values of δQ, positive and negative, as well as the zero value that corresponds to a redistribution of the energy within a thermally isolated group.

17. Changes in the Value of Z. Our attention was directed in Sec. 13 to the change in the value of Z when heat is admitted to, or removed from, a body. In the simple problem of Fig. 10 the change in Z corresponds to the change in the area under the curve; we need to know how this area depends on the total energy E. Now in obtaining (27) we have made the first step toward the desired knowledge, since the change in W corresponds to the change in the central ordinate of the curve in Fig. 10. We are interested not only in the central ordinate but in the ordinates throughout the curve; we need this information in order to evaluate the change in the area under the curve. It will be recalled that the right-hand half of Fig. 10 corresponds to distributions that differ somewhat from the strictly exponential, in that n_1 is relatively too large—n_1 being equal to $(\mathbf{n}_1 + 2p)$ in the notation of Sec. 11, while the left-hand half of Fig. 10 corresponds to distributions that differ somewhat from the strictly exponential, in that n_1 is relatively too small—n_1 being equal to $(\mathbf{n}_1 - 2p)$. That is to say, in the right-hand half of Fig. 9 or Fig. 10, the ratio n_1/n_0 is greater than $\mathbf{n}_1/\mathbf{n}_0$, while in the left-hand half it is less; for the ratio n_2/n_1 the converse statement is true. Suppose, for example, that by raising a particle from the level ϵ_0 to the level ϵ_1, we increase the total energy from E to $E + (\epsilon_1 - \epsilon_0)$. In Fig. 9 we need to know how the length of each vertical line is changed, in order to know how the sum of the lengths of the vertical lines will be changed. According to (14) and (15), the length of any vertical line will be changed in the ratio n_0/n_1 belonging to that line; the ratio n_0/n_1 has, of course, a different value for each line. Thus, if Fig. 9 or Fig. 10 were drawn for the same group of particles when they are sharing a slightly larger amount of energy, the diagram would not be an exact replica on a larger scale since the ordinates have not all been changed in the same ratio. Our problem is to inquire to what extent the diagram will differ from that which would result from a *uniform* change in the scale of ordinates.

We may now recognize that this question forms part of a much wider problem. In Sec. 5 it was asserted that, for a sufficiently large group of particles, all the distributions that occur at all frequently have practically the same shape. Now it is clear that, when this assertion is true, it is sufficient to dispose of the question under discussion here. To say that all the distributions that occur frequently have the same shape is to say that for each of these distributions the value of n_1/n_0 does not differ appreciably from the value of $\mathbf{n}_1/\mathbf{n}_0$; similarly that the values of n_2/n_0 and n_2/n_1 do not differ appreciably from $\mathbf{n}_2/\mathbf{n}_0$ and $\mathbf{n}_2/\mathbf{n}_1$; and further that, even if the required curve is not an *exact* replica of Fig. 10, the difference is quite negligible. Thus, if we can prove the assertion of Sec. 5, this will dispose of both questions at once; there are not two problems, but only one.

18. When the distributions of Figs. 1 and 3 were studied, the principle was introduced that the various distributions could be adopted by the particles in any random order; some will occur frequently, others seldom; the frequency with which any distribution is likely to occur is proportional to its value of w. When we suppose that these various alternatives in Fig. 10 are adopted in any random order, the frequency of occurrence of each alternative is proportional to the height of the appropriate ordinate. In the regions of Fig. 10 where the curve has fallen almost to the horizontal axis, the probability of occurrence is very small.

In order to focus our attention on the central region of Fig. 10, let us denote by p' and by $-p'$ the values of p on either side, where the curve has fallen almost to the horizontal axis—for example, where the ordinate has a value in the neighborhood of $\frac{1}{1000}$ of the central ordinate. If, as before, we denote by $\mathbf{n}_0$, $\mathbf{n}_1$, and $\mathbf{n}_2$ the strictly exponential population where p is zero, the population of the levels ϵ_0, ϵ_1, and ϵ_2 at the specified places on the diagram is as follows: on the right $(\mathbf{n}_0 - p')$, $(\mathbf{n}_1 + 2p')$, and $(\mathbf{n}_2 - p')$ and on the left $(\mathbf{n}_0 + p')$, $(\mathbf{n}_1 - 2p')$, and $(\mathbf{n}_2 + p')$. Recalling that $\mathbf{n}_2$ is smaller than $\mathbf{n}_1$ or $\mathbf{n}_0$, we may now define our problem by asking under what conditions the value of p' will be very small compared with $\mathbf{n}_2$. When p' is negligible compared with $\mathbf{n}_2$, it is clear that, over the whole central region between $-p'$ and p', the population will not differ appreciably from the central exponential population; *outside* this central range the population will deviate more and more from the exponential form, but this will not matter, since this part makes a negligible contribution to the area under the curve.

Starting from the central exponential population, if we shifted particles from the level ϵ_1 to the levels ϵ_2 and ϵ_0 and continued until all the $\mathbf{n}_1$ particles were exhausted, we could thereby obtain a new distribution of equal energy for each pair of particles shifted, that is to say, altogether $\frac{1}{2}\mathbf{n}_1$ distributions of the same total energy E. But if the assertion of Sec 5 is correct, very few of these distributions will have a value of w comparable with $w_{\max}$; for most of these distributions the value of w will be very small compared with $w_{\max}$.

Instead of removing particles from the middle level, we can obtain numerous new distributions of the same energy by shifting particles, one by one, from the higher level ϵ_2 to the middle level, at the same time bringing particles, one by one, from the lower level to the middle level to maintain the energy constant. If we were to continue this process until all the particles in the level ϵ_2 were exhausted, we would obtain by this process $\mathbf{n}_2$ new distributions of the same energy. In the early stages of this series, each new distribution has a value of w not differing appreciably from $w_{\max}$. But sooner or later, as more particles are shifted, the value of w begins to fall below $w_{\max}$.

19. When p particles have been shifted, the expression for w is

$$w = \frac{n!}{(\mathbf{n}_0 - p)!\,(\mathbf{n}_1 + 2p)!\,(\mathbf{n}_2 - p)!} \tag{28}$$

instead of the initial

$$w_{\max} = \frac{n!}{\mathbf{n}_0!\,\mathbf{n}_1!\,\mathbf{n}_2!}$$

The expression (28) is correct for negative as well as for positive values of p, that is, for particles shifted to or from the middle level. In either case the ratio of w to $w_{\max}$ is the product of three factors of similar form

$$\frac{w}{w_{\max}} = \frac{\mathbf{n}_0!}{(\mathbf{n}_0 - p)!} \frac{\mathbf{n}_1!}{(\mathbf{n}_1 + 2p)!} \frac{\mathbf{n}_2!}{(\mathbf{n}_2 - p)!} \tag{29}$$

As long as p is sufficiently small compared with n_0, n_1, and n_2, the value of (29) does not differ appreciably from unity. If n_2 is considerably smaller than n_1 or n_0, the term $(n_2 - p)!$ will be the first term to become important. In dealing with (29) we may make use of the following expansion, when p is small compared with n

$$\ln(n + p) = \ln\left[n\left(1 + \frac{p}{n}\right)\right]$$

$$= \ln n + \ln\left(1 + \frac{p}{n}\right)$$

$$= \ln n + \frac{p}{n} - \frac{1}{2}\left(\frac{p}{n}\right)^2 + \frac{1}{3}\left(\frac{p}{n}\right)^3 + \cdots$$

Using Stirling's approximation, we obtain

$$\ln\frac{n!}{(n+p)!} = n \ln n - n - \left(n \ln n + p \ln n + p + \frac{p^2}{n} - \frac{p^2}{2n} - \frac{p^3}{2n^2} + \frac{p^3}{3n^2}\right)$$
$$+ (n + p)$$

$$= -p \ln n - \frac{p^2}{2n} + \frac{p^3}{6n^2} + \cdots \tag{30}$$

Using this expression for each of the three terms in (29), we obtain

$$\ln\frac{w}{w_{\max}} = +p \ln n_0 - 2p \ln n_1 + p \ln n_2 - \frac{p^2}{2}\left(\frac{1}{n_0} + \frac{4}{n_1} + \frac{1}{n_2}\right)$$
$$- \frac{p^3}{6}\left(\frac{1}{n_0^2} - \frac{8}{n_1^2} + \frac{1}{n_2^2}\right) + \cdots \tag{31}$$

The first three terms on the right-hand side are together equal to zero since the numbers n_0, n_1, and n_2 are in a geometrical progression. As p increases from zero, the terms in p^3 will not become important until the value of p^3 becomes comparable with n_2^2. Omitting these terms,

$$\ln\frac{w}{w_{\max}} = -\frac{p^2}{2}\left(\frac{1}{n_0} + \frac{4}{n_1} + \frac{1}{n_2}\right)$$

Hence we obtain

$$\frac{w}{w_{\max}} = e^{-\alpha p^2} \tag{32}$$

where

$$\alpha = \frac{1}{2}\left(\frac{1}{n_0} + \frac{4}{n_1} + \frac{1}{n_2}\right) \tag{33}$$

This then is the expression for the curve in Fig. 10. We see that the value of α is greater than $1/2n_2$, but if n_0 and n_1 are large compared with n_2, the value of α will not be much greater than $1/2n_2$.

20. We began in Sec. 18 to denote by p' the value of p for which the value of w is one-thousandth of $w_{\max}$. From (32) we can now make an estimate of p' for a typical population. Since the numerical value of e^{-7} is a little less than $\frac{1}{1000}$, we may write approximately $\alpha p'^2 = 7$, or

$$p' = \sqrt{\frac{7}{\alpha}} = \sqrt{14n_2} = 3.7\sqrt{n_2} \qquad (34)$$

In the numerical example suggested, the value of $\sqrt{n_2}$ is 10^9, since we took $n_0 = 10^{20}$, $n_1 = 10^{19}$, and $n_2 = 10^{18}$. If with this initial distribution we started shifting particles to the middle level, keeping the total energy constant, we could obtain 10^{18} different distributions of equal energy before the particles in the level ϵ_2 were exhausted; but very few of these distributions resemble an exponential distribution, and very few have a high probability of occurrence. It follows from (34) that when 3.7×10^9 particles have been shifted from the level ϵ_2 (and an equal number from the level ϵ_0), the value of w will have already fallen to less than one-thousandth of w_{max}. It follows also that all the distributions that make an appreciable contribution to the area under the curve in Fig. 10 have a form extremely close to the strictly exponential. At the center the ratio n_2/n_1 is $10^{18}/10^{19}$. When p' particles have been shifted, this ratio is replaced by $(10^{18} - 3.7 \times 10^9)/(10^{19} + 7.4 \times 10^9)$, which does not differ from the central ratio by more than one part in 10^8.

Even if we consider a smaller group of particles, for example, a population with $n_0 = 10^{16}$, $n_1 = 10^{15}$, $n_2 = 10^{14}$, we find that, for all the distributions that are likely to occur, the value of n_2/n_1 does not differ from n_2/n_1 by as much as one part in 10^6.

According to (32) the area under the curve in Fig. 10 is given by

$$w_{max} \int_{-\infty}^{+\infty} e^{-\alpha p^2} \, dp$$

A method of evaluating this integral is given in Note 2 of the Appendix. Using the result given there, we obtain for the value of Z, the total number of states available to the group of particles

$$Z = w_{max}\sqrt{\frac{\pi}{\alpha}} \qquad (35)$$

In the numerical example, the value of Z would be of the order of 10^9 times as great as w_{max}.

21. We considered in Sec. 13 two bodies A and B, with energies E_A and E_B, placed in contact. We said that when contact is made, heat will flow from one body to the other if such a flow will enable the product $Z_A Z_B$ to attain values higher than its initial value. The transfer of heat is accompanied by an increase of Z for one body and a decrease in Z for the other body. An increase in the product $Z_A Z_B$ can only arise if the increase in Z for the one body is greater than the accompanying decrease in Z for the other body. To throw light on this problem, the proposal was made at the beginning of Sec. 17 to investigate in Fig. 10 how the area under the curve changes when the group of particles receives an amount of heat δQ. In obtaining the expression (27) we had already made the first step in this direction, since (27) gives the amount by which the central ordinate changes.

In conjunction with (32), it is clear that (27) gives us not only this but also all that we require for the problem of Fig. 10. When heat is admitted to that group of particles, particles may be raised from ϵ_0 to ϵ_1, from ϵ_0 to ϵ_2, and from ϵ_1 to ϵ_2. According to (15) the increase in w for each of the steps will be given by n_0/n_1, n_0/n_2, and n_1/n_2, respectively. If it is true that these three ratios differ by less than one part in 10^8 from $\mathbf{n}_0/\mathbf{n}_1$, $\mathbf{n}_0/\mathbf{n}_2$, and $\mathbf{n}_1/\mathbf{n}_2$—if this is true over the whole range from $-p'$ to $+p'$—then the ordinates of the curve in the whole of this central range will change together in the same ratio. We conclude that when energy is admitted to, or removed from, the group of particles, the area under the curve will be changed in the same ratio as $w_{\max}$.

We have used (14) and (18) to discuss distributions which differ from, as well as those which approximate closely to, the exponential form. In the greater part of this book we shall be concerned only with the latter; we are no longer interested in the contrast between $w_{\max}$ and small values of w. We may therefore conveniently drop the notation $w_{\max}$ and introduce instead a capital letter W. We have found that when a certain amount of energy is added to, or removed from, the group of particles, all the ordinates in Fig. 10 are changed in the same ratio W^*/W, and likewise the area under the curve. Thus we may write

$$\frac{Z^*}{Z} = \frac{W^*}{W} \tag{36}$$

or, using (27),

$$\delta \ln Z = \delta \ln W = \mu \, \delta Q \tag{37}$$

If we discuss a less simple problem, we clearly will not be able to give a detailed treatment, but the argument will be similar. Consider any arbitrary set of energy levels populated by a large group of particles. Fixing our attention on any two levels, let $\mathbf{n}_j$ and $\mathbf{n}_k$ denote the values required by (22) for a strictly exponential population sharing a certain total energy E. For the same value of E there will be many distributions in which n_j/n_k is very small compared with $\mathbf{n}_j/\mathbf{n}_k$, and others in which n_j/n_k is very large compared with $\mathbf{n}_j/\mathbf{n}_k$; these correspond to the regions of Fig. 10 where the curve has almost reached the horizontal axis. The existence of such distributions is important in connection with the same two questions as before: Is it true that all distributions that occur at all frequently have practically the same shape, and under what conditions is (37) valid? Both questions may be disposed of at once. Suppose that values of n_i, n_j, and n_k, differing markedly from $\mathbf{n}_i$, $\mathbf{n}_j$, and $\mathbf{n}_k$ but consistent with the same value of E, are inserted into the denominator of (1). The result depends on the size of the group of particles; if the group is very large, as it is in practice, we obtain thereby distributions that make a negligible contribution to Z. It follows that (36) and (37) are applicable to any group of particles with which we shall deal.

22. Equilibrium between Two Groups of Particles. The expression (37) may now be used to deal quantitatively with the problem of two substances placed in contact with each other. When contact is made between two solids A and B, the product $Z_A Z_B$ will not usually have its maximum value; heat will either flow from A to B or from B to A. If the flow of heat is from A to B, this is because the increase in Z_B, the number of states available to the B group, is greater than the simultaneous decrease in Z_A, the number of states available to the A group. The flow of heat will not continue indefinitely but will stop when the increase in Z_B is fully compensated by the decrease in Z_A. The condition for equilibrium is that the transfer of a quantity of energy from A to B, or vice versa, is accompanied by no change in the product $Z_A Z_B$ or in the product $W_A W_B$; that is to say,

$$\delta \ln W_A W_B = 0 \tag{38}$$

For this purpose we need to consider a rearrangement of the particles in the set of levels B such that the energy E_B is increased by a certain amount, and to consider a simultaneous rearrangement of the particles in the set of levels A such that the energy E_A is diminished by the same amount. If the levels of A are populated according to (13) with $\mu = \mu_A$, while the levels of B are populated according to (13) with $\mu = \mu_B$, we have

$$\begin{aligned}
\delta \ln Z_A &= \delta \ln W_A = \mu_A \, \delta Q_A \\
\delta \ln Z_B &= \delta \ln W_B = \mu_B \, \delta Q_B
\end{aligned} \tag{39}$$

When an amount of heat is transferred from A to B, we have

$$\delta Q_A = - \, \delta Q_B$$

and

$$\delta \ln Z_A Z_B = \delta \ln W_A + \delta \ln W_B = (\mu_B - \mu_A) \, \delta Q \tag{40}$$

The condition that this shall be zero is obviously that

$$\mu_A = \mu_B \tag{41}$$

23. The Temperature. We reach the conclusion that two bodies, whatever their sizes and whatever sets of energy levels they have, will be at the same temperature when the levels are populated according to the same value of μ. If the value of μ for one body is not initially equal to the value of μ for the other body, the product $Z_A Z_B$ is less than the greatest value consistent with the total energy $(E_A + E_B)$. Consequently, when the bodies are placed in thermal contact with each other, they will tend to adopt distributions possessing higher values of $Z_A Z_B$; that is to say, distributions for which μ_A and μ_B are more nearly equal, until finally equilibrium is attained. The right-hand side of (40) may have a positive, negative, or zero value. When μ_B is greater than μ_A, the value of (40) is positive and a spontaneous flow of heat from A to B will take place. But when a spontaneous flow of heat from one body to another takes place, we say that the former is at a higher temperature than the latter. Hence the smaller value of μ belongs to the higher temperature. In this way the temperatures of any number of substances can be arranged in order: $t_A > t_B > t_C > \cdots$ if $\mu_A < \mu_B < \mu_C < \cdots$. The possibility of an absolute scale of temperature, founded on (39), will be introduced in Sec. 29.

Consider two bodies of different sizes and let their thermal energy be such that the energy per particle in the one is equal to that in the other, that is, E_A/n_A is equal to E_B/n_B. Let us now ask how the value of $\dfrac{\partial \ln Z_A}{\partial E_A}$ compares with $\dfrac{\partial \ln Z_B}{\partial E_B}$. If the two bodies are of the same chemical substance, these two quantities are equal, no matter how great the difference in size. If, however, the set of levels for a particle in A is different from the set of levels in B, the values of the two quantities are in general different, for we have found that these two quantities are equal when the bodies are at the same *temperature*, and this is a condition that usually requires E_A/n_A not equal to E_B/n_B, since each substance has its own characteristic heat capacity and thermal energy.

24. Consider two bodies A and B at the same temperature. In a transfer of heat from A to B, some particles in B are raised to higher levels, while in A particles are taken down to lower levels; thus for the pair of bodies there are a simultaneous gain and loss of energy, which tend to cancel each other. We may arrange for the cancellation to be complete—so that the total energy $(E_A + E_B)$ remains constant, as above —or incomplete. When it is incomplete, we may expect to find a relation similar to (27); in fact, we can at once derive such a condition from (39). When δQ_A is not equal to $-\delta Q_B$, the pair of bodies gains a certain amount of energy from, or loses a certain amount of energy to, its surroundings. Let the quantity $(\delta Q_B - \delta Q_A)$ be denoted by δQ. When μ_A and μ_B have the same value μ, we obtain from (39)

$$\delta \ln W_A W_B = \mu \, \delta Q \tag{42}$$

Toward (42) we may take the same point of view as we took toward (27). As the condition of equilibrium we demand that, for any redistribution of the energy at constant E, there shall be no change in w. In practice we cannot thermally isolate either one body or a pair of bodies from its surroundings. But (42), like (27), prescribes the condition for equilibrium without the need for thermal isolation, for (42) covers all values of δQ, positive and negative as well as zero, and thus embodies (38) as a special case.

The expression (18) may be put into the form

$$\ln w^* - \ln w = -p \ln n_i + (p + q) \ln n_j - q \ln n_k \qquad (43)$$

Since p and q are respectively the number of particles added to the levels ϵ_i and ϵ_k, we may write $p = \delta n_i$, $q = \delta n_k$, and $\delta n_j = -(p + q)$, giving

$$\ln w^* - \ln w = -\ln n_i \, \delta n_i - \ln n_j \, \delta n_j - \ln n_k \, \delta n_k \qquad (44)$$

In general, if any number of energy levels are involved, the right-hand side will consist of terms of the form $-\ln (n_r) \, \delta n_r$. From (1), using Stirling's approximation, we obtain for $\ln w$ the expressions

$$\ln w = \ln (n!) - \Sigma \ln (n_r!)$$
$$= \ln (n!) - \Sigma(n_r \ln n_r - n_r) \qquad (45)$$

In any redistribution of the energy that leaves the total number of particles unchanged, we obtain the following expression for the change in $\ln w$

$$\delta \ln w = -\Sigma \ln n_r \, \delta n_r \qquad (46)$$

in agreement with (44). This quantity will be equal to zero when w has a maximum value.

Problems

1. Show that, for a given value of $(n_1 + n_2)$, the product of two factorials $n_1!$ and $n_2!$ has the smallest value when $n_1 = n_2$ and therefore that the value of $\dfrac{(n_0 + n_1 + n_2)!}{n_0! \, n_1! \, n_2!}$ is greatest when $n_0 = n_1 = n_2$. How is this to be reconciled with the statement of Sec. 9 that the value of (1) is a maximum when the values of n_0, n_1, and n_2 are in a geometrical progression?

2. A particle has a set of energy levels consisting only of three states ϵ_0, ϵ_1, and ϵ_2, which are like those of Sec. 19 except that they are not equally spaced. Taking $(\epsilon_2 - \epsilon_1)$ equal to $2(\epsilon_1 - \epsilon_0)$, consider a group of n particles and derive the expressions corresponding to (29), (31), and (32).

CHAPTER 2

The Use of Undetermined Multipliers—An Absolute Scale of Temperature—The Partition Function—Bose-Einstein Statistics —A Monatomic Gas

25. The Method of Undetermined Multipliers. The conventional derivation of (19) uses a notation like that of (46) and follows a mathematical procedure that is described in Note 3 of the Appendix.[1] When δn_r particles are added to a level whose energy is ϵ_r, the energy of the particles in this level changes from $n_r \epsilon_r$ to the value $(n_r + \delta n_r)\epsilon_r$, that is, it increases or decreases by the amount $\epsilon_r \delta n_r$ according as δn_r is positive or negative. The condition that in any arbitrary rearrangement of the particles in their levels, the total energy E remains unchanged is

$$\Sigma \epsilon_r \, \delta n_r = 0 \tag{47}$$

The condition that the total number of particles is constant is

$$\Sigma \, \delta n_r = 0 \tag{48}$$

We wish now to make use of the expression

$$\Sigma \ln n_r \, \delta n_r = 0 \tag{49}$$

obtained in Sec. 24, to determine the form of the population of the levels; we wish to find the distribution for which w has the maximum value consistent with the fact that a certain number of particles n are sharing a certain constant total energy E. On looking at (47), (48), and (49), it will be seen that the quantities n and E are not mentioned, nor are they represented by any other constants. It is necessary to introduce two constants, of which one is a pure number and the other has the dimensions of an energy; let these be denoted respectively by λ and $1/\mu$, where μ is the reciprocal of an energy.[2] The values of λ and μ will be determined later in terms of n and E. We make use of these undetermined multipliers in the manner described in the Appendix.

[1] An alternative approach to statistical mechanics, based on the same fundamental principles, will be introduced in Secs. 132–136 of Chapter 8; we shall consider there the assumptions that underlie the derivation of (19) and (57).

[2] For this constant we choose the notation μ, because it will be found to play the same part as the μ of the preceding chapter, whose dimensions were likewise the reciprocal of an energy.

The quantity in (47) becomes a pure number if it is multiplied by μ

$$\Sigma\mu\epsilon_r \; \delta n_r = 0 \tag{50}$$

We likewise multiply (48) by the other constant

$$\Sigma\lambda \; \delta n_r = 0 \tag{51}$$

We now add together (49), (50), and (51), obtaining

$$\Sigma(\ln n_r + \lambda + \mu\epsilon_r) \; \delta n_r = 0 \tag{52}$$

In this equation each r is to take the values 0, 1, 2 ... and (52) expresses the fact that the sum of all the expressions $(\ln n_0 + \lambda + \mu\epsilon_0) \; \delta n_0$ and $(\ln n_1 + \lambda + \mu\epsilon_1) \; \delta n_1$ ... is equal to zero. It is clear that *one* way in which this equation can be satisfied is that each of these bracketed expressions separately be equal to zero. It is shown in Note 3 of the Appendix that this is the *only* way in which (52) can be satisfied. For each value of r the bracketed expression must be zero. We obtain finally for each value of r

$$\ln n_r + \lambda + \mu\epsilon_r = 0 \tag{53}$$

That is to say, the value of w is a maximum when the population of the levels is in accordance with

$$n_r = e^{-\lambda}e^{-\mu\epsilon_r} \tag{54}$$

We thus obtain an exponential population, in agreement with (19). We can now see how values are to be assigned to λ and μ in terms of n and E. The total number of particles is

$$\begin{aligned} n &= n_0 + n_1 + n_2 + \cdots \\ &= e^{-\lambda}(e^{-\mu\epsilon_0} + e^{-\mu\epsilon_1} + e^{\mu\epsilon_2} + \cdots) \\ &= e^{-\lambda}\sum_r e^{-\mu\epsilon_r} \end{aligned} \tag{55}$$

Hence

$$e^{-\lambda} = \frac{n}{\Sigma e^{-\mu\epsilon_r}} \tag{56}$$

and we may write

$$n_r = \frac{ne^{-\mu\epsilon_r}}{P} \tag{57}$$

where

$$P = \sum_r e^{-\mu\epsilon_r} \tag{58}$$

The physical meaning of the quantity P will be discussed in Sec. 31. The total energy is given by

$$E = \sum_r n_r\epsilon_r = \frac{n}{P}\sum \epsilon_r e^{-\mu\epsilon_r} \tag{59}$$

26. Equilibrium between Two Groups of Particles. We discussed in Sec. 22 a group of particles in thermal contact with another group of particles of a different species. The method of Sec. 25 can be applied to the problem in two ways. We can treat each group of particles separately, introducing constants λ and μ for one group and λ' and μ' for the other group; we can then show, as was done in Sec. 22, that for equilibrium the condition is $\mu' = \mu$.

Alternatively, the problem can be treated as follows. When the two groups are in thermal contact, three conditions must be met. In one group the number of particles n is to remain constant, in the other group the number of particles n' is to remain constant, and the total energy $(E + E')$ is to remain constant. We shall therefore introduce three undetermined multipliers, two of which are to be pure numbers and the third an energy or the reciprocal of an energy. Denoting these by λ, λ', and μ, we shall write

$$\Sigma\lambda \, \delta n_r = 0 \tag{60}$$

$$\Sigma\lambda' \, \delta n_r' = 0 \tag{61}$$

$$\Sigma\mu(\epsilon_r \, \delta n_r + \epsilon_r' \, \delta n_r') = 0 \tag{62}$$

Following the same procedure as before, we obtain the equation

$$\Sigma(\ln n_r' + \lambda' + \mu\epsilon_r') \, \delta n_r' + \Sigma(\ln n_r + \lambda + \mu\epsilon_r) \, \delta n_r = 0 \tag{63}$$

From this we may draw the conclusion that for both sets of energy levels the population will be of the simple exponential form (57), with the same value of μ for the two groups of particles. We thus verify that two groups of particles are at the same temperature[1] when the energy levels are populated according to the same value of μ.

27. The Value of W. Returning to a single body, we may recognize again that when we say that the distribution is given by (57), we mean that so many configurations have the form (57) that all others occur seldom and may be neglected. In deriving (57) we had to pay attention to values of w that belong to those rare configurations, as well as to the maximum value that belongs to the most probable distribution of the energy E. In the remainder of this book we are mainly concerned with the value of w belonging to the most probable state. We shall denote this, as in (36), by a capital letter W. The value of W is obtained by substituting (57) in (45). We find

$$\ln W = n \ln n - \sum_r n_r \ln n_r$$

$$= n \ln n - \frac{n}{P} \sum e^{-\mu\epsilon_r} \ln\left(\frac{ne^{-\mu\epsilon_r}}{P}\right)$$

$$= n \ln n - n(\ln n - \ln P) \frac{\Sigma e^{-\mu\epsilon_r}}{P} + \mu \frac{n}{P} \sum \epsilon_r e^{-\mu\epsilon_r} \tag{64}$$

Comparing (64) with (59), we see that the last term in (64) is just μE. We have then

$$\ln W = n \ln P + \mu E \tag{65}$$

[1] A different and more satisfactory method of introducing the temperature will be given in Sec. 134.

It will be seen that the expression (27), obtained in Sec. 16 for a fixed set of levels, can be derived from (65). Let a small quantity of heat δQ flow into the body, sufficient to raise a few particles to higher levels. This process is not to be accompanied by a change in the value of any of the allowed energies, that is, it is a process at constant volume and without a change in the intensity of any external field. Since there is no change in P, the first term on the right-hand side is constant and furthermore $\delta E = \delta Q$; thus we arrive again at the expression (27). It will be shown in Sec. 54 that (27) and (37) are correct even when the volume is not maintained constant. In Sec. 28 we shall begin to consider processes where the volume is allowed to change.

28. Changes in Volume. We used in Sec. 1 the basic idea that the energy of a particle is quantized when the particle is confined in a certain volume. The allowed values of the energy, ϵ_0, ϵ_1, $\epsilon_r \ldots$, depend on the volume available for the vibration of the particle. It is hardly necessary to point out that this volume is quite different from the size of the particle; its value depends on the interatomic forces that restrain the motion of the particle. In one solid a large atom may have little freedom of vibration, while in another solid a small atom may have a larger amplitude.

Normally in the laboratory a solid is subject to atmospheric pressure. If this pressure is removed or reduced, the substance expands slightly; the additional volume is shared among the particles, and the volume available to each particle is larger than before. Conversely, if the solid is subjected to a higher pressure, the volume available to each particle is reduced. Any change in volume alters the allowed values of some or all of the energy levels. In general, a decrease in volume leads to wider spacing between the energy levels. This fact can be very simply understood in terms of wave mechanics,[1] where each particle is represented by a ψ-wave, whose wavelength is correlated with the average kinetic energy of the particle.

Quantization of the energy is ascribed entirely to the fact that only those energies will occur whose wavelengths are suitable to fit into the volume in which the particle is confined; no other energies are allowed. If we now subject the substance to an increased pressure, thereby diminishing the volume for each particle, clearly the original wavelengths will no longer be suitable; we shall need progressively shorter wavelengths. This means that the values of the allowed energies will be altered. Conversely, if we reduce the pressure and allow the volume to increase, the values of the allowed energies will be shifted in the opposite direction.

For any volume, the allowed values ϵ_0, ϵ_1, $\epsilon_2 \ldots \epsilon_r \ldots$ are the energies belonging to the different wave functions ψ_0, ψ_1, $\psi_2 \ldots \psi_r \ldots$. When the volume has a particular

---

[1] See, for example, R. W. Gurney, "Elementary Quantum Mechanics," 2d ed., Cambridge, 1940.

value v, two or more ψ-functions may happen to have energies that are the same or nearly the same, giving rise to what is sometimes called a "multiple level." In this book we usually assign the numbers 0, 1, 2 ... r ... to the individual ψ-functions, that is, to the separate energy states, so that the concept of a multiple level is usually avoided, as pointed out in the footnote to Sec. 14.

When we change the volume, each ψ-function may undergo a progressive change of form; no new ψ-functions are created, and none cease to exist. After a change of volume the number of possible states remains the same, but the set of allowed energies for a particle is different, and the spacing of the levels is different.

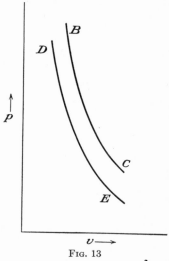

FIG. 13

In Secs. 13 and 23 we considered the thermal equilibrium between a group of particles A populating a certain set of levels and a group of particles B populating another set of levels, for example, a piece of copper and a piece of silver. We may notice now that the particles forming the group B need not be of a different species from those forming the group A. If we wish to discuss two slightly different sets of levels, we may consider two identical bodies subjected to different external pressures. The two bodies will be at the same temperature when the two sets of levels are populated with the same value of μ.

29. An Absolute Scale of Temperature. The relations between the volume of any body and the pressure are most easily seen on the familiar p-v diagrams. The curve showing the relation between p and v at any temperature is called the "isothermal" for this temperature. Normally, when an amount of heat is added to a solid, the body expands; the volume can be maintained constant by increasing the external pressure. A process at constant volume will be represented on Fig. 13 by a vertical line.

Let the curve BC be part of the isothermal for a body at a certain temperature, and let us consider the populations corresponding to different points on this curve. Any two points on BC correspond to different values of v and consequently to different sets of energy levels. According to (41) in Sec. 22, these energy levels will be populated with the same value of μ. Consider a short vertical line passing through the point B, corresponding to the addition of a small quantity of heat δQ at constant volume. The expression (27) in Sec. 16 gives the value of $\delta \ln W$ that accompanies this process. If we had chosen any other point on the curve BC, we would have obtained the same change in $\ln W$. On the other hand, if we had chosen any point *not* lying on the isothermal BC, we would certainly have obtained a different change in ln W for the same quantity of heat. Take, for example, any points on the isothermal DE, drawn for a different temperature, and consider the addition of the same amount of heat δQ as before, at constant volume. For any two points on DE the value of δ ln W will be the same but will be different from the value obtained for any point on BC or for any point that does not lie on DE. These considerations are true for any chemical substance.

Let us now put the argument in the reverse form. Fixing our attention on a certain value of δ ln W, let us ask how much heat, admitted at constant volume, is required to bring about this selected change in ln W. For any two points on the isothermal BC the same amount of heat is required; but this value is different from the amount required for any point on the isothermal DE. Let the ratio between these two amounts of heat be denoted by m. This proposal suggests the possibility of defining an absolute scale of temperature, by saying that the isothermal BC belongs to a temperature that is exactly m times the temperature to which the isothermal DE belongs. If, for example, m is equal to 2, we can say that one temperature is exactly *twice* the other temperature. If, in another case, m is equal to 100, one temperature is 100 times the other, and so on. If we define a scale of temperature in this way, it will be an absolute scale, in the sense that it will be the same for any chemical substance. According to (37) in Sec. 21, this definition says that the absolute temperature, which may be denoted by T, is to be proportional to the reciprocal of μ. This is consistent with the fact that has been mentioned more than once, that the smaller the value of μ, the higher the temperature. It will be recalled that μ has the dimensions of the reciprocal of an energy. If then we define T by writing

$$\mu = \frac{1}{kT} \tag{66}$$

the constant of proportionality k must be such that the product kT has the dimensions of an energy. The scale of temperature defined in this way corresponds to the absolute scale introduced by Lord Kelvin in 1854 (see Sec. 54). On this scale, when centigrade degrees are used, the value that must be assigned to k is 1.3805×10^{-16} erg per degree, which is equivalent to 8.62×10^{-5} electron-volt per degree. It is convenient to bear in mind that near room temperature the value of kT will be about $\frac{1}{40}$ electron-volt.

30. A Group of Particles at Temperature T. Substituting for μ in (57), we obtain a basic expression of statistical mechanics

$$n_r = \frac{ne^{-\epsilon_r/kT}}{P} \tag{67}$$

where

$$P = \Sigma e^{-\epsilon_r/kT} \tag{68}$$

The expression for the total energy becomes

$$E = \sum n_r \epsilon_r = \frac{n}{P} \sum \epsilon_r e^{-\epsilon_r/kT} \tag{69}$$

While (65) will now give the value of $\ln W$ in the form

$$\ln W = n \ln P + \frac{E}{kT} \tag{70}$$

the expression (27) derived in Sec. 16 for any fixed set of levels now takes the form

$$\delta \ln W = \frac{\delta Q}{kT} \tag{71}$$

The definition of the absolute temperature T and of the constant k are such that, if an amount of heat equal to kT is allowed to flow into any body, the increase in $\ln W$ is equal to unity. As we know that the value of W is extremely sensitive to the number of particles in the body, it may seem strange that (71) prescribes a change in $\ln W$ that is independent of the size and composition. One should, however, bear in mind that the smaller body will have a relatively smaller heat capacity and that the admission of a given quantity of heat will therefore tend to cause a greater incipient change of temperature. As a result, although for the smaller body $\ln W$ may have a much smaller value, the *change* in $\ln W$ will be just as great as for the larger body. At any rate, the expression (71) asserts that the addition of an amount of heat equal to kT will cause the value of W to be multiplied by the factor 2.718, irrespective of the size or composition of the body.

31. The Partition Function. The expression (67) gives the number of particles in any one quantized state of energy ϵ_r. For use in many problems, we need an expression that sums up concisely the character of the population of the set of levels at temperature T. Consider, for example, a solid that is partially vaporized; we need to know the value of the vapor pressure that will be in equilibrium with the solid. The point of view adopted in statistical mechanics is that in the vapor the particles have a set of energy levels available to them, and in the solid they have another set of energy levels available to them; a steady state is reached when the population of one set of levels is in equilibrium with the population of the other set. Every problem of equilibrium is approached in the same way and is described in terms of the way in which the available energy levels are populated. We should therefore have a simple way of prescribing the conditions for any equilibrium if for each set of levels we could find a compact expression that would describe, in convenient form, the way in which the set of levels is populated at temperature T. In fact, quantities can easily be derived that have the property that any equilibrium can be expressed in terms of a ratio between them. Such quantities are known as "partition functions."

Consider n particles distributed through energy levels having a set of values ϵ_r, populated in accordance with (67), and consider how the population would be different if the value of *one* of these allowed energies had been different. Obviously, the average number of particles in *each* of the occupied levels would be different, for if the number of particles in one level is changed, this leaves a different number of particles to be distributed among the remaining levels. It is clear then that the required expression, the partition function for this set of levels, must necessarily mention the energy ϵ_r of *every* occupied level, as well as the temperature T.

We have so far discussed sets of levels of only one type. It will be shown in Chapter 3 that for such a set of levels the sum $\Sigma e^{-\epsilon_r/kT}$, which occurs in the denominator of (67) and which was denoted by P, has the desired properties. This sum is sometimes known as the "sum-over-states." We shall provisionally adopt the quantity P as the partition function for a particle in a solid. It should, however, be borne in mind that when we come to look more closely at the behavior of particles in a solid, we may find it convenient to fix our attention on some other quantity and to introduce some other definition for our partition function. In the meantime we shall examine the properties of P as given by (68).

32. The numerical value of P will evidently depend on the zero of energy from which the values of ϵ_r are measured. We have seen that when the ground level ϵ_0 is chosen as the zero of energy, the thermal energy of the particles becomes identical with E and that this forms a natural zero of energy for any group of particles. In this case, the first term in the summation, namely, $e^{-\epsilon_0/kT}$ is equal to unity, since we have written $\epsilon_0 = 0$; and each of the succeeding terms is less than unity. The partition function takes the form

$$1 + e^{-\epsilon_1/kT} + e^{-\epsilon_2/kT} + \cdots \tag{72}$$

With increasing values of ϵ_r the values of succeeding terms diminish; when ϵ_r is large compared with kT the values are so small that further terms need not be included.[1] In Fig. 12 the population of a set of levels at a certain temperature was represented by means of a diagram. On a vertical scale the positions of the various allowed energies ϵ_0, $\epsilon_1 \ldots \epsilon_r \ldots$ were marked off; then, with the length of the base line representing the value of n_0, the exponential curve $e^{-\mu\epsilon}$ was drawn. The lengths of the other horizontal lines drawn to meet this curve had the values $n_0 e^{-\mu\epsilon_1}$, $n_0 e^{-\mu\epsilon_2}$, and so on, that is to say, the values of n_1, $n_2 \ldots$ enabling us to visualize the population of the levels at a particular temperature.

By a similar diagram in which the allowed energies are marked off on a vertical scale, we can obtain a useful graphic representation of the partition function. If the length of the base line is taken to be unity and the exponential curve $e^{-\epsilon/kT}$ is drawn as in Fig. 12, the lengths of the

[1] See Table 17.

other horizontal lines have the values $e^{-\epsilon_1/kT}$, $e^{-\epsilon_2/kT}$ .... The sum of the lengths of all the horizontal lines, drawn to meet the curve, is therefore

$$1 + e^{-\epsilon_1/kT} + e^{-\epsilon_2/kT} + \cdots$$

Thus, in this diagram, the sum of the lengths of the horizontal lines for any temperature T enables us to visualize the value of the partition function, just as in Fig. 9 the sum of the lengths of the vertical lines represented Z.

Figure 14c has been drawn for a set of levels that has on the average narrower spacing than those of Fig. 14a. Clearly the value of the partition function depends upon the spacing between the levels. When the spacing

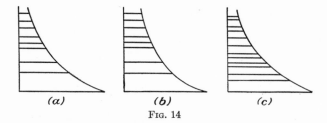

(a)   *(b)*   *(c)*

FIG. 14

is narrow, there are numerous horizontal lines, and the numerical value of P is large.

Let us consider next the variation of P with temperature. In Fig. 14b, again taking the base line to represent unity and drawing a curve for a smaller value of μ, the lengths of all the other lines are greater than in Fig. 14a; thus dP/dT is positive.

33. Consider now the population of any set of levels, which is given by

$$\frac{n_r}{n} = \frac{e^{-\epsilon_r/kT}}{P} \tag{73}$$

A rise of temperature throws particles up from the lower to the higher levels. That is to say, in each of the high levels the number of particles increases, while in the lowest levels the number decreases; in Fig. 12 some horizontal lines become longer, while others become shorter. By examining (73) one can see in what way the change in P is responsible for this behavior. With rise of temperature, both the numerator and the denominator on the right-hand side of (73) steadily increase, but at different rates. For a large value of ϵ_r the value of the numerator increases rapidly —more rapidly than the denominator. For the smallest values of ϵ_r, however, the numerator does not increase so rapidly as P. In particular, for the lowest level, when this level has been taken as the zero of energy, we have at all temperatures from (73)

$$\frac{n_0}{n} = \frac{e^0}{P} = \frac{1}{P} \tag{74}$$

Thus with rise of temperature the value of n_0 decreases in proportion as P increases; at any temperature the reciprocal of the partition function gives the fraction of the total number of particles that are in the ground level.

Referring again to Fig. 12, we see that, in constructing diagrams to represent the population of a set of levels at two different temperatures, the lengths of the base line in each case, representing n_0, must be taken inversely proportional to P. This ensures that the sum of the lengths of all the lines shall be the same, representing the same total number of particles n.

34. Although we usually take the lowest level as the zero of energy, we shall sometimes wish to use a partition function in which the levels are measured from a zero that lies below or above the ground level. Take, for example, a zero that lies below the ground level by an amount η. We may denote the new energies of the levels by ϵ_0', ϵ_1', ... ϵ_r', where ϵ_r' will be equal to $(\epsilon_r + \eta)$. The new value of the partition function is

$$P' = e^{-(\epsilon_0 + \eta)/kT} + e^{-(\epsilon_1 + \eta)/kT} + \cdots + e^{-(\epsilon_r + \eta)/kT} + \cdots \qquad (75)$$

But this is equal to

$$P' = e^{-\eta/kT}(e^{-\epsilon_0/kT} + e^{-\epsilon_1/kT} + \cdots + e^{-\epsilon_r/kT} + \cdots)$$

$$= e^{-\eta/kT}P \qquad (76)$$

Thus if we wish to take a new zero of energy that lies lower by an amount η, we have only to multiply the original partition function by the factor $e^{-\eta/kT}$. Conversely, if we take a zero that lies higher by an amount η, we shall have to multiply the original partition function by the factor $e^{\eta/kT}$.

The value of n_r/n in (73) for each of the populated levels must obviously be independent of the zero of energy to which we have chosen to refer the values of allowed energy. The result obtained in (76) ensures that this is so, since any alteration in the choice of a zero of energy will cause both the numerator and denominator in (73) to be multiplied by the same factor.

In later chapters it will often be necessary to consider, for each particle, two alternative sets of levels at the same time, and the values of the partition functions P_A and P_B belonging to the two sets of levels. We may notice at once that if the ratio of the numerical values of P_A and P_B has a certain value when a particular zero of energy has been chosen for both, then the ratio P_A/P_B will continue to have the same value whatever other zero of energy is used. This is because a shift in the zero of energy will multiply both P_A and P_B by the same factor, according to (76). In particular, if the values of P_A and P_B are equal when measured from some zero of energy, they are equal when measured from any other zero of energy.

35. We have already seen that dP/dT is positive; let us now obtain an expression for dP/dT.

We have

$$\frac{dP}{dT} = \frac{d}{dT}(e^{-\epsilon_0/kT} + e^{-\epsilon_1/kT} + \cdots + e^{-\epsilon_r/kT} + \cdots)$$

$$= \frac{\epsilon_0}{kT^2}e^{-\epsilon_0/kT} + \frac{\epsilon_1}{kT^2}e^{-\epsilon_1/kT} + \frac{\epsilon_r}{kT^2}e^{-\epsilon_r/kT} + \cdots \qquad (77)$$

Comparing (77) with (69), we obtain

$$\frac{n}{P}\frac{dP}{dT} = \frac{1}{kT^2}(n_0\epsilon_0 + n_1\epsilon_1 + \cdots + n_r\epsilon_r + \cdots)$$

$$= \frac{E}{kT^2}$$

Now

$$\frac{1}{P}\frac{dP}{dT} = \frac{d}{dT}(\ln P)$$

Hence we obtain a useful expression for the total energy

$$E = nkT^2\frac{d}{dT}(\ln P)$$

Mention was made in Sec. 28 of the fact that any change in volume is accompanied by changes in the values of the allowed energies. The character of these changes is such that, with increase in the volume available to a particle, the spacing becomes narrower, and with decrease in volume the spacing becomes wider. Under constant pressure, a rise of temperature is in general accompanied by an increase in volume, that is, thermal expansion. The volume may be maintained constant if the applied external pressure is raised by the required amount. We considered above how the partition function would vary with temperature; we must now recognize that we were discussing the variation of P at constant volume, since we took the values of ϵ_r to be constants. The above expression for E must therefore be written in the form

$$E = nkT^2\left(\frac{\partial \ln P}{\partial T}\right)_v \qquad (78)$$

36. A Monatomic Gas or Vapor. In applying statistical principles to the particles of a gas at low pressure, we find that the treatment must differ from that of a simple solid in two respects. In the first place we usually consider a gas to be contained in a vessel that has a volume of a few cubic centimeters at least, in contrast to the atomic volume available to a particle in the interior of a solid. We have seen that the spacing between the energy levels of a particle is determined by the volume in which the particle is free to move—the larger the volume the closer the spacing. Here the volume may be more than 10^{24} times larger than for an atom in the interior of a solid; consequently the spacing between successive energy levels is not wide, as in a solid, but is exceedingly narrow. Within a small range of energy there is an enormous number of quantized states. In a solid each particle has a comparatively small number of vibrational levels; in a gas, on the other hand, the number of levels available to each particle is not only very large but at ordinary pressure is much larger than the number of particles present.

In a solid, or in a gas, at any moment some particles have thermal energy considerably larger than the average; however, few particles have thermal energy five or six times larger than the average, and the total energy belonging to these few particles is a small fraction of E. In discussing the partition function, it was pointed out that beyond a certain point the terms in (72) make a negligible contribution, and that, in order to have a reasonably accurate value of P, it is only necessary to include the terms over a certain range of energy. When we speak of "the energy levels of a particle in a solid," we usually have in mind the levels that are included in a range of energy a little wider than that depicted in Fig. 12. In the same way, when we discuss a particle in a gas at ordinary temperatures, we shall have in mind all the possible quantized states contained in a similar range of energy. In any vessel the number of these states is much larger than the number of particles that will be present at ordinary pressures. (In a larger vessel we can have more molecules at the same pressure, but at the same time we shall have still more energy states because the spacing will be still narrower.)

In discussing a monatomic gas at low pressures, we begin, as is usual, by neglecting the volume occupied by the molecules themselves in comparison with the volume of the vessel, and we neglect the intermolecular forces of attraction and repulsion that only come into play during collisions between molecules. That is to say, in this chapter we discuss a perfect gas; we shall discuss an imperfect gas in Chapter 9.

For each particle there is a set of allowed energies, depending on the volume of the vessel. With the continual interchange of energy, the particles in the gas will be continually moving from one level to another. In a short interval of time all of these possible quantized states will have been represented. At any moment, on the other hand, few of them can be occupied. Even if every particle were in a different quantized state, there would not be enough particles to fill more than a few of these quantized states. We have then a dense set of levels, sparsely populated by the particles. In describing the population we shall of course be interested in the time average. Taking a time average, the number of particles in any quantized state will be a number less than unity; in fact, at ordinary pressures, it will be small compared with unity. The method of deriving an expression for the population is necessarily different from that followed in the case of a solid.

37. The other respect in which the statistics will differ is of a more fundamental nature. In introducing Fig. 1, we took a point A about which a particle was vibrating and assumed other points B and C about which similar particles were vibrating. In Fig. 2 we could distinguish, for example, the state in which the particle at the point A was in the level 3 from the state in which the particle at B or C was in the level 3. We carefully refrained from labeling the particles, which are not distinguishable from one another; we labeled only the points about which they vibrate. When a gas, on the other hand, is contained in a vessel, each particle is free to move through the same volume—the volume of the vessel. The pair of horizontal lines in Fig. 15 is intended to represent any two energy levels ϵ_r and ϵ_s and the two dots are intended to represent the state that may be described as one particle in the level ϵ_r and one particle in the level ϵ_s. If the particles are of the same species, there are not two states answering to this description; one cannot, by interchanging the particles, obtain a state distinguishable from the first; therefore to speak of interchanging the particles has no meaning. The same is true for any number of particles of the same species.

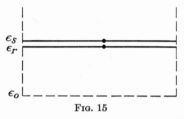

FIG. 15

Clearly the discussion must take a form quite different from that followed for a solid. The main focus of attention in Secs. 4–8 was the number of ways w in which each distribution could arise. In the problem of Fig. 5, for example, we supposed that we had 20 distinguishable sites for the particles. Given certain values of n_0, n_1, and so on we found that the particles could be rearranged among these 20 sites in more than 10^8 different ways. In the case of a gas, however, if we are told which quantum states are occupied, this distribution can arise in only one way because no distinguishable rearrangement is possible.

38. Consider a pure monatomic gas or vapor contained in a vessel having a volume of a few cubic centimeters. For each moving atom the kinetic energy ϵ is quantized. We may consider a small range of energy, say, between ϵ_r and $(\epsilon_r + \delta\epsilon_r)$, and find in this interval a large number of possible quantized states for a particle. Our attitude to these levels will be similar to that which we adopted in the case of a solid, that is, it is not the business of statistical mechanics to say how many possible quantized states lie in each interval of energy; that information must be supplied by quantum theory. Given this information, it is the aim of statistical mechanics to predict how these levels will be populated when a group of n particles is sharing a total energy E. Let us fix our attention on any narrow interval between ϵ_r and $(\epsilon_r + \delta\epsilon_r)$; in this interval let the number of quantized states for a particle be denoted by p_r. Then if the average number of particles populating this batch of states is n_r, the average number of particles per state is obviously n_r/p_r. If all the states in this narrow interval are regarded as having sensibly the same energy ϵ_r, then they are equally populated, and, taking a time average, each state in this batch is populated to the extent n_r/p_r. This is how we shall describe the population: If to every energy ϵ we can assign a quantity of the form n_r/p_r, we thereby describe how the whole set of levels is populated. In (67) we found, in the case of a solid, an expression for n_r that was applicable to any arbitrary set of levels. So here we do not need to have any previous knowledge of how the density of states varies with ϵ; we seek an expression

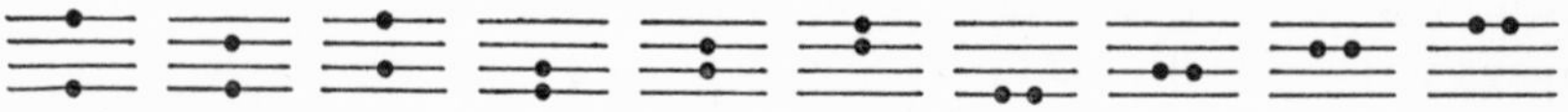

Fig. 16

for n_r/p_r that shall be applicable to any set of levels in which the density of states is high.

At atmospheric pressure 5 cubic centimeters of a monatomic gas contain more than 10^{20} particles. We could therefore divide the total range of energy into 10^{16} narrow intervals (not equal), each containing more than 1000 particles. In making this division into narrow intervals, it is convenient to choose each interval sufficiently wide that the average number of particles n_r present in these levels is large compared with unity; then we can use Stirling's approximation, or other approximations. In any sparsely populated set of levels, if we fix attention on the p_r quantized states in any one narrow interval of energy, it is clear that the n_r particles in this interval can be distributed among the p_r states in a variety of ways; this is true of any interval of energy. It thus comes about that for the whole population the value of w is very large, in spite of the fact mentioned above, that each distribution can arise in only one way.

39. Bose-Einstein Statistics. Taking first a small number of states, Fig. 16 shows, as an illustration, all the ways in which two particles can be distributed among a batch of four states. In contrast to the distributions of Fig. 3, each of these must be counted only once; there are thus altogether ten ways in which these two particles may be distributed among these four states. In general, the number of ways in which n particles may be distributed among p states without restriction on the number that may be put into each state[1] is

$$\frac{(n + p - 1)!}{n!\,(p - 1)!} \tag{79}$$

---

[1] For elementary particles such as electrons, on the other hand, the Pauli exclusion principle applies. According to this principle *only one* particle can be put into each

Substituting, for example, $p = 4$ and $n = 2$, we find the value 10, in agreement with Fig. 16. In practice, as was mentioned above, we shall choose much larger batches of levels. In every case we shall choose the value of p so large that the value of (79) will differ by a negligible amount from the following simpler expression, which we may use instead

$$\frac{(n + p)!}{n! \, p!} \tag{80}$$

For this purpose it is convenient to include a large number of energy states in each batch; on the other hand, the width of the range of energy must not be too great; otherwise it would be inaccurate to treat these states as all having the same energy ϵ. Even so, this leaves considerable latitude as to how successive batches of levels may be chosen; the essence of the method lies in the fact that the final result is independent of the particular way in which they have been chosen.

40. Starting with the lowest allowed levels (which almost coincide with zero kinetic energy) we designate a batch containing p_0 states, each having an energy ϵ_0; immediately above these we designate a batch of p_1 states, each having an energy ϵ_1; immediately above these a batch of p_2 states, each having an energy ϵ_2, and so on. For the particles within any one batch of states, (80) may be used. Furthermore, the arrangement of the particles within any one interval is independent of the arrangement of the particles within every other interval. Hence the value of w for the whole population is given by the product

$$w = \frac{(n_0 + p_0)!}{n_0! p_0!} \times \frac{(n_1 + p_1)!}{n_1! p_1!} \times \cdots \times \frac{(n_r + p_r)!}{n_r! p_r!} \times \cdots \tag{81}$$

This is the expression which, for a gas or vapor, replaces the expression (1) with which we have been, directly or indirectly, concerned in nearly every paragraph of the foregoing chapters. Corresponding to each conclusion that has been drawn from (1) there will now be either a similar or else a somewhat different conclusion to be drawn from (81).

41. We may begin by asking what will be the change in w if we remove a particle from the rth batch of levels without disturbing any other particles. In (81) only the rth term will be affected. In the denominator p_r is constant, but the first term of factorial n_r will fall out; and in the numerator the first term of $(n_r + p_r)!$ will fall out. We find immediately that w is reduced to the value w^*, given by

$$\frac{w^*}{w} = \frac{n_r}{n_r + p_r} \qquad \text{(removal of particle)} \qquad \cdots \tag{82a}$$

energy state; the Fermi-Dirac statistics that result from the exclusion principle will be discussed in Secs. 175 and 176. The statistics that result from the use of (79) are known as the "Bose-Einstein statistics."

At ordinary pressures n_r is small compared with p_r, and the right-hand side of (82a) is scarcely different from n_r/p_r, which is the degree to which the levels are populated in the interval of energy considered. Conversely, when a particle is added to any level in this interval, without disturbing the other particles, we obtain an expression that reduces to the reciprocal of (82a) when n_r is large compared with unity

$$\frac{w^*}{w} = \frac{n_r + p_r}{n_r} \qquad \text{(addition of particle)} \qquad \cdots \quad (82b)$$

which simplifies to p_r/n_r at ordinary pressures.

In Sec. 14, in the case of a solid, we found in (14) an expression for the change in w when a particle is shifted from one level to another. In the case of a gas we may use (82) to find the change in w when a particle is moved from one energy level to any distant energy level, say from the jth batch to the rth. For the removal of the particle from the former we use (82a) and for the addition of the particle to the latter we use (82b), giving

$$\frac{w^*}{w} = \frac{n_j}{n_j + p_j} \frac{n_r + p_r}{n_r} \tag{83}$$

At ordinary pressures this reduces to n_j/p_j divided by n_r/p_r, which may be expressed in the form of a rule, to replace the rule (15) that was obtained for a solid.

The expressions (82) and (83) are correct, whatever the form of the population. We are interested in finding what form will have the greatest value of w. This can be obtained from (81) by the method of undetermined multipliers, or from (83) by the method used in Sec. 9; that is, from any batch of states we take two particles and shift one to a higher and the other to a lower level, in such a way that the total energy remains constant. We need only to fix attention on any three energies that are equally spaced. For comparison with (14) these may be denoted by ϵ_i, ϵ_j, and ϵ_k. One particle is shifted from an arbitrary batch of states at ϵ_j to one at ϵ_k, while at the same time another particle is shifted from ϵ_j to ϵ_i; the total energy remains unchanged. The change in w is the product of two expressions like (83), one for each particle shifted. We find at once that the required condition is that three quantities must be in a geometrical progression; these three quantities are, namely,

$$\frac{n_i + p_i}{n_i}, \quad \frac{n_j + p_j}{n_j}, \quad \text{and} \quad \frac{n_k + p_k}{n_k}.$$

This condition must hold throughout the whole set of levels, whatever energies we choose to consider. Expressing the population as a function of ϵ, we obtain, as before, an exponential relation; for any energy ϵ_r we have

$$\frac{n_r + p_r}{n_r} = A e^{\mu \epsilon_r} \tag{84}$$

$$\frac{n_r}{p_r} = \frac{1}{A e^{\mu \epsilon_r} - 1} \tag{85}$$

If the constant μ has a positive value, the higher energy levels are progressively less populated, since with increasing ϵ_r the value of the denominator in (85) increases and the value of n_r/p_r declines. The lowest levels, as usual, are the most thickly populated.

42. We can now find the expressions corresponding to (23) and (27) that were obtained in Sec. 16 for a solid. Consider any two energies ϵ_j and ϵ_r, separated by an amount $\eta = (\epsilon_r - \epsilon_j)$. By substituting (84) into (81), we can find the change in w when an amount of heat η is admitted to or removed from, the group of particles. For a population that has the form (84), we find

$$\frac{W^*}{W} = \frac{A e^{\mu \epsilon_r}}{A e^{\mu \epsilon_j}} = e^{\mu \eta} \tag{86}$$

This result is precisely the same as that which was obtained for a solid in (23). If an amount of heat δQ, sufficient to shift many particles, is admitted or removed, we find as before that for any fixed set of levels

$$\delta \ln W = \delta Q \tag{87}$$

43. Before discussing (85) further, we shall now derive it by the method of undetermined multipliers. From (81) we have

$$\ln w = \ln \frac{(n_0 + p_0)!}{n_0! \, p_0!} + \ln \frac{(n_1 + p_1)!}{n_1! \, p_1!} + \cdots \tag{88}$$

$$= \Sigma (n_r + p_r) \ln (n_r + p_r) - \Sigma n_r \ln n_r - \Sigma p_r \ln p_r \tag{89}$$

The maximum value of $\ln w$ is found from the condition that $\delta \ln w$ is zero for any small shifts of particles from one batch of levels to another, the value of each p_r remaining constant. We have

$$\sum \frac{\partial \ln w}{\partial n_r} \delta n_r = \sum \ln (n_r + p_r) \, \delta n_r - \sum \ln n_r \, \delta n_r$$

$$= \sum \ln \frac{n_r + p_r}{n_r} \delta n_r \tag{90}$$

We wish to find the condition that $\ln w$ shall have its maximum value, subject to the restrictions that the total number of particles and the total energy have the given values n and E. Using as undetermined multipliers $- \lambda$ and $- \mu$, we write

$$\sum \left[\ln \left(1 + \frac{p_r}{n_r} \right) - \lambda - \mu \epsilon_r \right] \delta n_r = 0 \tag{91}$$

Whence

$$1 + \frac{p_r}{n_r} = e^\lambda e^{\mu \epsilon_r} \tag{92}$$

$$\frac{n_r}{p_r} = \frac{1}{e^\lambda e^{\mu \epsilon_r} - 1} \tag{93}$$

which agrees with (85).

44. Let us now consider the relations between p_r and n_r. In Sec. 40 we considered a narrow range of energy between ϵ_r and $(\epsilon_r + \delta \epsilon_r)$, and we denoted by p_r the number of energy states lying within this range of energy. The value of p_r depends on the volume of the vessel in which the particles move. The value of n_r, on the other hand, depends on the total number of particles that have been put into this vessel. If few particles have been put into the vessel, we can be sure that n_r/p_r is small compared with unity, even for the most highly populated batch of levels, namely, the lowest batch: In this case the term p_r/n_r, which occurs on the left-hand side of (92), is very large compared with unity for all values of r; we may substitute p_r/n_r for $(1 + p_r/n_r)$ in (92). Hence, taking the reciprocal, we obtain

$$\frac{n_r}{p_r} = e^{-\lambda} e^{-\mu \epsilon_r} \tag{94}$$

At any moment the majority of the states are unoccupied, but the graded character of the population may be expressed by saying that each batch of levels is less populated than any equal batch of lower energy and more populated than any equal batch of higher energy. The numerical magnitudes in (93) will be discussed in Sec. 177; it will be shown that the simple form (94) is accurate, not only at low pressures but under all conditions at which gases and vapors are usually studied. It is true that at very low temperatures the particles tend to crowd into the lowest levels, and (93) will differ appreciably from (94), but this takes place only very near the absolute zero, where the vapor will no longer behave like a perfect gas. In this chapter, in discussing a perfect gas, we shall confine our attention to the simple form (94).

The quantities $p_0, p_1 \ldots p_r$ are no longer of any interest. The arbitrary subdivisions of the set of levels have served their purpose and may now be eliminated. If we fix attention on any energy ϵ_r, the quantity n_r/p_r, which is a number small compared with unity, gives the degree to which the levels near ϵ_r are populated on the average, quite irrespective of the value of p_r. If we take small values of p_r, the values of n_r will be less than unity. Although hitherto this was to be avoided, it is no longer a disadvantage; in fact, we are at liberty in (94) to set p_r equal to unity. Whereas the letter r in (94) has hitherto referred to the numbering of the batches of energy states, it will now refer to the numbering of the individual energy states; n_r will denote the average number of particles in the particular state to which the letter r has been allotted. With this notation, we obtain

$$n_r = e^{-\lambda}e^{-\mu\epsilon_r} \tag{95}$$

Since $n = \Sigma n_r$, this gives

$$e^{-\lambda} = \frac{n}{\Sigma e^{-\mu\epsilon_r}} \tag{96}$$

and yields expressions identical with (57), (58), and (59) obtained in Sec. 25 for a group of localized particles:

$$n_r = \frac{ne^{-\mu\epsilon_r}}{P} \tag{97}$$

where

$$P = \Sigma e^{-\mu\epsilon_r} \tag{98}$$

We have been discussing a gas contained in a vessel having a certain volume v; the set of energy levels ϵ_r is the set belonging to this volume. As mentioned above, the lowest energy level ϵ_0 practically coincides with zero kinetic energy and is independent of the volume.

45. At ordinary pressures and temperatures, a population of the form (97) is the one that has the greatest value of w for the given value of E. There will be many distributions that do not have this form, but if the group of particles is sufficiently large, these distributions will not occur sufficiently frequently to warrant consideration.[1] Denoting by Z the total number of available states for the group, we can make the same remarks that were made for a group of localized particles in Sec. 17. According to (87), when heat is admitted or removed, the change in w is determined by the relative degree to which the levels are populated for different energies ϵ. If it is true that the only distributions that occur frequently are those which have the exponential form, then it follows that, when heat is admitted or removed, all the w's will be changed in the same ratio; since Z is the sum of all the w's, it follows that Z will be changed in the same ratio as w_{max} (as in Sec. 21). We shall have, as before,

$$\frac{Z^*}{Z} = \frac{W^*}{W}$$

$$\delta \ln Z = \mu \, \delta Q \tag{99}$$

When a gas or vapor is placed in thermal contact with a solid or with another gas, there will be a flow of heat, either from A to B or from B to A, unless they happen to be already at the same temperature. This flow

---

[1] Consider a population that does not have the form (97); the value of w will be less than w_{max}. As a result of collisions between molecules of the gas, a redistribution of the energy will tend to take place. R. C. Tolman, "The Principles of Statistical Mechanics," Chapters 11 and 12, Oxford, 1938, has discussed the probabilities of the various collisions according to quantum mechanical perturbation theory and has shown that we may expect the value of w to increase toward w_{max}.

of heat will continue until the product $Z_A Z_B$ has reached its maximum value. In view of (99), the problem is the same as for two solids in contact. The expressions (38) and (42), obtained in Secs. 22 and 24, apply to any two groups of particles; either or both may be solid, liquid, or gaseous, and the condition for equality of temperature is that the two populations be exponential with the same value of μ.

Without repeating the argument, we may then identify μ with $1/kT$, as before, and may write

$$n_r = \frac{ne^{-\epsilon_r/kT}}{P} \tag{100}$$

where

$$P = \Sigma e^{-\epsilon_r/kT} \tag{101}$$

$$E = \sum n_r \epsilon_r = \frac{n \Sigma \epsilon_r e^{-\epsilon_r/kT}}{\Sigma e^{-\epsilon_r/kT}} \tag{102}$$

For a gas or vapor the expression for the partition function (101) is the same as (68) obtained in Sec. 30 for a solid, but the numerical magnitude will be much larger. It was pointed out in evaluating (72) that those terms for which ϵ_r is large compared with kT make a negligible contribution and need not be included, so that the summation is over only a fraction of the number of possible states; even so, we shall find in Chapter 4 that at room temperature more than 10^{20} must be included.

With reference to Fig. 14, it may be mentioned here that for some solids the horizontal lines of Fig. 14 give a fairly correct idea of the magnitude of the partition function at room temperature. Thus, in Sec. 159 we shall find that for metallic magnesium at room temperature the value of P lies between 6 and 7. For softer substances the value of P is greater. Thus, for metallic sodium P reaches the value 40 near room temperature, while the value for metallic lead is still higher.

46. The expression (89) may be written in the following form

$$\ln w = \sum n_r \ln \left(\frac{n_r + p_r}{n_r} \right) + \sum p_r \ln \left(\frac{n_r + p_r}{p_r} \right) \tag{103}$$

In the remainder of this book we shall be mainly concerned with a gas in its most probable state. As in Sec. 27, we shall denote the value of w belonging to this state by a capital letter. The value of W is found by substituting (92) into (81) or (103).

$$\ln W = \sum n_r \ln \left(1 + \frac{p_r}{n_r} \right) + \sum p_r \ln \left(1 + \frac{n_r}{p_r} \right)$$

$$= \sum n_r (\mu \epsilon_r + \lambda) + \sum p_r \ln \left(1 + \frac{n_r}{p_r} \right)$$

Except at very low temperatures n_r/p_r, being small compared with unity, may be substituted for $\ln(1 + n_r/p_r)$; in this case the last term becomes just Σn_r, the total number of particles. Using (96), we find

$$\ln W = n\left(\ln \frac{P}{n} + 1\right) + \frac{E}{kT} \tag{104}$$

Although the expressions (100), (101), and (102) are identical with the expressions (67), (68), and (69) obtained in Sec. 30, nevertheless we find that (104) is not the same as (70). In each case the expression refers to a set of levels populated by a group of n particles sharing a total energy E. The difference lies in the fact that (70) was obtained for a set of localized levels, that is, where each particle was vibrating about its own recognizable site, whereas (104) applies to a set of unlocalized levels, that is, where all the particles in the group are free to move throughout the same communal volume.[1] We shall find that much of the behavior of matter will be discussed in terms of (70) and (104). It will be noticed that in these two expressions the last term E/kT is the same; the difference between the other terms will be investigated in Sec. 58.

47. Already in Sec. 3 it was pointed out that for a simple group of particles at the absolute zero of temperature the values of W and Z are unity, this being because each particle is in its lowest energy state. As soon as a little thermal energy is given to the group, the dispersal of the particles through the various energy levels begins; this dispersal is accompanied by a rapid increase in the value of W because there is an enormous number of choices as to the ways in which the energy E shall be shared. In connection with Fig. 10, we saw that each increment in E is accompanied by an increase in W; this is, of course, merely a continuation of the same process, the dispersal or distribution of the particles through the available levels to a progressively greater degree.

We recall these facts here because there is another way in which the distribution of the particles through a greater number of levels can take place. We have pointed out that an increase of volume always leads to narrower spacing between the levels; with continued increase of volume, the levels tend to crowd together. It is obvious that this will lead to a greater value of W for a given value of E; there will be a greater number of choices as to the way in which this energy E can be shared. If we were to carry out an increase in volume in such a way that the energy E shared by the particles remained constant, the value of W would show a progressive increase. Later we shall give a quantitative discussion of this aspect of the process.

---

[1] In both cases it is assumed that every particle in the group has the same set of levels. For a particle on the surface of a solid (or a liquid) the spacing of the levels will not be the same as in the interior. But the number of surface particles is relatively small. In a cube containing 10^{24} particles, for example, there would be, on the six faces, only 6×10^{16} particles, which is less than one in 10^7 of the total. Consequently, we do not have to pay especial attention to the surface.

If the population is initially in equilibrium, in each energy state ϵ_r the number of particles n_r is related to ϵ_r by the expression

$$n_r = n_0 e^{-\mu \epsilon_r}$$

where μ has the value appropriate to the amount of energy E shared by the n particles. As soon as the values of ϵ_r begin to change appreciably, the initial values of n_r are no longer appropriate and a rearrangement of the particles spontaneously takes place. The details of this rearrangement will depend on the way in which the change of volume is carried out, that is, whether it is isothermal (μ constant) or adiabatic (μ changing). Our aim must be to understand clearly the nature of, and the reasons for, this rearrangement of the particles. The most fundamental cause is the fact that, in a set of levels, some levels are likely to be more sensitive to a change of volume and others less sensitive. If for some populated states the value of ϵ_r is changed appreciably while for others the value remains nearly constant, it is obvious that the spacing of the energy levels is upset in such a way that the initial values of $n_0, n_1, n_2 \ldots n_r \ldots$ are no longer an exponential function of the energy ϵ—are not exponential with any value of μ, either the initial value or any other value.

If a sudden or very rapid change of volume were made, the population would be momentarily seriously out of equilibrium. In a thermodynamic discussion, however, we are usually interested in reversible changes, in which the body is practically in equilibrium at all stages throughout the process. In our terms this means that the change is made so slowly that at all stages of the process the population has the particular exponential form that is appropriate to the amount of energy E shared by the particles at the moment. That is to say, the value of μ may change but in a reversible process the population is always exponential with $some$ value of μ.

In Sec. 16, where we dealt with a fixed set of levels, a change in the appropriate value of μ could only come about if we allowed a quantity of heat to enter or leave the group. As soon as we allow the volume to change, this is no longer true; the initial value of μ will cease to be appropriate except in the special case where the process has been carried out isothermally. Thus, when the volume is allowed to change, all the quantities that determine the form of the population are likely to change: the values of the allowed energies ϵ_r are altered, the total energy is usually altered, and the value of μ is usually altered.

48. External Work Done in a Reversible Process. Consider a body initially at a certain temperature T and subject to an external pressure p, and let its volume be v. The pressure that the body can support under these conditions is the same whether the body is thermally isolated or is in contact with a thermal reservoir at temperature T. If dA is the external work that must be done on the body to cause a change of volume

equal to dv, the quantities dA and dv are of opposite sign and the value
of the pressure is by definition

$$p = -\frac{dA}{dv} \tag{105}$$

In any process in which there is an infinitesimal change dv in the volume,
the work done on the body has the same value $dA = -pdv$, whether the
body is thermally isolated or not. If no heat is allowed to enter or leave,
that is, during an adiabatic compression or expansion, the energy E
shared by the n particles changes by an amount δE equal to δA. If, in
addition, an amount of heat δQ is admitted, the change in the energy E
shared by the particles will be

$$\delta E = \delta Q + \delta A$$

In a kinetic description of the process we usually imagine the substance
compressed by means of a piston, and we consider the molecules of the
substance rebounding from the moving surface. When the piston is
moving inward, the molecules rebound with increased energy; conversely,
when the piston is moving outward, they rebound with reduced energy.

In a quantized description of a reversible process, the necessity of doing
work enters as the result of the changes in the allowed values of the
energy. During the change, the energies must of course be measured
from a zero of energy that remains fixed. When a level of initial energy
ϵ_r contains n_r particles, their energy is $n_r \epsilon_r$. If now (owing to a small
reduction in the volume) the allowed value of the energy changes from
ϵ_r to $(\epsilon_r + \delta\epsilon_r)$, where $\delta\epsilon_r$ has a positive value, the increment in energy
$n_r \delta\epsilon_r$ must be supplied by the agent carrying out the compression. Since
the same is true for each of the energy levels, the total work done in
reducing the volume by an amount δv will be $\Sigma n_r \delta\epsilon_r$. Conversely, if the
body is allowed to expand, this expression, taken with opposite sign, gives
the amount of energy lost by the body in doing external work. This loss
of energy is not associated with particles falling from one energy level to
another. During a reversible expansion there is no reason why the
usual interchange of energy should cease; a particle may fall from an
energy level ϵ_k to a lower energy level ϵ_j, but there is no mechanism for
transforming the amount of energy $(\epsilon_k - \epsilon_j)$ into external work; this
amount of energy is therefore either transferred to other particles within
the body or represents heat flowing out of the body. There is no direct
connection between the doing of external work on the body or by the body,
and the rearrangement of the particles that usually takes place at the
same time, but independently. The external work arises from the necessity
of obtaining a shorter or longer wavelength for the wave functions of the
particles when the volume is changed.

49. As an approach to the problem, it is useful to ask whether we can imagine an artificially simple case in which no rearrangement of the particles will be required, no matter how large the change of volume. The answer is that we can imagine such hypothetical cases, namely, where the change that distorts the set of levels is of an especially simple character. In a certain set of levels, consider the gaps between successive energy levels $(\epsilon_1 - \epsilon_0)$, $(\epsilon_2 - \epsilon_1)$, $(\epsilon_3 - \epsilon_2)$, and so on; and let us suppose that when the volume changes all these quantities change in the same ratio; and let no heat enter or leave the body. Then if the various values of n_r are initially exponential, they will remain exponential, though with a changing value of μ. The value of μ is, in fact, always the value appropriate to the value of E that the particles share at the moment. Thus, in this case there is no need for any rearrangement of the particles to take place in order for the population to have its optimum form at all times. The temperature will change but the number of particles in each level will remain the same. The value of W therefore remains the same, since according to (1) the value of W depends only on the values of n_r in the denominator.

Of the hypothetical cases we have just considered, the simplest would be a set of uniformly spaced levels in which, when the volume changes, the spacing remains uniform, becoming merely uniformly wider or narrower. In this case, if the particles in successive levels are in a geometrical progression and if they remain in the same geometrical progression, this is satisfactory; there is no reason why any of the n_r should change, provided that the change of volume is carried out adiabatically.

50. In practice, as mentioned in Sec. 47, the various levels will not be sensitive to changes of volume in any such simple regular manner; the various energy differences are altered in different ratios, and the original values of n_r thus cease to be appropriate. To illustrate the kind of rearrangement that takes place, Fig. 17 shows a simple example of three levels. (We may suppose that the level ϵ_3, not shown in Fig. 17, is so much higher that it contains negligibly few particles.) Let us suppose that the levels ϵ_2 and ϵ_0 are equally insensitive to a change of volume, while the level ϵ_1 is more sensitive, so that the quantity $(\epsilon_2 - \epsilon_0)$ remains constant, while the ratio of $(\epsilon_2 - \epsilon_1)$ to $(\epsilon_1 - \epsilon_0)$ is progressively diminished during a compression and similarly increased during an expansion.

In Fig. 17a, let the lengths of the three horizontal lines represent the values of n_0, n_1, and n_2 in the initial exponential population, in equilibrium at a certain temperature. In Figs. 17b and 17c the same curve has been drawn; the three horizontal lines have been drawn in their new relative positions but with the same lengths as in Fig. 17a, to show what the situation would be if no rearrangement of the particles had taken place. In Fig. 17b it is impossible to draw an exponential curve through the three points A, B, and C; it is impossible with *any* value of μ. We see that there are relatively *too many* particles in the middle level ϵ_1. In a reversible process this state of affairs will not occur; in a reversible adiabatic compression, therefore, particles will spontaneously leave the level ϵ_1 so as to preserve the exponential shape for the population. Similarly, in Fig. 17c, which is intended to depict the result of an expansion, there are *too few* particles in the middle level ϵ_1. In a reversible expansion, therefore, in order to avoid this state of affairs, a certain number of particles will spontaneously be shifted to this level from the other levels.

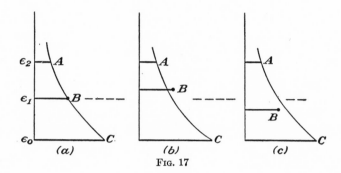

Fig. 17

Throughout this chapter we have been making use of the fundamental idea, introduced in Sec. 5, that if a group of particles is left undisturbed, when once the population has adopted that form which gives w its maximum value, no further rearrangement of the particles will take place, apart from momentary fluctuations. If, however, owing to some change imposed on the group, an opportunity arises of attaining a greater value of w, a rearrangement of the particles will take place. Caution must be exercised in applying these ideas; we may make a brief digression at this point to consider the following argument, which is fallacious.

Let us make use of Figs. 17a and 17b to study again a very slow adiabatic change of volume. Consider a resultant change in the energy ϵ_1 that is just sufficient to cause the numbers n_0, n_1, and n_2 to deviate appreciably from an exponential relation. It appears correct to say that a rearrangement of the particles takes place because these initial values n_0, n_1, and n_2 no longer suffice to give w its maximum value. If the values n_0, n_1, and n_2 had remained unchanged during the process, the value of w would obviously, by (1), have remained unchanged; the rearrangement allows a value W', slightly greater than W, to be attained. Let the rearrangement lead to the values n_0', n_1', and n_2'. With the modified values of the energy levels, this set of values n_0', n_1', and n_2' gives an exponential form, though with the original energy levels they, of course, would not do so. If the change of volume were continued, values differing still more from the original n_0, n_1, and n_2 would be required.

Instead, let us suppose that we allow the body, by a slow adiabatic process, to recover its original volume. If the values n_0', n_1', and n_2' were retained during this second step, the value W' would persist. But now the values n_0', n_1', and n_2' do not give the population the required exponential form. Another rearrangement of the particles takes place, to allow w to attain its maximum value. But this is an absurd conclusion, since W' cannot be greater than W and at the same time be less than W. If we have successfully carried out a reversible process, the population must have returned to its original form, with its initial value of W. If the source of the fallacy in the above argument is not already apparent to the reader, it will become clear in the following paragraphs.

51. If it is true that during a reversible process the population of the levels never departs appreciably from the exponential form, it is clear that in considering a rearrangement of the particles we may use the values of ϵ_0, ϵ_1 ... ϵ_r ... that prevail at the moment and may disregard the fact that the values of ϵ_r have been different in the recent past and will again be different in the near future, as the change in volume proceeds. That is to say, there is no reason why we should not use the expressions that have been derived in Sec. 16 for dealing either with a rearrangement that leaves the total energy unchanged, or one that involves an admission or loss of heat. As a result of this, it is simple to give a description of any change, isothermal or adiabatic.

Let us deal first with a reversible adiabatic process. In thermodynamic discussions a process is sometimes carried out by a series of alternating steps; by making each of these steps smaller, one can reach, in the limit, a reversible process. So here we can come as near as we like to a reversible adiabatic process by a series of alternating steps. To go from the levels of Fig. 17a to those of Fig. 17b for example, by a change of volume, we shall proceed as follows. Starting with an exponential population, (1) we shift some particles from the middle level ϵ_1 to the other levels, arranging that there shall be no change in the total energy E; then (2) we change the volume by an amount δv, causing the values of the allowed energies to change slightly. We then repeat the process (1) at constant volume, again allowing no heat to enter or leave; after this the process (2) is repeated, introducing a further change in the spacing of the energy levels. By a succession of such small steps, we obtain an adiabatic change of volume; the smaller the steps, the nearer we approach to a reversible change of volume.

Now the striking feature of these steps is that, neither in the steps of type (1) nor in those of type (2) is there a change in W. Starting with an exponential population, we know that a rearrangement that leaves E unchanged also leaves W unchanged; and in step (2) there is obviously no change in W because the number of particles in each level does not change. It is only necessary that each pair of steps should leave the population in an exponential form; then the succession of alternating steps can be continued indefinitely without a progressive change in W.

In Sec. 49 mention was made of a set of levels with uniform spacing which, during a change in volume, was assumed to become uniformly wider or narrower. We noticed that in this case during an adiabatic change the value of w would remain constant. We see now that this constancy of w is not peculiar to that special case but is a general property of any reversible adiabatic change.

52. The manner in which the rearrangement takes place may be illustrated from Fig. 10. It will be recalled that in this problem there is, for constant n and constant E, a value of n_1 that gives w its maximum value; in Sec. 17 this was denoted by $\mathbf{n}_1$. The quantity chosen for abscissas in Fig. 10 was $(n_1 - \mathbf{n}_1)$, which was denoted by p. Obviously, with an appropriate shift of the origin, the curve may equally well be taken to be a plot of w against n_1. Suppose then that Fig. 10 corresponds to the initial state of a body that we shall subject to an adiabatic change of volume—a change that raises the level of ϵ_1 relative to the levels ϵ_0 and ϵ_2, as depicted in Fig. 17b. In this case, we have seen that the number of particles in the level ϵ_1 must be progressively diminished. The value of $w_{\max}$ must occur at a lower value of n_1; in Fig. 10 the curve must be shifted to the left. Conversely, for the change depicted in Fig. 17c, the value of $w_{\max}$ must occur at a higher value of n_1; the curve must be shifted to the right.

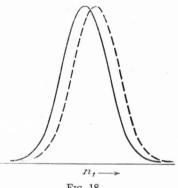

FIG. 18

If in this process a distribution with a greater value of $w_{\max}$ became available, we would take it for granted that a spontaneous rearrangement of the particles would take place. The problem is to describe how a continual rearrangement of the particles takes place spontaneously without any change in the value of $w_{\max}$. In Fig. 18 the dotted curve shows a displacement to the right without an increase in $w_{\max}$. We see that on the left the dotted curve lies below the original curve, while on the right the dotted curve lies above.

In the initial state of the body distributions with n_1 appreciably smaller than $\mathbf{n}_1$ will often occur; during and after this change of volume they will occur *less* frequently; and with further change of volume they will occur still less frequently. In the initial state of the body, values of n_1 greater than $\mathbf{n}_1$ likewise occur; during and after this change of volume they will occur *more* frequently.

53. If, finally, we wish the substance to follow any path on a p-v diagram that is not an adiabatic path, we must allow some appropriate amount of heat to enter or leave. At any moment the total thermal energy of the body is $\Sigma n_r \epsilon_r$. In any change of volume δv the total change in energy is equal to the work done on the body plus the heat δQ that has been added

$$\delta E = \delta A + \delta Q \tag{106}$$

For this change we have also the expression

$$\delta E = \Sigma n_r \, \delta \epsilon_r + \Sigma \epsilon_r \, \delta n_r \tag{107}$$

We have seen that each term in (107) is equal to the corresponding term in (106).

In an adiabatic change of volume the term $\Sigma\epsilon_r\ \delta n_r$ is zero; for some energy levels the δn_r is positive and for other levels the δn_r is meanwhile negative, in such a way that, at any stage, compensation takes place; this continual rearrangement of the particles, as we have seen, leaves the values of Z and w_{max} unchanged.

The first term on the right-hand side of (107), which is equivalent to δA, may be expressed in terms of the partition function. Consider the change in P produced when the energy levels are shifted by various amounts $\delta\epsilon_r$. In any isothermal compression or expansion we shall have

$$\delta P = \sum \frac{\partial}{\partial \epsilon_r} e^{-\epsilon_r/kT}\ \delta\epsilon_r = -\frac{1}{kT}\sum e^{-\epsilon_r/kT}\ \delta\epsilon_r$$

Comparing this with (107), we find

$$\delta A = \sum n_r\ \delta\epsilon_r = \sum n\frac{e^{-\epsilon_r/kT}}{P}\ \delta\epsilon_r$$

$$= -nkT\frac{\delta P}{P} = -nkT\ \delta \ln P \tag{108}$$

We can thus find a relation between the rate of change of the partition function and the external pressure p. From (105) and (108), we obtain

$$nkT\frac{\partial \ln P}{\partial v} = -\frac{\partial A}{\partial v} = p \tag{109}$$

It was pointed out in Sec. 47 that an increase in volume at constant E must be accompanied by an increase in W. If we were to arrange that the process involves a simultaneous decrease in E, we could maintain the value of W constant (or even bring about a diminution in W). While the levels tend to crowd together, we could arrange that a progressive decrease in E should keep pace with this and so prevent the increase in W that would otherwise occur. Conversely, during a compression, while the spacing of the energy levels becomes wider, we could arrange that a progressive increase in E should keep pace with this and so prevent the decrease in W that would otherwise occur. In Sec. 49 we considered two cases in which the distortion of the set of energy levels was of an especially simple character, and we saw that in an adiabatic compression there was no reason why any of the n_r should change. It must be because the rate of increase in E in this process is always just sufficient to prevent the decrease in W that would otherwise occur. In general, we achieve this result if we ensure that no heat enters or leaves the body.

54. The expression (27), obtained in Sec. 16, gave the change in $\ln W$ that accompanies the process of adding a small quantity of heat at constant volume. We see now that if, after this process, we allow the body to expand adiabatically, this second step will not entail any further change in $\ln W$. Starting from the point B, repetition of these two steps will lead to a curve like that shown in Fig. 19. In this way one can go from any point B to any point C lying on the same isothermal.   Since the adiabatic steps make no contribution, the change in ln W is equal to the sum of the contributions from the steps represented by the vertical lines, each of which may be made to cut the isothermal.   If the steps between B and C are made exceedingly numerous, the length of each of the vertical lines becomes small, so that the temperature scarcely differs at any point from that of the isothermal.   In the limit the value of T may be taken as constant during the admission of every amount of heat δQ.   In the limit likewise the zigzag curve coincides with the isothermal, and we see

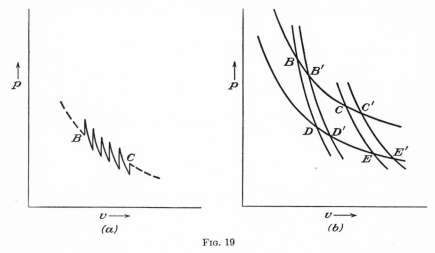

Fig. 19

that the expression (71) in Sec. 30 is valid for an isothermal change of volume as well as for a process at constant volume.   The new feature is that δQ is not to be identified with δE, because some of the energy has been used in doing work against the external pressure.   We have

$$\delta \ln W = \frac{\delta Q}{kT} = \frac{\delta E + p\,\delta v}{kT} \tag{110}$$

In this connection we may examine the basis of Kelvin's absolute scale of temperature.

In Fig. 19b, let BC and DE be any two isothermals, as in Fig. 13, and let BD and $B'D'$ be a pair of adiabatics.   If, starting from B, we take the substance round the cycle $BB'D'DB$, the quantity W must return to its original value, since this value is determined entirely by the values of the various n_r.   For the adiabatic steps $B'D'$ and DB, the change in W has been zero; hence for the steps BB' and $D'D$ the changes must have been equal and opposite.   It follows that for steps such as BB' and DD' between any two adiabatics, the values of $\delta \ln W$ must be equal.

It will be recalled that, in defining an absolute scale of temperature in Sec. 29, use was made of just such steps with equal values of $\delta \ln W$; we may now inquire whether this scale is the same as that introduced by Lord Kelvin, whose definition had the following basis. On going from B to B' in Fig. 19b, a certain amount of heat δQ is absorbed; on going from D to D' a different amount would be absorbed. Let the value of the former be m times the latter. On going from C to C' a certain amount of heat will be absorbed, and, on going from E to E', a different amount. The thermo-dynamic argument must first show that, if CE and $C'E'$ are a pair of adia-batics, the ratio of these two amounts of heat has the same value m as before—that, in fact, it has the same value for any pair of adiabatics inter-secting the isothermals BC and DE. Kelvin, drawing attention to this fact, proposed that the ratio m be used to define an absolute scale of tem-perature. In view of what has just been said about steps with equal values of $\delta \ln W$, it will be clear that this scale is the same as that proposed in Sec. 29.

55. Alternative Sets of Energy Levels. In each problem so far we have dealt with a group of particles to which one definite set of levels was available and we have pointed out the convenience of choosing the lowest level of this set as the zero of energy. The more interesting problems of statistical mechanics are those where two or more alternative sets of levels are available to each particle. Suppose, for example, that in dis-cussing the particles of a monatomic vapor we have taken as our zero of energy the energy ϵ_0 of an atom at rest in the vapor. If we go on now to consider the condensation of part of the vapor to form a solid (or a liquid), we introduce a set of levels that are lower than ϵ_0. When some solid has been formed, to remove a particle from its surface and leave the particle at rest in the vapor, a certain amount of work must be done; conversely, when particles condense onto the surface of the solid, they fall to energy levels that are lower than the level ϵ_0, which has been chosen as zero. The energies of the lowest and most populated levels of the solid have therefore negative values, relative to our zero of energy. The total energy of the solid will be negative; if more particles are added to the solid, its total energy will continue to decrease with every additional particle; conversely, if particles are removed from the solid its energy will increase.

On the other hand, the thermal energy of the particles—their energy of thermal vibration—is, of course, a positive quantity; it is increased when particles are added at constant temperature and diminished when particles are removed. In studying these problems, it is important that there should not be at any time a doubt as to the relation between the thermal energy and the total energy E. It will be convenient, therefore, to put on record here some of the salient facts, beginning with a single set of levels and going on later to the relations between two or more sets of levels.

Consider, as usual, a group of n particles. If all the n particles were in their lowest energy level, the total energy would be $n\epsilon_0$. Consequently, when the total energy has a greater value E, the thermal energy is $(E - n\epsilon_0)$. Dividing by n, the average thermal energy per particle is $(E/n - \epsilon_0)$.

At any moment, in the group of particles, some particles will have energy greater than E/n, while some will have energy less than E/n; that is to say, for some of the populated levels the energy ϵ_r is greater than E/n, while for other populated levels it is less. In a set of widely spaced levels, E/n will usually not have a value coinciding with one of the energy levels. In a diagram the value of E/n can conveniently be represented by a horizontal broken line lying somewhere between two of the energy levels, as has been drawn for each of the sets of levels in Fig. 20 below.

For a given set of levels, the value of E/n is sufficient to fix the value of the temperature T; that is to say, there is one particular value of μ that corresponds to the given value of E/n. The converse of this is not true; for a group of n particles, the value of T does not prescribe a value of E in the same way. In Sec. 22, where we introduced and examined the idea of two bodies at the same temperature, we did so by transferring energy from one body to the other. When we have a population that is exponential with a certain value of μ, it is necessary to move many particles in order to produce an appreciably different value of μ. It is therefore legitimate to discuss a change in E at constant μ, or at constant temperature.

56. The evaporation of a solid or a liquid and the condensation of a vapor were referred to above. We have drawn attention to the fact that in such problems the central fact is that two alternative sets of energy levels are available to the particles. There are many other processes of a similar character, for example, the partial dissociation of a diatomic gas and the recombination of atoms to form molecules, the melting of a solid and the freezing of a liquid, the transformation of a solid from one modification to another. In each of these processes, particles are transferred from one set of levels to another. Both sets of levels are, or become, populated; since we are interested in thermal equilibrium, the two populations will be exponential with the same value of μ.

We may begin to visualize the state of affairs in these various problems by considering two sets of energy levels, like those depicted in Figs. 20a to d. For particles of a gas or vapor the spacing between the energy levels will be many million times narrower than for those of a solid; in Fig. 20 we have merely drawn sets of energy levels of comparable spacing. In each set of levels the position of the horizontal broken line is intended to indicate the value of E/n at the same temperature. In Fig. 20a the broken line for B lies below that of A, although the ground level for B lies above that of A. In Fig. 20b the situation is different, while in Fig. 20c the ground level of B lies above the broken line of A. Figure 20d shows a hypothetical case, which has merely been added for comparison; it depicts two sets of levels where the spacing is the same but where one set of levels has been shifted with respect to the other by an amount $(\epsilon'_0 - \epsilon_0)$. If we compare the value of E_B/n_B with that of E_A/n_A at the same temperature, the values of E_A and E_B must be referred to the same zero of energy and E_B/n_B will be different from E_A/n_A. In Fig. 20d, however, the thermal

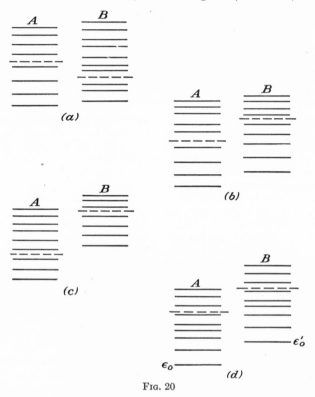

Fig. 20

energy per particle in B will be the same as the thermal energy per particle in A at the same temperature. In Figs. 20a to c the thermal energy per particle in B will be different from that in A, this difference being the result of the different spacing of the levels, not of the difference in the positions of the ground levels. When we come to consider the partition functions for the populations of A and B, we shall find that the values are affected both by the difference in the spacing and the difference in the position of the ground level; sometimes one of these factors will be the more important, sometimes the other.

We shall consider next the addition or removal of particles from a group of n particles sharing an energy E. With a fixed set of energy levels, as long as the number of particles is unchanged, constant E ensures constant temperature. But when the number of particles changes, this is no longer so. The expression $\left(\dfrac{\partial \ln W}{\partial n}\right)_E$, for example, denotes for any group of particles the change in ln W with change in n, while the total energy E shared by the group remains constant. If we remove q particles from the group, we have the original energy E now shared by $(n - q)$ particles.

Consider any one of the sets of levels in Fig. 20; some energy levels lie above and some lie below the broken line. If we remove q particles from levels lying *above* the broken line, the average energy per particle for the remaining $(n - q)$ particles will be less than the original value of E/n. On the other hand, if we remove q particles from levels lying *below* the broken line, the average energy per particle for the remaining particles will be greater than the initial value. If we wish to maintain the energy per particle constant while we add or remove particles, levels such as ϵ_j, ϵ_k, ϵ_r . . . must be chosen such that the sum of these energies is equal to q times E/n; thus

$$\epsilon_j + \epsilon_k + \epsilon_r + \cdots = q\left(\frac{E}{n}\right) \tag{111}$$

In this way the value of the energy per particle for the particles remaining in the group is maintained constant.

If a large number of particles is to be added or removed, the exponential form of the population can be maintained, with its original value of μ, if the number of particles added to or removed from each level is proportional to the number of particles in that level. For any group of n particles populating a fixed set of levels and sharing energy E, the expression $\left(\dfrac{\partial E}{\partial n}\right)_T$, signifying the change in E with n at constant temperature, is merely another name for the average energy per particle in the group; it is simply E/n.

In any set of levels, suppose that we have chosen a certain level ϵ_j as our zero of energy, writing $\epsilon_j = 0$. Then the removal of particles from this level or the addition of particles to this level leaves the total energy unchanged, by definition. If any level in the set is taken as the zero of energy, it is usually the ground level that is so chosen; in this case addition of particles or removal of particles from the ground level leaves the value of E unchanged.

Problems

1. It was stated in Sec. 39 that there is considerable latitude as to the ways in which the subdivision of the levels may be made. To prove this, show that if two adjacent batches of energy states are fused into a single wider batch, the value of the contribution to w is unchanged. Conversely, show that if a wide batch of levels is split into narrower batches, according to (81) their contribution to w will be unchanged.

2. To a certain group of particles, an amount of heat $k\theta$ is added, where k is Boltzmann's constant. If this addition causes an increment in ln W equal to b, show that the temperature on the Kelvin scale is θ/b.

CHAPTER 3

The Distribution of Particles through Alternative Sets of Energy Levels—Conditions for Equilibrium—A Saturated Vapor—Order and Disorder in Crystals

57. Addition or Removal of Particles. We discussed in Sec. 22 two groups of particles containing n_A and n_B particles, respectively. The numbers n_A and n_B were fixed. In many problems, on the other hand, we are interested in the equilibrium between two groups where the particles are all of the same species but the number in each group is free to change. When, for example, a solid (or a liquid) is in contact with its own vapor in a closed vessel, the attainment of equilibrium depends on the freedom of particles to enter or leave the vapor, until the pressure of the vapor adopts its "saturation value." In all such problems it is important to know how the value of w for a group of particles will be changed when particles are added to or removed from the group.

Let us first consider a solid to which the expression (1) is applicable. From (1) we can at once say how the value of w will be changed if a particle is removed from any level ϵ_r without disturbing any of the other particles. In the first place, in the numerator the $n!$ is to be replaced by $(n-1)!$, and at the same time in the denominator $n_r!$ is to be replaced by $(n_r - 1)!$. None of the other factors are altered; hence we find that the value of w for the group will be reduced to w^*, given by

$$\frac{w^*}{w} = \frac{n_r}{n} \qquad \text{(removal of particle)} \qquad \cdots \quad (112a)$$

Conversely, if a particle is added to the group and is placed in the level ϵ_r, we find that the value of w is increased to w^*, given by $w^*/w = (n+1)/(n_r+1)$; when the numbers are large, this is indistinguishable from n/n_r. The change is thus the converse of $(112a)$.

$$\frac{w^*}{w} = \frac{n}{n_r} \qquad \text{(addition of particle)} \qquad \cdots \quad (112b)$$

We notice that the change in w will be smallest when n_r is most nearly equal to n—when it is the most populated level to which the particle is added or from which the particle is removed.

When a particle is added to any level ϵ_r, we are obviously at liberty to think of this addition as having been made in two steps: (1) the addition of a particle to the ground level ϵ_0, and (2) the raising of the particle from ϵ_0 to ϵ_r. Now we know that in an exponential population the raising of a particle from ϵ_0 to ϵ_r is accompanied by an increase in w in accordance with (24) and (27) in Sec. 16. The change in w should be smallest when it is the ground level to which the particle is added, since in this case there is no increase in the thermal energy. This is, in fact, the result given by (112), since in an exponential population the most populated level is the ground level.

When a particle is added to, or removed from, the ground level, there is no change in the thermal energy of the group, and the change in ln w is due solely to the fact that the number of particles in the group has been increased or diminished by unity. From (112) we can find an expression for this quantity, and we can then verify that when a particle is added to any higher level, the excess is in accordance with (27). For an exponential population, if we take the ground level as our zero of energy, we may use the expression (74) obtained in Sec. 33 and find that when a particle is added to this level, (112b) takes the form

$$\frac{W^*}{W} = \frac{n}{n_0} = P \tag{113}$$

From (23) we expect to find that when a particle is added to a higher level, the change is greater than this by the factor $e^{\mu\eta}$, where $\eta = \epsilon_r$. In fact, from (57) we verify that when a particle is added to any level ϵ_r

$$\frac{W^*}{W} = \frac{n}{n_r} = P e^{\mu\epsilon_r} \tag{114}$$

This is greater than (113) in the expected ratio.

The value of W that we are discussing is for n particles that form a strictly exponential population. If we add a particle to the group without changing the value of E, the value of W is increased, because the number of different ways in which the energy E can be shared among $(n + 1)$ particles is greater than the number of ways it can be shared among n particles. Further, if the increase in n is accompanied by some increase in the thermal energy, the resulting value of W will be still larger; thus the increase in W consists of two parts. The case of special interest is an addition of particles where the increase in E is such as to leave the value of the energy per particle unchanged; this corresponds to an isothermal addition of particles.

58. Suppose that we start with a small group of n particles sharing a total energy E and that we add successive contingents of particles, each having the same average energy per particle. In this way we can build up a very large group of particles isothermally. Consider the value of $\ln W$ for this large group. We may expect that the expression for $\ln W$ will consist of two parts, one part made up of the increments arising from the successive increments in n, and the other part made up of the increments $\mu \, \delta Q$ arising from the successive increments in the thermal energy. Now in Secs. 30 and 46 we have already obtained expressions for the value of $\ln W$ for a group of localized and for a group of unlocalized particles. In order to facilitate comparison between these two expressions, it will be convenient to repeat them here. In (70) we obtained for a group of localized particles

$$\ln W = n \ln P + \frac{E}{kT} \tag{115}$$

and in (104) we obtained for a gas

$$\ln W = n\left(\ln \frac{P}{n} + 1\right) + \frac{E}{kT} \tag{116}$$

In each case the expression for $\ln W$ consists of two terms, and we may at once verify that the two terms correspond to the two quantities that we have just described.

Let us deal first with the localized particles of a solid. Taking a group of n particles sharing an energy E, suppose that we add q additional particles in the manner suggested in Sec. 56, that is, selecting levels ϵ_i, ϵ_k, ϵ_r . . . so that the sum of these energies is equal to q times E/n. According to (112), the total change in w will be the product of q factors

$$\frac{w^*}{w} = \frac{n}{n_i} \times \frac{n}{n_k} \times \frac{n}{n_r} \times \cdots \tag{117}$$

This expression is correct, whatever the form of the population. If the population is exponential, we may use (57) and substitute for each of the q factors, thus obtaining

$$\frac{W^*}{W} = \frac{P}{e^{-\mu\epsilon_i}} \times \frac{P}{e^{-\mu\epsilon_k}} \times \frac{P}{e^{-\mu\epsilon_r}} \cdots \tag{118}$$

and

$$\ln W^* - \ln W = n \ln P + \mu(\epsilon_i + \epsilon_k + \cdots) \tag{119}$$

If we make use of (111), we see that (119) leads naturally to an expression containing two terms that evidently correspond to the two terms on the right-hand side of (115), which may be written in the form

$$\ln W = n\left(\ln P + \frac{E/n}{kT}\right)$$

When a large group of n particles has been built up isothermally, the term E/kT is the sum of the increments due to the growth of the energy, while the term $n \ln P$ is a basic or intrinsic term, independent of the growth of the energy.

This interpretation of the two terms on the right-hand side of (115) becomes still clearer if we suppose that the addition of each particle is made by means of the two steps mentioned above; that is, the particles are first placed in the ground level (in this step the group receives no thermal energy), and the particles are then raised to their respective levels. In this second step the group receives thermal energy equal to E/n per particle added. In the first step, according to (113), the value of $\ln W$ is increased by the amount $\ln P$ for each particle added to the ground level; this accounts for the first term on the right-hand side of (115). We shall find that this basic or intrinsic term in (115) plays an important role in the discussion of problems of equilibrium.

It is convenient, at the same time, to mention here the order of magnitude of the terms in (115) when the ground level is chosen as the zero of energy. As for $\ln P$, it has already been mentioned at the end of Sec. 45 that for most solids at room temperature the value of P lies in the range between 7 and 100, so that the values of the first term on the right-hand side of (115) will lie between $2n$ and $5n$. At ordinary temperatures the average energy per particle is somewhat greater than kT, so the last term in (115) is of the same order of magnitude.

Recalling that W is another notation for w_{max}, we may consider the numerical difference between the $\ln Z$ and $\ln w_{max}$ of (35) in Sec. 20. According to (33) the value of $(\pi/\alpha)^{\frac{1}{2}}$ lies between $\sqrt{n_2}$ and $\sqrt{n}$. The value of $\ln w_{max}$ is greater than n, while the value of $\frac{1}{2} \ln n$ is extremely small in comparison.

We have discussed above the expression (115), which is applicable to a solid. Similarly, if particles are added to a gas, we can imagine that each particle is first placed in the lowest level ϵ_0 and then raised to its appropriate level. Since the expression (71) in Sec. 30 is of universal application, the thermal term in the increase of $\ln W$ should be the same as in the case of a solid.

On comparing (116) with (115), we see that the last term is the same, namely, E/kT. From (116) we obtain

$$\left(\frac{\partial \ln W}{\partial n}\right)_T = \ln \frac{P}{n} + \frac{E/n}{kT}$$

Using (82b) and (96), it may easily be verified that the quantity $\ln(P/n)$ is just the amount by which $\ln W$ will be increased by the addition of a particle to the ground level when this level has been chosen as the zero of energy.

59. Distribution of Particles through Alternative Sets of Levels. We have made a preliminary survey of some changes that accompany the addition or removal of particles from a homogeneous group. At the beginning of Sec. 57 it was pointed out that such a study is necessary before one can attack such problems as saturated vapor pressure, and so on, where particles are free to move from one homogeneous group to another. In such problems we discuss two groups of particles of the same species; the only difference between the groups A and B is that one set of energy levels has different spacing from the other and a different ground level.   A prerequisite for equilibrium between the two is that the populations be exponential with the same value of μ; this condition, however, is not sufficient for equilibrium.   Let E_A be the total energy shared by one group and let Z_A denote, as usual, the total number of states available to the particles when they share energy E_A; let E_B and Z_B be the corresponding quantities for the other group.   We shall suppose that the energy $(E_A + E_B)$ has to remain constant.   If some particles pass from one group to the other, the values of Z_A and Z_B will be changed.   If, for example, the increase in $\ln Z_B$ is greater than the simultaneous decrease in $\ln Z_A$, this transfer of particles allows the product $Z_A Z_B$ to take larger values. Such a flow will therefore take place spontaneously and will continue until the product $Z_A Z_B$ attains its maximum value consistent with the total energy $(E_A + E_B)$.   In some cases it may happen that $Z_A Z_B$ continues to increase until all the particles have been transferred to one set of levels, leaving the other set empty; this means that, under the given conditions, no equilibrium between the two phases is possible.   The cases that interest us are those where $Z_A Z_B$ has its maximum value when both sets of levels are partially populated.

In order to discuss the product $Z_A Z_B$, we must first consider Z_A and Z_B separately.   The problem will be quite similar to that of Sec. 22 except that here we are dealing with the addition and removal of particles, whereas there we were dealing only with the addition and removal of heat. In Fig. 10, for example, when we discussed the change in the central ordinate and the change in the area under the curve, we were concerned with the change of Z with E.   Here, on the other hand, we shall be concerned with the change of Z with n.   We saw in Sec. 12 that when energy is added to, or removed from, the group, the curve of Fig. 10 will rise or fall.   Depending on the size of the group of particles, there are two possibilities: the area under the curve changes either in the same ratio as w_{max} changes or in a different ratio.   Here likewise the addition or removal of particles will cause the curve to rise or fall, in accordance with (112) and there are the same two possibilities, depending on the size of the group of particles.   At the center of Fig. 10 the strictly exponential values $\mathbf{n}_0$, $\mathbf{n}_1$, and $\mathbf{n}_2$ provide in (112) the ratios $n/\mathbf{n}_0$, $n/\mathbf{n}_1$, and $n/\mathbf{n}_2$.   To the right and to the left of Fig. 10 other values n_0, n_1, and n_2 provide ratios n/n_0, n/n_1, and n/n_2.   The question is whether these differ appreciably from the ratios at the center; if so, the area representing Z will not change at the same rate as w_{max}.   On the other hand, if the group of particles is sufficiently large, it may easily be shown by differentiating (35) with respect to n that the result is similar to that found in Sec. 21 for the change of Z with E.

In general, we can deal with the problem as was done in Sec. 21, by considering the basic assertion that, in a sufficiently large group of particles, only distributions that approach very closely to the strictly exponential form will occur frequently. Whenever this is the case, Z will change at the same rate as w_{max}, since the values of n/n_r that will occur in (112) will not differ appreciably from the strictly exponential values $n/\mathbf{n}_r$. We have then

$$\delta \ln Z = \delta \ln W$$

60. Before applying this expression to the equilibrium between two populations, it will be convenient to recall the familiar kinetic aspects of such a problem. When, for example, a solid or a liquid is in contact

Fig. 21

with its own vapor and a uniform temperature prevails, the equilibrium is not a static affair but is the result of a kinetic balance; a large number of particles are condensing and at the same time a large number are evaporating. When these numbers are unequal, the lack of balance is observed as a condensation or an evaporation; in our terminology particles are spontaneously transferred from the levels of A to those of B, or vice versa, because this transfer enables the product $Z_A Z_B$ to attain higher values. The same is true when both A and B are solids. Many substances can exist in two modifications—rhombic sulfur and monoclinic sulfur are a familiar example. In the modification A the particles have a certain set of energy levels, and in the modification B they have a different set of levels. When both sets of levels are populated, we can ask whether equilibrium between one group of particles and the other group is possible.

Let the groups A and B initially contain n and n' particles, respectively, and let the levels of B be denoted by $\epsilon'_0, \epsilon'_1 \ldots \epsilon'_r \ldots$ as in Fig. 21, to distinguish them from the levels of A, which are to be referred to the same zero of energy. Suppose that the populations are exponential with the same value of μ. It will be convenient to suppose that there is a level of B that has the same energy as a populated level of A; suppose, for example, that the level ϵ'_r on the right-hand side of Fig. 21 happens to lie opposite to the level ϵ_k on the left. Then a particle may move from the level ϵ_k to the level ϵ_r', or vice versa, without any change in energy and without any change in the total energy $(E_A + E_B)$, since $\epsilon_r' = \epsilon_k$.

Let ϵ_j be any level of A lying below the level ϵ_k. We can now consider a rearrangement of the particles in which a particle is transferred to the level ϵ_r'. The particle may have been taken from the level ϵ_k, in which case the total energy remains unchanged, or it may have been taken from the lower level ϵ_j, in which case we must admit the necessary amount of heat $(\epsilon_r' - \epsilon_j)$ that is equal to $(\epsilon_k - \epsilon_j)$. The transfer from ϵ_j to ϵ_r' is obviously equivalent to two steps: a particle is transferred from ϵ_k to ϵ_r', and another particle is raised from ϵ_j to ϵ_k. Since the particles are all of the same species and indistinguishable, the final result is exactly the same as if a particle had been transferred direct from ϵ_j to ϵ_r'. We may concentrate our attention on the transfer from ϵ_k in A to ϵ_r' in B, since the raising of a particle from ϵ_j to ϵ_k within a set of levels has already been dealt with in (23) in Sec. 16.

The transfer of a particle from one group to the other will be accompanied by a change in both W_A and W_B. According to (112a), when the particle leaves the level ϵ_k, we shall have

$$\frac{W_A^*}{W_A} = \frac{n_k}{n}$$

and, according to (112b), when the particle arrives in the level ϵ_r', we shall have

$$\frac{W_B^*}{W_B} = \frac{n'}{n_r'}$$

We may substitute from (57) for n_k/n and for n'/n_r' and obtain

$$\frac{(W_A W_B)^*}{W_A W_B} = \frac{n_k}{n} \div \frac{n_r'}{n'}$$

$$= \frac{e^{-\mu\epsilon_k}}{P_A} \div \frac{e^{-\mu\epsilon_r'}}{P_B} \tag{120}$$

Now, since $\epsilon_r' = \epsilon_k$, (120) reduces to

$$\frac{(W_A W_B)^*}{W_A W_B} = \frac{P_B}{P_A} \tag{121}$$

We know from Sec. 34 that the value of the ratio P_B/P_A will not depend on the particular zero of energy chosen but will have the same value when referred to any zero of energy.

Although we supposed that there was a level of B that had the same energy as a level of A, this device is not necessary. Let q particles be transferred simultaneously from various levels of A to various levels of B; if this is done in such a way that the total energy remains unchanged, we shall reach the same result as before. The particles taken from A contribute factors like those of (118), leading to an exponent of the form

$- \mu(\epsilon_i + \epsilon_j + \cdots)$. At the same time the particles added to B lead to a similar expression, and it is clear that if the total energy of A and B is to remain unchanged, the sum of the energies in one exponent must be equal to that in the other. Hence, in writing down the change in $W_A W_B$, the exponential terms will cancel each other as they did in (120), leaving the result

$$\frac{(W_A W_B)^*}{W_A W_B} = \left(\frac{P_B}{P_A}\right)^q \tag{122}$$

In (122) the value of the ratio P_B/P_A may be greater than unity, less than unity, or equal to unity. When it is greater than unity, the transfer of one or more particles from A to B will be accompanied by an increase in the product $W_A W_B$. Conversely, when it is less than unity, the transfer of particles in the opposite direction will be accompanied by an increase in $W_A W_B$. *A state of equilibrium implies that there is no preferred direction of flow.* In our kinetic picture of the equilibrium, when the two populations are sharing a constant energy $(E_A + E_B)$, particles will be moving to and fro between the two sets of levels, without a bias in either direction. From (122) it is clear that, under certain conditions at least, we can say that when the partition function for one set of levels is equal to the partition function of the other set of levels at the prevailing temperature, particles can move in either direction without any change in $W_A W_B$ when $(E_A + E_B)$ remains constant.

In the two groups of particles of Sec. 22, where the number of particles in each group was fixed, we saw that the condition (38) could be generalized to the form (42) and regarded as a special case of (42). Here, if we set (122) equal to unity, this is equivalent to writing

$$\delta \ln (W_A W_B) = 0 \tag{123}$$

for a rearrangement of the particles that includes transfers from one set of levels to the other at constant energy. Let us now discuss the transfer of q particles from A to B without arranging for the total energy to remain unchanged. Suppose, instead, that we arrange for an amount of energy δQ to enter. In (120) the exponential terms will not cancel but will imply an additional change in $\ln W$ equal to $\mu \, \delta Q$; this will be so, whether P_B is equal to P_A or not. Hence we may say that the change in $\ln W$ will be greater than $\mu \, \delta Q$, less than $\mu \, \delta Q$, or equal to $\mu \, \delta Q$, according as P_B is greater than, less than, or equal to P_A. Thus, if we write

$$\delta \ln (W_A W_B) = \mu \, \delta Q \tag{124}$$

this embodies (123) as a special case when δQ is zero; in this case (124) prescribes the condition $P_A = P_B$, as before. The fact that a pair of bodies cannot in practice be thermally isolated from their surroundings is not of importance, since (124) predicts the same conditions for equilibrium as (123), namely, P_A equal to P_B at the prevailing temperature.

61. We can now approach the problem of equilibrium between two populations A and B, where one or both are of the gaseous type. The discussion that derived (121) and (122) was based on equations (112a) and (112b), which were in turn derived from (1). For a gas or vapor we have to use (81) instead of (1), which is applicable only to localized particles. When a solid is in equilibrium with its own vapor, one group consists of localized particles while the other consists of particles all of which are free to move through the communal volume of the vessel. Let us again discuss two populations A and B, but let us suppose that B is of the gaseous type while A is of the type already discussed in (121).

Using the same notation as before, we fix attention on any quantized state of B that has the same energy as a particular level ϵ_k of A. As before, a particle can move from ϵ_k to ϵ_r', or vice versa, without any change in $(E_A + E_B)$, but this will be accompanied by a change in the values of both W_A and W_B. When the particle leaves the level ϵ_k we have the first term on the right-hand side of (120), namely,

$$\frac{W_A^*}{W_A} = \frac{e^{-\mu \epsilon_k}}{P_A}$$

When this particle arrives in the level ϵ_r', belonging to the vapor, we have to use (82b) and obtain

$$\frac{W_B^*}{W_B} = \frac{n_r' + p_r'}{n_r'} = \frac{P_B e^{\mu \epsilon_r'}}{n_B} \tag{125}$$

To obtain the change in $W_A W_B$, this expression must be multiplied by W_A^*/W_A. The two exponential factors cancel, as they did in (109), since $\epsilon_r' = \epsilon_k$, and we obtain

$$\frac{(W_A W_B)^*}{W_A W_B} = \frac{1}{P_A} \frac{P_B}{n_B} \tag{126}$$

As in Sec. 60, we can now consider the transfer of any number of particles from one set of levels to the other, arranging either that the total energy shall remain constant or that the total energy shall be changed by the admission of an amount δQ; the argument and conclusions will be similar to those of Sec. 60.

62. Saturated Vapor. We have given a preliminary discussion of a number of particles $(n_A + n_B)$ that are distributed through two sets of levels, forming two groups, of which one occupies a set of localized levels and the other a set of unlocalized levels. In later chapters we must ask to what extent these populated levels are adequate to represent a solid and a vapor, respectively, and under what conditions the equilibrium will have the character predicted here. We shall verify that (126) is a correct expression for dealing with the problem.

Anticipating this result, we may briefly discuss here the significance of (126), changing for this purpose the subscripts. Let the vessel contain n_v particles of vapor and let the partition functions be denoted by P_v for the vapor and P_s for the solid. From (126) we have then

$$\frac{(W_s W_v)^*}{W_s W_v} = \frac{P_v/n_v}{P_s} \qquad (127)$$

The value of (127) may be greater than, less than, or equal to unity. We give to (127) the following interpretation. The solid and the vapor are at the same temperature T. If particles evaporate from the solid, this is because the value of P_v/n_v is greater than P_s; if particles condense onto the solid, this is because the value of P_v/n_v is less than P_s. Equilibrium implies that there is no preferred direction of flow; from (127) we see that the required condition is that the number of particles of vapor in the vessel shall be given by

$$n_v = \frac{P_v}{P_s} \qquad (128)$$

When n_v has a value less than this, the vapor is unsaturated; an evaporation of particles from the solid will, according to (127), be accompanied by an increase in the product $W_s W_v$ without any change in $(E_s + E_v)$. When n_v has a value greater than (128), the vapor is supersaturated, and a condensation will be accompanied by an increase in the value of $W_s W_v$. When the number of particles of vapor in the vessel is given by (128), particles can move from either set of levels to the other without any change in $W_s W_v$ and without any change in the energy.

63. We have seen in Secs. 41 and 57 that the removal of a particle from a group of n particles is always accompanied by a diminution in W, that is to say, the value of W^* belonging to the $(n - 1)$ particles that remain in the group is smaller than the original value of W; this is so from whichever of the energy levels the particle is taken.

As we are so often interested in leaving the value of W unchanged, we shall find the following question useful. Suppose that we intend to remove one or more particles from the level ϵ_r. We know that we can, if we wish, prevent this diminution in the value of W, namely, by allowing a certain amount of heat to flow into the body at the same time. We know that the addition of an amount of thermal energy always has the effect of increasing the value of W; if then this amount of heat is properly chosen to be of the right magnitude, the value of W can be maintained at its original value while the particle is removed.

Conversely, when a particle is *added* to a solid or to a gas, we can prevent the increase in $\ln W$ if we arrange for an appropriate amount of heat δQ to flow out of the body at the same time. Such a loss of heat is always accompanied by a decrease in $\ln W$, and if the amount is properly chosen, it will compensate for the particle or particles added to the group. For a solid at temperature T the correct quantity of energy can immediately be seen on inspection of the expression

$$\ln W = n \ln P + \frac{E}{kT}$$

If the sum of the two terms on the right-hand side is to remain constant, one term must decrease when the other increases. If particles are added to the group, the first term on the right-hand side increases by the amount $\ln P$ per particle added. To compensate for this, the change in E per particle added must clearly be given by

$$\left(\frac{\partial E}{\partial n}\right)_W = -kT \ln P \tag{129}$$

In the same way, if we consider the addition of particles to a gas or vapor, the required amount of energy to maintain W constant can be seen by inspection of (116); the amount per particle must be

$$\left(\frac{\partial E}{\partial n}\right)_W = -kT \ln \frac{P}{n} \tag{130}$$

64. We began in Sec. 60 to discuss particles that are free to distribute themselves between two sets of energy levels A and B. We considered particles transferred without any change in $(E_A + E_B)$, and we asked what further condition must be satisfied in order that there should likewise be no change in the product $W_A W_B$.

Now it is clear that there is an alternative method of dealing with this problem. We could consider a process in which particles are transferred from A to B without any change in the product $W_A W_B$, and we could ask what further condition must be satisfied in order that there shall be likewise no change in the value of $(E_A + E_B)$. The expressions (129) and (130) are evidently all that is needed in order to carry through this argument. These expressions, properly handled, will enable us to remove particles from the group A without any change in the value of W_A and then to add the particles to the group B without any change in the value of W_B. Choosing levels in accordance with (111), we ensure that the temperature remains unchanged.

Consider, for example, a solid in contact with its own vapor, in a vessel that contains n_v particles of this vapor. Both solid and vapor are at temperature T. The condition (130) requires that, for each particle transferred from solid to vapor, the vapor shall at the same time lose an amount of energy $kT \ln (P_v/n_v)$, while the condition (129) requires that the solid receive an amount of energy $kT \ln P_s$. In this case the constancy of the product $W_A W_B$ is ensured. If the total energy is likewise to remain unchanged and if P_s and P_v are referred to the same zero of energy, we must have

$$kT \ln P_s - kT \ln \frac{P_v}{n_v} = 0 \tag{131}$$

In order that this condition may be satisfied, the value of n_v must be given by

$$n_v = \frac{P_v}{P_s}$$

in agreement with (128). This problem will be discussed later; in the meantime we may conclude that, under certain conditions at least, the vapor will be saturated when the number of particles in the vessel is equal to the ratio of the two partition functions at the prevailing temperature.

In the same way, if the two sets of levels A and B belong to two modifications of a solid, we shall have to use (129) for both in order to maintain the product $W_A W_B$ constant. The condition that ensures that the total energy shall likewise remain constant is

$$kT \ln P_A - kT \ln P_B = 0 \tag{132}$$

This condition is satisfied if the partition function for one set of levels is equal to that of the other at the prevailing temperature, in agreement with the conclusion that was reached in Sec. 60.

65. Vacant Lattice Points in Crystals. The significance of the quantities that we have found in (131) and (132) will be considered in Chapter 5. Before discussing those problems further, we shall examine here two examples of equilibrium of rather different type. In doing so, we shall pay more attention to the physical processes by which the equilibrium is attained.

In recent years it has become clear that in solids not all the particles are completely immobile, but that in some solids even at room temperature a few particles have considerable mobility. In other solids the particles become mobile at temperatures rather above room temperature. Let Fig. 22*a* represent a perfect crystal and let it consist of N atoms of a certain species, occupying N contiguous lattice points. Suppose now that one atom moves out to an unoccupied lattice point, as indicated by the arrow in Fig. 22*a*; and suppose that an underlying atom moves into the hole thus created. We have now a crystal with one interior lattice point unoccupied, as shown in Fig. 22*c*. Since an adjacent atom may move into this hole at any time, this means that the hole will wander at random through the crystal. Consider now the state of the crystal with one vacant interior lattice point. If there are N interior lattice points, any one of which may be the vacant lattice point, this state of the crystal can arise in N different ways, whereas the original state of the crystal can arise in only one way, namely, when all the contiguous lattice points are occupied. The value of w for the crystal is increased.

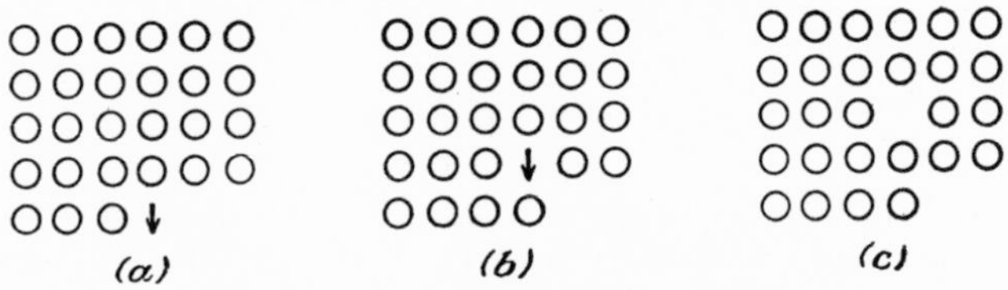

FIG. 22. Formation of a vacant lattice point.

In Chapter 1, when we considered any hypothetical state of the crystal in which all the particles were in the same energy level, for example, the level ϵ_1, this state could arise in only one way—w was equal to unity. But here, in a crystal with one vacant lattice point, w could be very large, even if all the particles were in the same energy level. When the particles form an exponential population the value of w will, of course, be still larger. Recalling the footnote to Sec. 46, let us consider next a crystal with two vacant lattice points, that is to say, with two mobile holes in the interior. There are N choices for the position of the first hole, $(N - 1)$ choices for the position of the second, and so on, if there are three or more holes.

To take an atom from the interior and put it on the surface of the crystal, leaving a hole in the interior, requires a certain amount of work. If the crystal is thermally isolated, it is obvious that the process illustrated in Fig. 22 will not produce more than a certain number of vacant lattice points, since the production of each hole will use up a certain amount of energy. There will be a decrease in the thermal energy, just as if there had been a flow of heat from the crystal. This loss of thermal energy will be accompanied by the usual decrease in w, which will tend to counteract the increase in w just mentioned. As a result, if a certain amount of heat is given to a crystal, the formation of holes will not continue indefinitely but will come to a stop when the number of holes has risen to a certain value appropriate to the total energy E. The greater the value of E, the greater the number of holes that will be present in the crystal. On the other hand, if the crystal is cooled, the number of holes will fall to a smaller value.

Certain properties of crystals leave no doubt that vacant lattice points are present and behave in the manner described. At room temperature, however, their number is so small that their presence can be neglected when discussing the value of w for a solid. We shall study in Sec. 66 the more striking phenomena that occur in certain alloys.

The density of a crystal containing vacant lattice points would be less than the ideal density. Accurate measurements of density have been made only at room temperature. A careful study[1] of the results appears to show that in such crystals as calcite, diamond, sodium chloride, and potassium chloride the number of vacant lattice points at room temperature is less than one in 10^4. Crystals with lattice defects will be briefly discussed in Sec. 173.

66. Order and Disorder in Certain Alloys. In many binary alloys the atoms of the component metals A and B are distributed *at random* among the lattice points of the mixed crystal. In some binary alloys, on the other hand, the atoms of A and the atoms of B tend to take up a regular arrangement and to form two interpenetrating lattices, as indicated in Fig. 23*a*. Such an arrangement can, of course, be *perfect* only if the numbers of A atoms and B atoms are equal or bear some simple ratio corresponding to a simple composition of the crystal, such as A_3B. We shall discuss here the case of equal numbers of A and B.

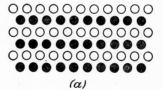

The degree of order in the crystal is investigated experimentally by measuring the scattering of X rays from the mixed crystal. It is found that as the temperature is raised toward its melting point, the A and B atoms tend to change places, producing disorder as indicated in Fig. 23*b*. As a result, at high temperatures the crystal approaches a completely disordered state in which the A and B atoms occupy the available sites at random.

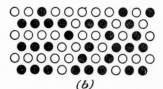

(b)

FIG. 23.   Order and disorder in an alloy.

Further, it is found that if the temperature is lowered somewhat and held constant at a particular value T, a definite degree of order returns. In fact, to each temperature T belongs an appropriate degree of order.

This is a typical problem of statistical mechanics. For if we ask why the crystal adopts a certain degree of order at temperature T_1 and a different state of order at temperature T_2, the answer must be given in terms of w, the number of ways in which any state of the crystal can arise. At temperature T_1, the crystal possesses a total energy E_1, and a certain degree of order gives to w the maximum value consistent with this amount of energy. At temperature T_2 the crystal has a total energy E_2, and it is a different degree of order that now gives to w the maximum value consistent with the total energy.

In Sec. 174 we shall give a treatment of this problem that is applicable over the whole range from complete order to complete disorder. Here we shall attempt to treat only small amounts of disorder, and we shall choose an especially simple crystal for discussion.

The sites that, in a perfectly ordered crystal, are occupied by the A

[1] F. Seitz, *Rev. Modern Physics*, **18**, 398 (1946).

atoms are often called "α-sites," while those occupied by the B atoms are called "β-sites." A definite degree of disorder is specified by saying that a certain number of A and B atoms have been interchanged, so that a number of A atoms occupy β-sites, while the same number of B atoms occupy α-sites. Let us take a crystal containing equal numbers of A and B atoms, namely, n atoms of A and n atoms of B. Let us consider the state of the crystal specified as "one pair of atoms interchanged and occupying wrong sites"; this state can arise in n^2 different ways, since any one of the A atoms can be interchanged with any one of the B atoms. In saying this we are, of course, not referring at all to the number of ways in which the particles can be distributed among their energy levels, but only to the number of ways in which the two species can be arranged on lattice sites of given type. In this problem, as in Sec. 65, there is thus a configurational W, which may be denoted by W_{cf}, in addition to the usual thermal W, which may be denoted by W_{th}. It is the thermal W that has been under discussion hitherto in this book but it has not before been necessary to specify it by means of a subscript.

67. When any liquid solidifies and forms a crystal, the atoms adopt their regular lattice arrangement because this is a state of low potential energy. In a mixed crystal AB the atoms tend to form their interlocking lattices for the same reason; in other words, when the crystal is in an ordered state, it takes a definite amount of work to interchange one A atom with one B atom, putting them onto wrong sites; this amount of energy may be denoted by V. (In Sec. 174 we shall take into account the fact that when the crystal is disordered, the value of V becomes smaller; here we shall consider only states with a high degree of order and shall take V to be a constant, independent of temperature.) For simplicity we shall suppose that in this crystal the set of energy levels for a particle of species A has the same spacing, whether the particle is on a right or a wrong site, and the same for the particles of species B. In this case the situation is like that depicted in Fig. 20d; the value of the thermal energy of a particle at any temperature T will be the same whether it is on a right or a wrong site; consequently, the value of W_{th} for the crystal at this temperature will not be influenced by the number of particles occupying wrong sites. The number of ways in which any particular state of the crystal can arise will be given by the product $W_{th}W_{cf}$. When the crystal possesses a certain total energy E, the state of the crystal that will be adopted is the one for which this product has its maximum value. Writing

$$\ln W = \ln W_{th} + \ln W_{cf} \tag{133}$$

we want to find the condition under which this has the greatest value consistent with the possession of a total energy E.

Suppose then that the mixed crystal, having any small degree of disorder and possessing any arbitrary total energy E, is thermally isolated and allowed to come to equilibrium. In this process of coming to equilibrium we may find that more atoms of A and B go into "wrong" places. This can come about only if the necessary energy (V per pair interchanged) is borrowed from the thermal energy, since the crystal is thermally insulated. That is to say, the degree of disorder increases only if at the same time particles fall into lower energy levels. We know by (27) in Sec. 16 that the value of W_{th} is thereby diminished. Thus when such a crystal is thermally insulated, an increase in W_{cf} is accompanied by a decrease in W_{th}. Conversely, if an A atom and a B atom that are occupying "wrong" sites go back to "right" sites, an amount of energy V is liberated and is added to the thermal energy. By (27), when an amount of energy is injected into the thermal energy, the value of W_{th} is increased; thus a decrease in W_{cf} is accompanied by an increase in W_{th}. It is not difficult to see how a compromise is reached and an equilibrium established.

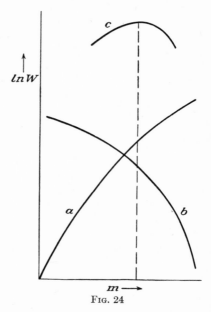

Fig. 24

68. In Fig. 24 let the abscissa be m, the number of particles on "wrong" sites, and let curve a be a plot of $\ln W_{cf}$ as a function of m. Taking a thermally insulated crystal with a fixed total energy E, let curve b be a plot of $\ln W_{th}$ against m. With increasing m, more and more of the energy is used up and the value of W_{th} falls, as described above; each point on this curve corresponds to a certain temperature of the crystal. If we add the ordinates of curve a and curve b, we shall by (133) obtain the curve for $\ln W$. Curve c obtained in this way possesses a maximum. The point on the horizontal axis lying below this maximum specifies the degree of order that the crystal possessing a total energy E will adopt.

The important feature of the situation is that at equilibrium the total energy E is divided into two parts; a certain fraction is used up in putting atoms on to wrong sites, while the remainder, which may be denoted by E_{th}, plays the usual role of energy of thermal agitation. We may write

$$E = E_{cf} + E_{th} \tag{134}$$

If a greater fraction of the energy were to go into the form E_{cf}, the value of W_{cf} would be greater, but only at the expense of W_{th}; if a greater fraction of the energy were to go into the form E_{th}, the value of W_{th} would be greater, but only at the expense of W_{cf}. A compromise is reached; the condition that W shall be a maximum determines how much of the energy shall go into the form E_{cf} and how much shall remain as energy of thermal agitation.

Consider now what would be the situation if we had given to the crystal a greater total energy—greater than before by an amount qV, where q is an integer and V is, as before, the work required to displace an additional pair of atoms. In constructing Fig. 24, curve a would be the same as before. Curve b would have the same shape as before but would be displaced to the right a distance q, since the thermal energy, and consequently W_{th}, would have the same values as before if the number of atoms on wrong sites were greater by q. If we add the ordinates of curve a and curve b, we obtain a curve with a maximum lying farther to the right, indicating, as we should expect, a lower degree of order.

The crystal has come to equilibrium by adopting a certain degree of disorder, at the same time adopting a certain temperature. We supposed that this state was reached because the crystal was thermally isolated. But once the crystal has come to a steady temperature, then of course we do not upset its equilibrium if we now put the crystal into thermal contact with a heat reservoir that is at the same temperature T. Although the crystal is no longer thermally isolated and small quantities of heat will flow to and fro between the reservoir and the crystal, the crystal will not depart from the state that it has adopted, except momentarily.

In the discussion of the insulated crystal, the basic idea was that W_{cf} would not increase beyond a certain point because the displacement of additional atoms used up more and more of the thermal energy and so led to a decrease in the value of the product $W_{cf}W_{th}$. If, however, the crystal is not insulated, this is no longer true. If we obtain the requisite energy from the reservoir, we can displace additional atoms to wrong sites without drawing upon the thermal energy of the crystal. The argument in its original form does not seem to apply to this case.

Let us take a mixed crystal that has come to equilibrium at a certain temperature T and place it in contact with a heat reservoir at this temperature T. Suppose now that, in this crystal, we move q additional atoms to wrong sites, drawing the necessary energy qV from the reservoir. In doing so, we have increased the value of W_{cf} without at the same time diminishing the value of W_{th}. The value of the product $W = W_{cf}W_{th}$ has certainly increased, and the thermal energy of the crystal still has the value appropriate to the temperature T. It would seem then that the crystal would spontaneously change in this direction, since it obtains a larger value of W by so doing.

The solution of this problem lies in the fact that, although it is true that this new value of W is greater than the previous value, it is *not the greatest value of W consistent with the new value of E*. As we shall see below, there are still greater values of W; consequently the crystal is unable to remain in the condition to which we have brought it, and the final result will be that the additional atoms that we have displaced to wrong places will spontaneously go back to right places, until the original equilibrium is restored.

69. The argument proving these statements can be more simply set forth if we first make a short digression and study more closely the problem of Sec. 22, where we discussed the value of $\ln W_A W_B$ for a pair of bodies in contact. If the total energy $(E_A + E_B)$ remains fixed, it is clear that, taking E_A as abscissa, we could obtain a diagram analogous to Fig. 24, with three curves—one similar to curve a for $\ln W_A$, another similar to curve b for $\ln W_B$, and, on adding the ordinates, a curve for $\ln W_A W_B$ that has a maximum. When the bodies A and B have come to equilibrium and adopted a certain temperature T, let them be placed so that B is in contact with a heat reservoir at this temperature T.

Now suppose that a certain amount of energy is transferred from the reservoir to B. The value of W_B is increased while the value of W_A remains unchanged. We can no longer use the argument that an increase in W_B *must* be accompanied by a decrease in W_A, as we could in the case of thermal isolation. The value of $W_A W_B$ has certainly been increased; the greater the amount of energy admitted to B, the greater will be the increase in $W_A W_B$. We are, however, in no danger of supposing that this process will continue spontaneously. Although the value of $W_A W_B$ is greater than the initial value, it is not the *greatest* value appropriate to the new value of the total energy. We supposed that the value of E_B was increased while the value of E_A remained unchanged. The pair of bodies will not accept this situation; the additional energy will be shared between the two bodies, since this allows $W_A W_B$ to attain the maximum value appropriate to the new value of the total energy.

Returning to the problem of disorder in the mixed crystal, the quantities E_{cf} and E_{th} play a role similar to that of E_A and E_B. In transferring particles to wrong sites at constant temperature, we have increased E_{cf} without any change in E_{th}. But this one-sided arrangement will not be maintained; particles will spontaneously return from wrong to right sites and thereby E_{th} will receive its share of the added energy. An increase in E_{th} means a rise in temperature; in fact, the temperature of the crystal is now higher than that of the thermal reservoir, and heat will therefore flow out of the crystal. The details of this process may be understood from Fig. 25, which reproduces the curves from Fig. 24. The original state of the crystal in equilibrium at temperature T is shown by the point D, where the length $AD = AB + AC$. When q additional atoms have been displaced, the curve b is shifted to the right, as shown by the curve b'; the ordinates of b' must now be added to the ordinates of curve a.

If a horizontal line BE is drawn, the point E evidently belongs to the same temperature as B because the values of W_{th} are the same, while all points on the portions of the curves b and b' lying above BE correspond to temperatures higher than the initial temperature T, since the value of W_{th} is larger. The value of $\ln W_{cf}W_{th}$ for the new state of the crystal will be found by adding the ordinate of the point E to the ordinate of the point

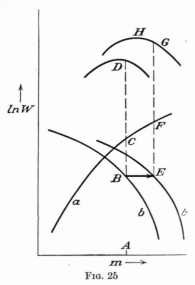

FIG. 25

F immediately above it. The point G obtained in this way lies higher than the initial point D; that is to say, the value of W is greater than the initial value. But the point G does not lie at the maximum of the curve obtained by adding the ordinates of the curve b' to the ordinates of the curve a. As stated above, there are still greater values of $\ln W$ available; the crystal will change spontaneously toward the state represented by the point H. In this process, since H lies to the left of G, some of the displaced atoms go back to right sites, thereby injecting energy into the thermal energy of the crystal and raising its temperature. However, as soon as the temperature rises above that of the heat reservoir, heat will flow out of the crystal, and this flow will continue until finally the crystal returns to its original state, represented by the point D.

We found in (134) that the total energy E was divided into two parts. Disregarding the relation between these two parts, we tried in this imaginary experiment to displace more atoms at constant temperature, increasing the value of E_{cf} without at the same time increasing the value of E_{th}. When the crystal is left to itself, however, part of the added energy will at once be converted into a thermal energy, as described above, and this process will be repeated until the whole of the added energy is given back to the reservoir.

We have discussed this problem in some detail because it shows in simple form certain aspects that are shown less clearly in many other equilibrium problems. Consider, for example, a solid and its vapor, enclosed in a vessel and thermally isolated; and let the whole come to equilibrium. The removal of additional particles from the solid into the vapor would now be accompanied by an increase in W were it not for the fact that a certain amount of work must be done to transfer the particles; thermal energy is used up, and the value of W_{th} decreases for every particle removed from the solid; a compromise is therefore reached. Conversely, if particles of vapor were condensed on to the solid, the heat liberated thereby would cause an increase in W_{th}; but here again, when the vapor pressure has its saturation value, this increase in W_{th} is exactly compensated and W is unchanged.

When the vessel is placed in contact with a heat reservoir, the transference of particles from solid to vapor no longer necessarily causes a diminution in W_{th}. But we must say, as above, that the new value of W, though larger than the initial value, is not the largest value consistent with the new value of the total energy. The temperature will spontaneously rise, and the energy taken from the reservoir will be given back, until the pressure of the vapor has returned to its saturation value.

Problem

In (115) and (116) the value of E depends on the zero of energy to which the energy levels have been referred. Verify that the value of W, however, according to (115) and (116) is independent of the zero of energy chosen.

CHAPTER 4

*The Partition Function and Properties of Monatomic and Diatomic
Gases—Localized and Unlocalized Particles*

70. The Partition Function of a Monatomic Gas or Vapor. Consider
a monatomic gas contained in a rectangular vessel, the sides of which have
lengths a, b, and c, the atoms of the gas each having a mass m. As in
Sec. 28, those energies are allowed for which the ψ-wave fits into the
vessel; each ψ-wave is a standing wave that has a nodal plane coinciding
with each of the six walls of the vessel. That is to say, for free motion
of a particle in the x-direction the allowed wavelengths are those for which
an integral number of half-wavelengths are equal to a; likewise in the y-
and z-directions, those for which an integral number of half-wavelengths
are equal to b and c, respectively, the ψ-functions being given by

$$\psi = \left(\frac{8}{abc}\right)^{\frac{1}{2}} \sin\frac{n_x\pi x}{a} \sin\frac{n_y\pi y}{b} \sin\frac{n_z\pi z}{c} \tag{135}$$

where n_x takes all positive integral values from unity upward, and the
same for n_y and n_z. The energies to which these ψ-waves belong are
given by

$$\epsilon = \frac{h^2}{8m}\left(\frac{n_x^2}{a^2} + \frac{n_y^2}{b^2} + \frac{n_z^2}{c^2}\right) \tag{136}$$

where h is Planck's constant. To obtain the partition function, (136) must
be substituted in (101) in Sec. 45, giving

$$P = \sum_{n_x}\sum_{n_y}\sum_{n_z} e^{-\frac{h^2}{8mkT}\left(\frac{n_x^2}{a^2} + \frac{n_y^2}{b^2} + \frac{n_z^2}{c^2}\right)} \tag{137}$$

where the summation must be taken over all values of n_x, n_y, and n_z.
The exponential term in (137) may be split into three factors, whereby
the sum may be expressed as the product of three separate summations
over values of n_x, n_y, and n_z:

$$P = \sum_{n_x} e^{-\frac{gn_x^2}{a^2}} \sum_{n_y} e^{-\frac{gn_y^2}{b^2}} \sum_{n_z} e^{-\frac{gn_z^2}{c^2}} \tag{138}$$

where

$$g = \frac{h^2}{8mkT} \tag{139}$$

88

We have then to evaluate three sums of the form

$$\sum_n e^{-\alpha n^2}$$

in which there is a term for every integral value of n. This may be done by the method that was used in Figs. 9 and 10 for the evaluation of Z, in which there was a term for every integral value of p. It will be recalled that the area under the curve of Fig. 10 was numerically equal to the sum of lengths of the vertical lines in Fig. 9. Here, if n is taken as abscissa and if vertical lines equal in length to $e^{-\alpha}$, $e^{-4\alpha}$, $e^{-9\alpha}$ . . . are erected at $n = 1, 2, 3 \ldots$, the required sum is the sum of the lengths of all the vertical lines. But this will be numerically equal to the area under the bounding curve, which is given by the integral

$$\int_0^\infty e^{-\alpha n^2}\, dn \qquad (140)$$

A method of evaluating this integral is given in Note 2 of the Appendix. Since the integration is to be taken from zero to infinity, the value will be one-half the integral (35) in Sec. 20, namely, $\frac{1}{2}\sqrt{\pi/\alpha}$. Substituting in (138), we find that for the translational energy levels of a monatomic gas or vapor the partition function is given by

$$P_{\text{tr}} = \left(\frac{2\pi m k T}{h^2}\right)^{\frac{3}{2}} abc \qquad (141)$$

But abc is the volume of the vessel containing the gas. We find the important result that the partition function is proportional to the volume of the vessel.

71. We have been attempting to evaluate the quantity $\Sigma e^{-\epsilon_r/kT}$ summed over the energy states available to each particle of a perfect monatomic gas or vapor. For many species of atoms (141) is the required result. For some species, however, including the atoms of alkali metals, an additional numerical factor must be introduced. We have not yet mentioned the various electronic states of the atom, and for most gases there is no need to do so, since for most species all the particles are in the same electronic state and will remain so at all terrestrial temperatures. In a free atom of any of the alkali metals, on the other hand, what is usually called the "lowest electronic state" consists of two electronic states with an extremely small difference of energy between them. In the vapor, almost exactly half of the atoms will be in one of these states and the other half will be in the other state, irrespective of their kinetic energy of translation.

The value (141) for the partition function was arrived at by assuming that if we assign to n_x in (136) an integral value and an integral value to n_y and to n_z, this prescribes *one* possible state for the particle. But, in the case of an alkali atom, there are two possible states associated with this one state of translational motion, and likewise two states associated with every other state of translational motion given by (136). The correct value of the partition function in this case will thus be double the value given by (141). In general (141) may be multiplied by a factor g, where g is an integer expressing the multiplicity of the lowest electronic state of the atom. Denoting by v the volume of the containing vessel, we obtain from (141)

$$P_{\text{tr}} = \left(\frac{2\pi mkT}{h^2}\right)^{\frac{3}{2}} gv \tag{142}$$

For later use in Sec. 92 we shall write this in the form

$$P_{\text{tr}} = Bv \tag{143}$$

where B is independent of the volume of the vessel.

Since the mass of the particle m occurs in (142), it is clear that when the monatomic gas consists of a mixture of isotopes, the values of the energy levels and of the partition function (142) are slightly different for each isotope. The numerical values of (142) for different elements will be discussed in Chapter 6.

72. Properties of a Perfect Monatomic Gas. The zero of energy for (136) and (142), as already mentioned, coincides with the energy of a molecule at rest; hence, if E is evaluated from (78) in Sec. 35 using this zero of energy, the value found will be the kinetic energy of the molecules of the gas.

If we compress the gas isothermally reducing the volume, we have to do an amount of work $\int p\,dv$. But none of this energy remains in the gas; it is all passed on to the surroundings in the form of heat. In other words, although many or all of the values of ϵ_r are altered by the change in volume, the value of the sum $\Sigma n_r\epsilon_r$ remains the same, for we have from (142)

$$\left(\frac{\partial \ln P_{\text{tr}}}{\partial T}\right)_v = \frac{3}{2T} \tag{144}$$

and substituting in (78), we obtain for the kinetic energy

$$E_{\text{tr}} = nkT^2\left(\frac{\partial \ln P_{\text{tr}}}{\partial T}\right)_v = \frac{3}{2}nkT \tag{145}$$

This is independent of the volume of the vessel containing the gas. A change in the volume of the vessel alters the energy levels of the particles, that is, it alters the allowed values of the translational energy; in spite of this the value of the thermal energy is unchanged. This behavior is peculiar to a "perfect gas." We notice that E/n, the average kinetic energy per particle is equal to $\frac{3}{2}kT$, in agreement with the value obtained from a discussion of the kinetic theory of gases (or from classical statistics; see Sec. 141).

73. Consider now a closed vessel divided into two chambers by a dividing wall that is a conductor of heat (compare Fig. 29a). Let one chamber contain n_A particles of a perfect gas A sharing a total energy E_A, while the other chamber contains n_B particles of another perfect gas B sharing a total energy E_B. Suppose now that the wall that permanently separates the gases can move without friction and can so allow the separate gases to adopt the state that can arise in the greatest number of ways consistent with the total energy $(E_A + E_B)$. From (104) in Sec. 46

$$\ln W_A W_B = n_A\left(\ln \frac{P_A}{n_A} + 1\right) + \frac{E_A}{kT} + n_B\left(\ln \frac{P_B}{n_B} + 1\right) + \frac{E_B}{kT} \qquad (146)$$

If the volume of one chamber increases at the expense of the other, we have $\delta v_A = -\delta v_B$. No external work is done, and the kinetic energy of the particles at temperature T is independent of the volume. We find then that the gases will not be in equilibrium unless

$$\delta \ln W_A W_B = \left(n_A \frac{\partial \ln P_A}{\partial v_A} - n_B \frac{\partial \ln P_B}{\partial v_B}\right) \delta v = 0$$

$$n_A \frac{\partial \ln P_A}{\partial v_A} = n_B \frac{\partial \ln P_B}{\partial v_B} \qquad (147)$$

To see the significance of (147), we must compare it with (109) in Sec. 53. Clearly, from (109), the state adopted by the gases is the one where their pressures are equal; this condition gives to $W_A W_B$ its maximum value. The expression (109), which has just been cited, is of general application. In the case of a perfect gas contained in a vessel of volume v, we obtain from (142)

$$\left(\frac{\partial \ln P_{\mathrm{tr}}}{\partial v}\right)_T = \frac{d \ln v}{dv} = \frac{1}{v} \qquad (148)$$

Consider now Boyle's law; for one mole of gas $pv = RT$; for a quantity of gas containing n molecules $pv = nkT$. From (148), we obtain

$$p = \frac{nkT}{v} = nkT \frac{\partial \ln P_{\mathrm{tr}}}{\partial v}$$

$$= \left[\frac{\partial}{\partial v}(nkT \ln P_{\mathrm{tr}})\right]_T \qquad (149)$$

which is in agreement with (109) in Sec. 53.

From (145) we find that for a perfect gas the heat capacity at constant volume is

$$\left(\frac{\partial E}{\partial T}\right)_v = \frac{3}{2} nk \qquad (150)$$

On the other hand, if the rise of temperature dT takes place at constant pressure, it will be accompanied by an increase in volume dv. The external work done per degree rise of temperature is thus $p(dv/dT)$. For a gas that obeys Boyle's law, dv/dT is equal to nk/p. When we are dealing with one mole of any substance, $nk = R$, the molar gas constant. Thus the difference between the molar specific heat at constant pressure and the molar specific heat at constant volume for a perfect gas is

$$C_p - C_v = p\frac{nk}{p} = R$$

$$C_p = \frac{5}{2}R \qquad C_v = \frac{3}{2}R \tag{151}$$

74. In discussing the states of translational motion of the particles of a perfect gas in Sec. 45, we obtained in (100) an expression for the degree to which the states of any energy ϵ would be populated at temperature T. If we wish to know how many particles will have energies between ϵ and $(\epsilon + \delta\epsilon)$, we have to know how many allowed values of the energy will lie in this interval. Although the partition function (142) was evaluated by taking into account all the energy states of a particle, we have not yet written down an expression for the density of states, which for large vessels is independent of the shape of the vessel. Let $N(\epsilon)\,d\epsilon$

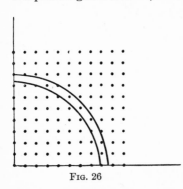

Fig. 26

denote the number of energy states for a particle lying between ϵ and $(\epsilon + d\epsilon)$; this function can be derived most simply by means of a geometrical construction. For a vessel of cubical shape (136) takes the form

$$\epsilon = \frac{h^2}{8ma^2}(n_x{}^2 + n_y{}^2 + n_z{}^2) \tag{152}$$

In (152) every combination of an integral value of n_x, an integral value of n_y, and an integral value of n_z gives one energy state. Consider now Fig. 26, where the positions of the dots correspond to integral values of x and y. The distance of any dot from the origin is given by $r^2 = x^2 + y^2$, where x and y have integral values. If we imagine a three-dimensional lattice of this kind, there will be a lattice point for every combination of integral values of x, y, and z; there will be one lattice point per unit volume. The distance of any lattice point from the origin will be given by $r^2 = x^2 + y^2 + z^2$, where x, y, and z have integral values. The resemblance to (152) is clear if we take r^2 equivalent to ϵ multiplied by the factor $8ma^2/h^2$. Any lattice points that are equidistant from the origin will correspond to energy states that have the same value of ϵ. The total number of states having energies less than some value of ϵ will be equal to the number of lattice points lying within a sphere of radius r, or rather, lying within one octant of this sphere, since in (152) we are concerned only with positive values of n_x, n_y, and n_z. The volume of this octant is $\pi r^3/6$; since in the construction there is one point per unit volume, this gives the number of points in the octant. Hence the number of states having energy less than ϵ is

$$\frac{\pi v}{6}\left(\frac{8m\epsilon}{h^2}\right)^{\frac{3}{2}} \tag{153}$$

where v has been written for a^3, the volume of the cubical vessel containing the gas.

In the same way $\mathrm{N}(\epsilon)\,d\epsilon$, the number of states having energy between ϵ and $(\epsilon + d\epsilon)$, will be equal to the total number of points lying within a spherical shell between r and $(r + dr)$, or rather within one octant of this shell. Thus

$$\mathrm{N}(\epsilon)\,d\epsilon = 4\pi v 2^{\frac{1}{2}}\left(\frac{m}{h^2}\right)^{\frac{3}{2}}\epsilon^{\frac{1}{2}}\,d\epsilon \tag{154}$$

With increasing ϵ, the density of the energy states increases in proportion to $\sqrt{\epsilon}$.

The expression (93) gives the degree to which states of energy ϵ are populated. If (154) is multiplied by (93) or (100), it gives the number of particles having energies lying between ϵ and $(\epsilon + d\epsilon)$. Although this may seem an important quantity, it will be noticed in the following chapters that we never actually need to make use of it. We do not directly make use of (154) either. Use of the partition function suffices, since the partition function is a summation carried out over the whole set of states.

If in (135) the sides of the vessel, a, b, and c, are strictly equal, various states given by (136) will coincide in energy; it is clear that when, for example, the bracketed expression in (152) has the value 6, this can occur in three different ways, namely, when $n_x^2 = 4$, or when $n_y^2 = 4$, or when $n_z^2 = 4$. The lowest level, ϵ_0, given by (136) or by (152), however, is strictly single, corresponding to $n_x = n_y = n_z = 1$. In the x-direction the side a is equal to one half-wavelength, in the y-direction the side b is equal to one half-wavelength, and in the z-direction, the side c is also equal to one half-wavelength.

The expressions (153) and (154) refer to the number of states of translational motion, given by (136). If the lowest electronic state of the atom or molecule has a multiplicity g different from unity, (153) and (154) must be multiplied by g.

75. Partition Function of a Diatomic Gas.

When a diatomic gas is contained in a vessel, the energy levels for translational motion of the molecule are similar to those of a monatomic gas. When the pressure is so low that it may be treated as a perfect gas, the allowed values of the energy are found by inserting in (136) the mass of the molecule. In addition to translational motion, a diatomic molecule may possess a large or a small amount of internal energy—energy of vibration and rotation.

It will be unnecessary here to distinguish between the rotational or vibrational origin of the internal levels. In the whole set of internal energies, let the allowed values be denoted by $\zeta_0, \zeta_1 \ldots \zeta_j \ldots$. In addition the molecule may have any allowed value of the translational energy, given by (136). It will be convenient to denote, as usual, the total quantized energy of a single molecule by ϵ_r. This is the sum of the internal energy and the translational energy. The allowed values of the translational energy, given by (136), will be denoted by $\eta_0, \eta_1 \ldots \eta_k \ldots$. Let w_{in} be the value of w belonging to the population of the levels of internal energy, given by (1). Let w_{tr} be the value of w belonging to the population of the levels of translational energy; its value will be given by (81) in Sec. 40. At ordinary temperatures and low pressures of the gas, (93) reduces to (94) and w_{tr} has its maximum value when its population has the exponential form

$$n_k = \frac{n e^{-\mu \eta_k}}{\Sigma e^{-\mu \eta_k}} \tag{155}$$

while w_{in} has its maximum value when its population has an exponential form

$$n_j = \frac{n e^{-\mu' \zeta_i}}{\Sigma e^{-\mu' \zeta_i}} \tag{156}$$

Although the translational energy of a molecule at any moment is independent of its internal energy, there must be for the gas as a whole a division of the total energy E between the total internal energy, which amounts to $\Sigma n_j \zeta_j$, and the total translational energy, which amounts to $\Sigma n_k \eta_k$. A certain number of calories are in the form of internal energy and a certain number in the form of kinetic energy of translation, and we are led to inquire how this division is determined.

Consider any state of the gas in which part of the total energy is internal and part translational. Suppose now that we convert an amount of energy δE from, say, the translational to the internal form and suppose that this transfer is accompanied by an increase in the product of $w_{\text{tr}} w_{\text{in}}$; in this case such a transfer of energy will occur spontaneously and will continue until the product $w_{\text{tr}} w_{\text{in}}$ reaches its maximum value. According to (27) in Sec. 16, when an amount of energy dE is converted from the translational to the internal form, the value of $\ln w_{\text{in}}$ is increased by the amount $\mu' \, dE$, while the value of $\ln w_{\text{tr}}$ is diminished by the amount $\mu \, dE$. The change in the product $w_{\text{tr}} w_{\text{in}}$ will be zero if $\mu' = \mu$. This is the most probable state, and it is this condition that determines how the total energy shall be distributed between the translational and internal forms. The state adopted by any diatomic gas therefore has the property that the conversion of any small amount of internal energy into translational energy, or vice versa, is not accompanied by a change in W.

Since the internal and the translational parts of the energy are evidently in equilibrium with each other, we need only pay attention to the allowed values of the total energy of a molecule. If these allowed values are denoted by ϵ_0, $\epsilon_1 \ldots \epsilon_r \ldots$, the number of molecules that have total energy ϵ_r will be given by an expression of the usual form

$$n_r = \frac{ne^{-\epsilon_r/kT}}{P}$$

Now any combination of an amount of internal energy ζ_j with an amount of translational energy η_k gives one allowed value of ϵ. Thus, in the denominator we shall perform the summation over the correct values of ϵ_r if we sum over every possible combination of a ζ_j with an η_k. Thus, we obtain

$$n_r = \frac{ne^{-\epsilon_r/kT}}{\sum_j \sum_k e^{-(\zeta_j + \eta_k)/kT}} \tag{157}$$

$$= \frac{ne^{-\epsilon_r/kT}}{\sum_j e^{-\zeta_j/kT} \sum_k e^{-\eta_k/kT}} \tag{158}$$

The second sum in the denominator of (158), being a summation over the translational energy levels, is simply P_{tr} and is obtained by inserting the mass of the molecule into (142). We find then for a diatomic gas

$$P = P_{tr}P_{in} = P_{tr}\Sigma e^{-\zeta_j/kT} \tag{159}$$

where the summation is over all the allowed values of the internal energy. For a diatomic particle the partition function is thus greater than for a monatomic particle of the same mass; its value is P_{in} times as great. In considering the allowed values of the internal energy in Chapter 11, we shall find it necessary to distinguish between those diatomic molecules in which the two nuclei are identical and those in which they are not. The latter class is called "heteronuclear"; examples are the molecules CO and NO, and the Cl_2 molecule $Cl^{35}Cl^{37}$, which contains nuclei of masses 35 and 37. The molecules $Cl^{35}Cl^{35}$ and $Cl^{37}Cl^{37}$ are examples of the former class, which is called "homonuclear."

We can now consider the possibility of tabulating values of the partition functions for various substances. Since the numerical value will depend on the zero of energy adopted, it is necessary to introduce some convention for this choice. For the translational energy of a diatomic molecule, the use of (136) and (142) has taken the zero of energy to be the energy of a molecule at rest; at the same time, for the internal energy, it is natural to take the lowest vibrational-rotational level to be the zero of energy. In Chapter 6 we shall begin to use for any set of levels the symbol **P** to denote the values of P when referred to the lowest level of the set. When the partition function is referred to any other zero, **P** will have to be multiplied by an appropriate factor $e^{-\eta/kT}$ in accordance with (76) in Sec. 34.

In (159) we have P equal to the product $P_{tr}P_{in}$; although P_{in} is independent of the volume of the vessel containing the gas, P_{tr} is of course proportional to the volume. Many of the results obtained for a monatomic gas will apply here. Thus the value of $\ln W$ will be given by (116); for the total energy, we shall have the expression

$$E = nkT^2 \frac{\partial}{\partial T} (\ln P_{tr} + \ln P_{in})$$

$$= \frac{3}{2}nkT + nkT^2 \frac{\partial \ln P_{in}}{\partial T} \tag{160}$$

Thus each diatomic molecule has the kinetic energy $\frac{3}{2}kT$, as in a monatomic gas.

We have considered the division of the total energy into the two forms, translational and internal. The argument may be extended to describe the division into three forms, translational, vibrational, and rotational. In this case, in the denominator of (157) we shall have the product of three summations; in Chapter 11 we shall write the partition function of a diatomic molecule in the form $P_{tr}P_{vib}P_{rot}$.

For a perfect monatomic gas, W is the number of different ways in which the particles can be distributed over their levels of translational energy. For a diatomic gas this must be multiplied by the number of different ways in which the particles may be distributed among their levels of internal energy. The value of $\ln W$ will be greater by the presence of the additional term $n \ln P_{in}$.

76. In both the expressions (115) and (116) the quantity denoted by P is the summation $\Sigma e^{-\epsilon_r/kT}$ taken over the allowed energy states of a particle. But we have noted that in the case of a perfect gas the quantity $\left(\ln \frac{P}{n} + 1\right)$ is continually turning up, instead of the quantity $\ln P$ for a solid. In the general discussion of the behavior of matter we like to use expressions that are applicable to all states of matter. The two states that we have discussed, the compact solid and the perfect gas, are two extreme forms between which lie dense gases, vapors, and liquids. We may then regard it as likely that the quantities $\left(\ln \frac{P}{n} + 1\right)$ and $\ln P$ are special cases, that is, extreme forms, between which we may expect to find intermediate expressions.

To show that this is so, let Fig. 27a depict a vessel of a certain size containing n particles of a monatomic gas, and let Fig. 27b depict schematically a vessel of the same size containing the same number of particles, but let the vessel be divided into n equal compartments, each containing one particle. The allowed energies for a particle in any compartment will be given by (136); hence its partition function will be obtained by inserting in (142) the volume of one compartment. If P denotes the partition function for the undivided vessel, the partition function P^* for a compartment will be equal to P/n, since the volume is one nth the total volume. For the gas in the undivided vessel, the value of ln W will be given by the usual expression (116). We shall now discuss the value of ln W when the dividing walls are present, assuming that the whole gas is at temperature T and that the dividing walls do not interfere with the usual exchange of energy between the particles of the gas. The distribution of energy is to be the same as it would be in the undivided vessel but the value of W will not be the same.

Let the various compartments be labeled A, B, C, and so on. The particle in the A compartment may be in any one of its set of levels. The particle in the B compartment has a similar set of levels. When the particle in the A compartment is in its rth level and the particle in the B compartment is simultaneously in its sth level, this configuration is distinguishable from the situation where the former is in its sth level and the

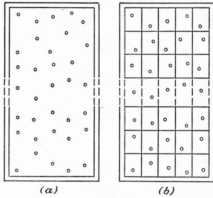

(a)   *(b)*

Fig. 27

latter is in its rth level. In fact, the statistics are no different from those of a solid. The value of W will be given by (1) if, in the denominator of (1), each factor n_r denotes the number of compartments that contain a particle in the rth level. The expression for ln W will be one of the simple form (115),

$$\ln W = n \ln P^* + \frac{E}{kT} \tag{161}$$

$$= n \ln \frac{P}{n} + \frac{E}{kT} \tag{162}$$

Our intention is to remove the dividing walls piecemeal. We know that when all the dividing walls have been removed, the expression for ln W will be (116) containing an extra term,

$$\ln W = n\left(\ln \frac{P}{n} + 1\right) + \frac{E}{kT} \tag{163}$$

By a gradual removal of the dividing walls, we may hope to see clearly the origin and significance of the extra term; we shall presumably obtain expressions that are intermediate between (162) and (163).

It will be convenient to carry out this discussion in two parts. Suppose that, for example, starting with the n compartments, we were to remove dividing walls in such a way as to leave $n/2$ equal compartments, each containing *two* particles. Two changes would thereby be introduced: in the first place, the discussion of Fig. 15 in Sec. 37 will now apply to the pair of particles in each compartment; at the same time the set of energy levels for every particle has been altered, since the size of each compartment has been doubled. In order to deal with one factor at a time, it will be convenient to make a digression and to consider the case where only the first of these changes is introduced.

77. Starting again with the vessel divided into n compartments, let us compare this with a vessel of *half* the size divided into $n/2$ equal compartments, each containing two particles; we have then, as before, a gas at temperature T containing n particles, and the set of energy levels for each particle is the same in the two cases. Many configurations, however, which were distinguishable for the separate particles, one per compartment, are indistinguishable for the pairs of particles. The value of W must be reduced by a certain factor. To evaluate this factor, we have to ask in how many ways n particles can be arranged in pairs.

Similarly, if we consider a vessel in which there are m particles in each compartment (there being n/m equal compartments) we have to ask in how many ways n particles can be arranged in groups of m. The required expression has the same form as (1), namely,

$$\frac{n!}{m! \times m! \times m! \times \cdots} = \frac{n!}{(m!)^{n/m}} \tag{164}$$

It is clear that, on going from $m = 1$ to $m = 2$, for example, the value of this expression is reduced by the factor $2^{n/2}$; and that, in general, on going from one particle per compartment to m particles per compartment, the value is reduced by the factor $(m!)^{n/m}$. Hence, to remove duplicate configurations, we shall have to subtract from (161) the quantity $\frac{n}{m} \ln (m!)$.

At the same time, in order to carry out our original program of progressively removing the dividing walls, we shall have to take into account the change in the size of the compartments. We denoted by P the partition function for the undivided vessel. When the vessel was divided into n equal compartments, the partition function for each was P/n. When the vessel is divided into n/m equal compartments, the partition function for any particle will be mP/n. Combining this with (164), we can complete the discussion and can verify that we obtain expressions intermediate between (162) and (163). When there are n/m compartments with m particles in each, the expression for $\ln W$ will be

$$\ln W = n \ln \frac{mP}{n} - \frac{n}{m} \ln (m!) + \frac{E}{kT}$$

$$= n\left[\ln \frac{P}{n} + \ln m - \frac{1}{m} \ln (m!) \right] + \frac{E}{kT}$$

$$= n\left[\ln P^* + \ln m - \frac{1}{m} \ln (m!) \right] + \frac{E}{kT} \qquad (165)$$

On writing $m = 1$, we see that (165) reduces to (161), the form characteristic of a solid. On the other hand, when m is large, we may use Stirling's formula and obtain

$$\ln W = n\left[\ln \frac{P}{n} + \ln m - \frac{1}{m}(m \ln m - m) \right] + \frac{E}{kT}$$

$$= n\left(\ln \frac{P}{n} + 1 \right) + \frac{E}{kT}$$

which is the expression for the undivided vessel.

We can now verify that, for any intermediate stage between $m = 1$ and $m = n$, the expression (165) gives us a value intermediate between (162) and (163). When, for example, we have two particles in each compartment, we obtain from (165)

$$\ln W = n\left(\ln P^* + \ln 2 - \frac{1}{2} \ln 2 \right) + \frac{E}{kT}$$

$$= n\left(\ln \frac{P}{n} + 0.347 \right) + \frac{E}{kT} \qquad (166)$$

As we remove more dividing walls, the numerical term in the parentheses rises rapidly from 0.347 toward 1.00. We find, for example, that with $m = 27$ the value of the numerical term is already greater than 0.9. There is thus no great difference between having 27 particles per compartment and having 10^{19} particles per compartment. When, starting with $m = 1$, we begin to remove the dividing walls, nearly the whole of the change in the value of $\ln W$ occurs in the early stages.

At the beginning of Sec. 76, we introduced this discussion to discover why in the expressions (104) and (130) we have to use $\left(\ln \frac{P}{n} + 1 \right)$ for a gas or vapor and only $\ln P$ for a solid. We suspected that these were special forms of an expression that would apply to all forms of matter. We have found now that we can obtain expressions intermediate between (115) and (116). When there is one particle per compartment, we have

$$\ln W = n \ln P^* + \frac{E}{kT}$$

When there are two particles per compartment, (165) may be written

$$\ln W = n \ln (\sqrt{2}P^*) + \frac{E}{kT}$$

When there are three or more particles per compartment, the numerical factor multiplying P^* is greater than $\sqrt{2}$. When all partitions have been removed, (154) may be written

$$\ln W = n \ln (eP^*) + \frac{E}{kT}$$

Thus, the numerical factor tends to the limiting value 2.718 when the particles of the gas or vapor move in an undivided vessel.

Problems

1. The partition function (142) is to be substituted in the denominator of (100); when the multiplicity g is different from unity, to what extent does this affect the distribution of energy among the particles? See footnote to Sec. 14.

2. Combining (154) with (94), find an expression for the number of particles in a perfect monatomic gas having energy between ϵ and $(\epsilon + d\epsilon)$. Then find the number of particles having a speed between c and $(c + dc)$, the "Maxwellian" distribution.

3. Taking as abscissa the number of particles per cell, plot a curve to show how the numerical factor in (166) rises from 0.347 toward unity.

CHAPTER 5

The Relation between Statistical Mechanics and Thermodynamics

78. Latent Heat. Section 22 dealt with two populations with the same value of μ and with the study of a rearrangement of the particles in their levels, involving a small transfer of energy from one group to the other. The amount of energy transferred was, of course, not large enough to alter appreciably the value of μ for either group. In Sec. 60 we were again concerned with two populations having the same value of μ. This time the rearrangement could include the transfer of both particles and energy but was again on the submicroscopic scale and not large enough to produce a visible change in either group. We may now draw attention to an important difference between these two problems; whereas there is no large-scale isothermal process corresponding to the problem of Sec. 22, the discussion of Sec. 60 may readily be extended to include the transference of matter in bulk, involving large quantities of energy capable of calorimetric measurement.

Consider a cylinder provided with a piston and placed in contact with a heat reservoir at temperature T; suppose that the cylinder contains a small quantity of a solid in equilibrium with its own vapor, which fills the vessel. If the piston is very slowly withdrawn, the solid will gradually evaporate at constant temperature. If the change is extremely slow, the vapor will never depart appreciably from the saturation value as long as there is any solid present. Particles are transferred to and fro between one set of energy levels A (solid) and another set of levels B (vapor), but the number transferred from A to B exceeds the number transferred from B to A. During this process the total energy $(E_A + E_B)$ does not remain constant; energy is continually withdrawn from the heat reservoir to supply the latent heat of evaporation. The process may be continued until the whole of the solid has been evaporated; (conversely, we can cause the vapor to condense at constant temperature).

The kinetic mechanism by which the vapor is maintained at its saturation value is the continual exchange of particles between one set of levels and the other. These exchanges take place on a submicroscopic scale and the amounts of energy involved are too small to be detected. On the

other hand, as the evaporation of the solid proceeds at constant temperature, the amount of heat admitted becomes a macroscopic quantity,
capable of calorimetric measurement; from an experimental point of view,
therefore, not only this process but any other similar process is worthy
of study. Whenever we have a number of particles partially distributed
through two alternative sets of levels, a large quantity of matter may be
transferred from one phase to the other at constant temperature by
allowing heat to enter or leave. In this way we have latent heats of melting,
heats of transition from one modification to another, heats of molecular
dissociation, heats of solution, and so on.

79. Consider, for example, the two sets of levels depicted in Fig. 20c;
in the group A the energy per particle is E_A/n_A, represented by the position
of the broken line on the left, while in group B at the same temperature
the energy per particle is E_B/n_B, represented in Fig. 20 by the other broken
line. Suppose now that a certain number of particles are removed from
A without changing its temperature (and without causing any modification
of the set of levels for the particles left in A); in this contingent of particles
(removed) the average energy per particle must be E_A/n_A. Similarly, if a
contingent of particles is to be added to B without altering its temperature
(and without causing any modification of the set of levels in B), the
average energy per particle in the contingent must be E_B/n_B. Thus when
particles are transferred from the group A to the group B at constant
temperature, this is equivalent, in Fig. 20, to transferring particles from
one broken line to the other and the amount of energy added per particle
is evidently

$$\frac{E_B}{n_B} - \frac{E_A}{n_A} \tag{167}$$

The same quantity can be written in the form

$$\left(\frac{\partial E_B}{\partial n_B}\right)_T - \left(\frac{\partial E_A}{\partial n_A}\right)_T \tag{168}$$

From the point of view of quantum theory, the value of (167) for any
two sets of levels A and B is in no sense a fundamental quantity; the
value depends on various factors and changes continuously with temperature. Nevertheless, such amounts of energy, being susceptible to measurement, played a part in nineteenth-century physics. The science of
thermodynamics is, in fact, largely concerned with a system whereby the
behavior of matter may be deduced from an empirical mass of such calorimetric data. It is of interest to examine the relation between thermodynamics and statistical mechanics. For this discussion two courses are
open to us. It would, on the whole, be more satisfactory to postpone this
discussion until after Chapters 8, 9, and 10. From another point of view,
however, it is more convenient to open the question here, with reference
to our problem of a number of particles partially distributed through
two sets of levels.

80. Changes at Constant Volume and at Constant Pressure. It will be recalled that, in writing down (121), we took both sets of energy levels as fixed and considered only a rearrangement of the particles among the given levels. If this is to remain so during a bulk transfer of matter, this transfer must be carried out in such a way as not to distort the energy levels, which means that the volume in which each particle moves must remain unchanged. This may sound, at first, as if it were equivalent to the requirement that the process be carried out "at constant volume." In the case of a solid, however, this is obviously not so. If the number of particles in a solid be increased from n to $(n + m)$ at constant volume v, this means that the m additional particles are crammed into the volume that initially held only n particles. As a result, the volume available to each particle is smaller than before and the set of energy levels tends to be distorted. It is when the particles are added or removed at constant pressure that the set of energy levels for each particle remains unchanged.

In the case of a perfect gas, however, the statement must be reversed. If n particles are moving in a vessel of volume v, the energy levels remain unchanged so long as the volume of the vessel is constant. On the other hand, if particles are added to the gas at constant pressure, the volume will increase and the set of energy levels for each particle will be progressively modified.

When a crystal at temperature T, containing n particles, is subject to an external pressure p, let its volume be v. If particles are added to the crystal at constant pressure and temperature, work is done against the external pressure. The increment in the volume of the crystal per particle added is v/n, which is the same as $(\partial v/\partial n)_{p,T}$. The conversion of a solid from one modification to another usually involves external work. Consider, for example, rhombic and monoclinic sulfur. The density of the latter is some 6 per cent less than that of the former; that is to say, the monoclinic crystal occupies a volume about 6 per cent larger. In such cases, however, if the external pressure does not exceed a few atmospheres, the numerical magnitude of the work done is negligible in comparison with the total change of energy. If we can neglect the external work done, we can substitute (167) in (42). When dm particles are transferred from A to B, we have $dm = dn_B = - dn_A$, and (42) may thus be written in the following forms, which are equivalent:

$$\delta \ln W_A W_B = \frac{1}{kT}\left(\frac{E_B}{n_B} - \frac{E_A}{n_A}\right) \tag{169}$$

$$\left[\frac{\partial}{\partial n_A}\left(E_A - kT \ln W_A\right)\right]_{T,v} = \left[\frac{\partial}{\partial n_B}\left(E_B - kT \ln W_B\right)\right]_{T,v} \tag{170}$$

$$\left\{\frac{\partial}{\partial m}\left[(E_A + E_B) - kT \ln W_A W_B\right]\right\}_{T,v} = 0 \tag{171}$$

These expressions, as mentioned above, apply to a process where the energy levels remain unchanged and where the work done is either zero or small enough to be neglected; that is to say, the expressions apply to a gas at constant volume, or to a solid or liquid at constant pressure, when the external work is small enough to be neglected.

For a gas at constant pressure, the increment in volume and the work done must be included in (169), as in (110). With the extra terms, (170) and (171) take the form

$$\left[\frac{\partial}{\partial n_A}(E_A - kT \ln W_A + pv_A)\right]_{T,p} = \left[\frac{\partial}{\partial n_B}(E_B - kT \ln W_B + pv_B)\right]_{T,p} \quad (172)$$

$$\left\{\frac{\partial}{\partial m}\left[(E_A + E_B) - kT \ln W_A W_B + p(v_A + v_B)\right]\right\}_{T,p} = 0 \quad (173)$$

81. On either side of (170) we have the quantity $kT \ln W$ differentiated with respect to the number of particles in the group. From (115) and (116), respectively, we at once obtain the following expressions:

for a solid

$$\left[\frac{\partial}{\partial n}(kT \ln W)\right]_T = kT \ln P + \frac{\partial E}{\partial n} \quad (174a)$$

and for a gas or vapor

$$\left[\frac{\partial}{\partial n}(kT \ln W)\right]_{T,v} = kT \ln \frac{P}{n} + \frac{\partial E}{\partial n} \quad (174b)$$

Substituting in (170), it is evident that (170) and (171) are alternative forms for the conditions that we found in Secs. 60 and 61 for equilibrium, namely, if both A and B are solids

$$P_A = P_B \quad (175)$$

and, if A is solid and B is gaseous,

$$n_B = \frac{P_B}{P_A} \quad (176)$$

The basic idea in Sec. 78 was that, with a slowly moving piston, the vapor would not depart appreciably from the saturation value. As far as the equilibrium is concerned, it obviously can make no difference if this piston is firmly locked instead of being mobile; it can make no difference whether we consider the system at constant volume or at constant pressure. That is to say, we should be able to recover (175) and (176) as readily from (172) as we did from (170). For this purpose, we have to differentiate $kT \ln W$ at constant pressure; this means that we have to include an extra term, to allow for the fact that the change in volume causes a change in the partition function. Thus, from (70),

$$\left[\frac{\partial}{\partial n}(kT \ln W)\right]_{T,p} = kT \ln P + nkT \frac{\partial \ln P}{\partial v}\left(\frac{\partial v}{\partial n}\right) + \frac{\partial E}{\partial n} \quad (177)$$

If the second term on the right-hand side is compared with (109), it will be seen that the term contains the pressure p. In fact, when we substitute the right-hand side of (177) into (172), with negative sign, the term pv is canceled; thus for two solids we again recover the relation $P_A = P_B$. Similarly, if (104) is differentiated with respect to n at constant pressure, the additional term is the same as the second term in (177). When substitution in (172) or (173) is made, the same cancellation takes place and we obtain the condition (176), as before.

In deriving the conditions for any equilibrium, it is clearly more convenient to use (170) than (172), for when we use (172) we merely burden ourselves with two extra terms that cancel each other.

82. Entropy and Free Energy. In thermodynamics it is to some extent recognized that when a system spontaneously approaches and adopts a state of equilibrium, this is because in so doing the system adopts the states that can arise in the greatest number of ways. Although no attempt is made to say anything about the molecular character of these states, the concept of entropy, tending toward its maximum value, expresses the same idea as the tendency for a population to adopt the form with the greatest value of Z. Entropy has the same dimensions as those of Boltzmann's constant k, namely, "energy per degree of temperature." We have seen in Sec. 59 that when we are dealing with any change involving a large group of particles, the difference between the numerical value of $\delta \ln Z$ and that of $\delta \ln W$ is negligible. Since only *changes* in entropy are discussed in themodynamics, we need not distinguish between $k \ln Z$ and $k \ln W$. If in (170), (171), (172), and (173) we write S for $k \ln W$, we obtain the four equations

$$\left[\frac{\partial}{\partial n_A} (E_A - TS_A)\right]_{T,v} = \left[\frac{\partial}{\partial n_B} (E_B - TS_B)\right]_{T,v} \tag{178}$$

$$\left[\frac{\partial}{\partial m} (E - TS)\right]_{T,v} = 0 \tag{179}$$

$$\left[\frac{\partial}{\partial n_A} (E_A - TS_A + pv_A)\right]_{T,p} = \left[\frac{\partial}{\partial n_B} (E_B - TS_B + pv_B)\right]_{T,p} \tag{180}$$

$$\left[\frac{\partial}{\partial m} (E - TS + pv)\right]_{T,p} = 0 \tag{181}$$

this substitution being based on the fundamental expression for any change of entropy

$$\frac{\delta Q}{kT} = \frac{\delta S}{k} = \delta \ln W \tag{182}$$

When this identification of S with $k \ln W$ is made, it is clear that (180) and (181) express the condition that when particles are transferred from group A to group B, or vice versa, at constant temperature and pressure, there shall be no change in the Gibbs free energy G, which is defined as

$$G = E - TS + pv \tag{183}$$

Similarly, (178) and (179) express the condition that when particles are transferred at constant temperature and volume, there shall be no change in the Helmholtz free energy F, which is defined as

$$F = E - TS \tag{184}$$

Through a discussion of W we have been led to a consideration of the free energy. For a solid containing n particles, we have from (115)

$$E - TS = E - kT \ln W = - nkT \ln P \tag{185a}$$

Similarly, for a gas or vapor, from (116)

$$E - TS = E - kT \ln W = - nkT \left(\ln \frac{P}{n} + 1 \right) \tag{185b}$$

For one mole of substance, RT will be written for nkT in these expressions. In the isothermal compression or expansion of any substance (gas, liquid, or solid) the change in the Helmholtz free energy is equal to the work done on the substance. If the identifications made in (178) and (179) are correct, this change in F should be equal in both cases to δA, as given by (108). Either from (185a) or (185b) we obtain

$$\left(\frac{\partial F}{\partial v} \right)_T \delta v = - nkT \frac{\partial \ln P}{\partial v} \delta v \tag{186}$$

in agreement with (108).

When the number of particles in the group is changed at constant temperature, we have, per particle, from (183) and (185), in the case of a solid

$$\left(\frac{\partial F}{\partial n} \right)_{v,T} = \left(\frac{\partial G}{\partial n} \right)_{p,T} = - kT \ln P \tag{187a}$$

and in the case of a gas or vapor

$$\left(\frac{\partial F}{\partial n} \right)_{v,T} = \left(\frac{\partial G}{\partial n} \right)_{p,T} = - kT \ln \frac{P}{n} \tag{187b}$$

It will be recalled that the quantities on the right-hand sides of (187a) and (187b) were the quantities that were equated in Sec. 61, to prescribe the condition for equilibrium between a solid and its vapor.

At the end of Sec. 81 it was pointed out that in prescribing the conditions in any equilibrium problem it is more convenient to use the Helmholtz than the Gibbs free energy. In the following chapters we shall use the term *free energy* to mean the Helmholtz free energy unless otherwise stated.

We often have to deal with the free energy of two or more independent populations in contact. The additivity of the free energies may either be derived from a study of the partition function, as described in Sec. 138, or it may be simply regarded as arising from the fact that the value of W is equal to the product of W_A, W_B, $W_C \ldots$ belonging to the component parts; as a consequence the value of $\ln W$ is the sum of $\ln W_A$, $\ln W_B \ldots$, while the total energy E is the sum of E_A, $E_B \ldots$. Hence we have the result that has already emerged in (171)

$$E - kT \ln W = (E_A + E_B + \cdots) - kT(\ln W_A W_B \cdots) \qquad (188)$$

When, for example, a solid is in contact with its own vapor at temperature T, the free energy of the whole is equal to the free energy F_s of the solid and the free energy F_v of the vapor.

$$F_s + F_v = n_s kT \ln P_s + n_v kT \left(\ln \frac{P_v}{n_v} + 1 \right) \qquad (189)$$

When dm particles are transferred from solid to vapor, we have

$$dm = dn_v = - dn_s$$

or

$$\frac{\partial}{\partial m} = \frac{\partial}{\partial n_v} = - \frac{\partial}{\partial n_s}$$

For equilibrium according to (179), we write

$$\left(\frac{\partial F}{\partial m} \right)_{T,v} = \left(\frac{\partial G}{\partial m} \right)_{T,p} = kT \ln P_s - kT \ln \frac{P_v}{n_v} = 0 \qquad (190)$$

which leads to the result obtained in Chapter 3

$$n_v = \frac{P_v}{P_s}$$

This expression will be discussed in Sec. 91.

83. The expressions (185a) and (185b) assign to F a numerical value depending on the zero of energy that has been chosen for the energy levels. In a thermodynamic treatment, the free energy of a body is measured from some arbitrarily chosen zero of energy. When dealing with a set of energy levels, we choose, whenever possible, the ground level as our zero of energy. Provided that this ground level consists of a single energy state, the value of P tends to unity at the absolute zero of temperature and the value of F given by (185) goes to zero. At other temperatures $\ln P$ is positive; thus according to (185) F is a negative quantity and takes larger negative values as the temperature rises. This is depicted by the lower curve in Fig. 28. The slope of such a curve depends on the character of the spacing between the energy levels; when the spacing is narrow, the value of P at any temperature is relatively large, and hence the curve for F will fall more rapidly than for a set of levels with wide spacing.

The negative value of F can also be ascribed to the fact that when the ground level is chosen as the zero of energy, the term TS in (184) is always greater than E, except at zero temperature when E and TS are both equal to zero.

When we are dealing with two alternative sets of levels, like those of Fig. 20, where η is the difference in energy between the two ground levels, we usually choose the ground level of the lower set as the zero of energy. In this case the partition function for the upper set of levels tends to the value of $e^{-\eta/kT}$ at the absolute zero of temperature; the value of F therefore

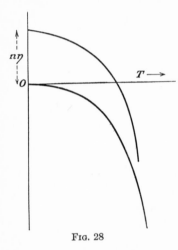

FIG. 28

reaches the value of $+ n\eta$, as shown in the upper curve of Fig. 28. This quantity $n\eta$ is of course the total energy of the particles at this temperature, since E and F become identical at the absolute zero.

84. We can now give to the free energy an interpretation based on the discussion of Sec. 58. We saw there that when a particle is added to a group, the increase in $\ln W$ usually consists of two terms, one arising from the thermal energy and the other, an intrinsic term, arising from the fact that the number of particles has been increased by unity. When a particle is added to the ground level, there is no increase in thermal energy. If from $\ln W$ we subtract the term E/kT and express the difference in thermodynamic notation, we obtain

$$\ln W - \frac{E}{kT} = \frac{S}{k} - \frac{E}{kT} = -\frac{F}{kT}$$

Thus the quantity $- F/kT$ is seen to correspond to the first term on the right-hand side of (115) or to the first term on the right-hand side of (116). It is these terms that are used in prescribing a state of equilibrium. The quantity $- \dfrac{1}{kT}\dfrac{\partial F}{\partial n}$ is that part of the change in $\ln W$ which accompanies the increase or decrease in the number of particles in a group, irrespective of the change in thermal energy. The term E/kT plays no part; it is subtracted from $\ln W$; hence the minus sign that occurs in the expressions $(TS - E)$ or $(E - TS)$.

In any phase containing either one or several species, the chemical potential of the ith species (per mole) may be defined[1] as

$$\mu_i = L\left(\frac{\partial E}{\partial n_i}\right)_{S,v,n_j} \tag{191}$$

[1] E. A. Guggenheim, "Modern Thermodynamics," p. 10. Methuen, 1933.

where L is Avogadro's constant and where n_j refers to any other species that may be present in this phase. We shall find now that we have used this quantity in Sec. 64. In discussing vapor pressure, it was pointed out that the increase in W, on adding particles to the vapor, could be avoided if at the same time we arranged to remove a properly chosen amount of energy. We assumed a fixed set of energy levels, that is, a constant volume for the vessel containing the vapor; only one species was present, so the n_j in (191) can be omitted. Since constant entropy implies a constant value of W, it is clear that (191) is (per particle) equivalent to (130); we thus obtain an interpretation of (191). When particles are added to a phase, there is ordinarily an increase in S; but this increase in S could be avoided if a properly chosen amount of energy were, at the same time, removed from the group as described in Sec. 63. The way in which this concept may be used in prescribing equilibrium has been illustrated in Sec. 64. We have already seen that, for a gas or vapor, the quantity $- kT \ln(P/n)$ is equal to $(\partial F/\partial n)_{v,T}$ and to $(\partial G/\partial n)_{p,T}$.

As noticed in Sec. 80, in the case of a solid, a fixed set of energy levels implies constant pressure but not constant volume. We may use the alternative definition of the chemical potential

$$\left(\frac{\partial H}{\partial n_i}\right)_{S,p,n_j} = \left[\frac{\partial}{\partial n_i}\,(E + pv)\right]_{S,p,n_j} \tag{192}$$

bearing in mind that when a solid is subjected to a pressure of 1 atmosphere or less, the contribution from the term pv is negligibly small. When particles are added to a solid at constant pressure, the usual increase in S can be avoided if a properly chosen amount of heat is removed at the same time.

According to (185b), the entropy of a perfect gas is equal to

$$k \ln \dot{W} = nk \ln \frac{P}{n} + nk + \frac{E}{T} \tag{193}$$

The term nk has been called the "communal entropy" of the gas molecules, since it arises, as described in Sec. 77, from the fact that the particles occupy a common volume v. At one time it was suggested that when a solid melts, the particles of the liquid thereby acquire a communal entropy equal to nk. It was, however, pointed out by N. F. Mott and the author that there is no reason to think that this is so.[1] If the temperature of the liquid is raised through the critical temperature and beyond, as the density decreases the particles have a steadily increasing communal entropy, which will eventually in the vapor reach the value nk.

85. A Mixture of Perfect Gases. Since the discussion of Fig. 15, it has been clear that in a mixture of isotopes the number of different ways w in which a total energy E can be shared among n particles will be larger than for n particles of a single isotope occupying the same volume. This

[1] See R. H. Fowler and E. A. Guggenheim, "Statistical Thermodynamics," p. 330, Cambridge, 1939.

question of the additional entropy may be approached from a different point of view. Figure 29a is intended to depict a vessel divided into two

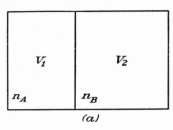

unequal compartments having volumes v_1 and v_2. Let the first contain a certain amount of a perfect gas A, while the other contains an amount of another perfect gas B at the same pressure and temperature. Suppose now that we remove the thin dividing wall and allow the gases to mix. It is of interest to ask whether there is a change in the entropy and the free energy. Let $B_A v_1$ denote the partition function for a particle of species A when confined in the volume v_1 of Fig. 29, and let $B_B v_2$ be the partition function for a particle of species B confined in the volume v_2. According to (159) and (143), when each particle is free to move through the whole vessel, the partition functions will be

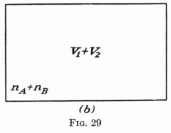

(b)

Fig. 29

$B_A(v_1 + v_2)$ and $B_B(v_1 + v_2)$. Initially, we have from (116)

$$\ln W_A W_B = n_A\left(\ln \frac{B_A v_1}{n_A} + 1\right) + n_B\left(\ln \frac{B_B v_2}{n} + 1\right) + \frac{E_A + E_B}{kT} \quad (194)$$

Since for any perfect gas the energy E is independent of the volume, there will be no change in the last term. We find then that (194) will be increased by an amount

$$n_A \ln\left(\frac{v_1 + v_2}{v_1}\right) + n_B \ln\left(\frac{v_1 + v_2}{v_2}\right) \quad (195)$$

Since the gases in the two compartments were initially at the same pressure, their densities must have been such that $n_A/n_B = v_1/v_2$. Accordingly, (195) may be written in the form

$$n_A \ln\left(\frac{n_A + n_B}{n_A}\right) + n_B \ln\left(\frac{n_A + n_B}{n_B}\right) \quad (196)$$

In any mixture, the quantities $n_A/(n_A + n_B)$ and $n_B/(n_A + n_B)$ are known as the "mole fractions" of the components A and B of the mixture and may be denoted by x_A and x_B, respectively. The change of entropy, on removing the dividing wall, is thus

$$S' - S = -(n_A \ln x_A + n_B \ln x_B)k \quad (197)$$

Since both of the logarithms are negative, (197) represents an increase in entropy.

Returning to a perfect gas consisting of isotopes, it can readily be shown that for a mixture of two isotopes, A and B, which are present in the ratio n_A/n_B, the expressions (196) and (197) give the amounts by which the values of $\ln W$ and S for the mixture are greater than those for a single isotope. The corresponding decrease in the free energy is

$$F' - F = (n_A \ln x_A + n_B \ln x_B)kT \tag{198}$$

A solid or liquid consisting of two or more isotopes will be discussed in Chapter 7.

86. Partial Dissociation of a Diatomic Gas. We can go on now to discuss an equilibrium involving three sets of energy levels. Consider a vessel containing a diatomic gas AB, which is partially dissociated into atoms

$$AB \rightleftarrows A + B \tag{199}$$

In the vessel let the number of diatomic molecules be n_{AB}, while the number of atoms of species A is n_A and the number of atoms of species B is n_B. If we break up one diatomic molecule into atoms, we diminish n_{AB} by unity and at the same time add one particle to n_A and one particle to n_B. Suppose that the pressure of the whole is so low that each species may be treated as a perfect gas. Each species of particle has its own set of energy levels in the vessel, depending on the mass of the particle in accordance with (136) and (159); let the three partition functions referred to the same zero of energy be P_{AB}, P_A, and P_B. The value of W is the product of W_{AB}, W_A, and W_B. To predict the equilibrium, the method of Sec. 61 could be used; here we shall write down the free energy of the whole:

$$F = F_{AB} + F_A + F_B \tag{200}$$

$$= - n_{AB}kT\left(\ln \frac{P_{AB}}{n_{AB}} + 1\right) - n_A kT\left(\ln \frac{P_A}{n_A} + 1\right) - n_B kT\left(\ln \frac{P_B}{n_B} + 1\right) \tag{201}$$

If dm molecules are dissociated into atoms, we have

$$dm = - dn_{AB} = dn_A = dn_B$$

Hence we write

$$\left(\frac{\partial G}{\partial m}\right)_p = \left(\frac{\partial F}{\partial m}\right)_v = kT\left(\ln \frac{P_{AB}}{n_{AB}} - \ln \frac{P_A}{n_A} - \ln \frac{P_B}{n_B}\right) = 0 \tag{202}$$

This is satisfied by

$$\frac{n_A n_B}{n_{AB}} = \frac{P_A P_B}{P_{AB}} \tag{203}$$

where the three partition functions are referred to the same zero of energy. We shall discuss the significance of (203) in Chapter 6.

87. Treatment of Free Energy in Physical Chemistry. In studying reactions between elements and compounds, chemists find it convenient to select at each temperature a "standard reference state" for each reacting species. Thus for any gas a pressure of 1 atmosphere is usually chosen. To illustrate this procedure in relation to the discussions given in this book, let us consider again a partially dissociated gas AB contained in a vessel of volume v; if each species behaves as a perfect gas, the equilibrium condition is given by (203). Suppose that, for the species A, we have selected the standard state such that at the temperature considered the volume v will contain n_A^0 particles. The Helmholtz free energy of these n_A^0 particles will be

$$F_A^0 = -n_A^0 kT\left(\ln\frac{P_A}{n_A^0} + 1\right)$$ (204)

Similarly, for the species B and AB, let the standard states at the same temperature be such that the volume v will contain n_B^0 and n_{AB}^0 particles. Consider now the ratios n_A/n_A^0, n_B/n_B^0, and n_{AB}/n_{AB}^0. There is no reason why these three quantities should bear any simple relation to each other. Using (203), we obtain

$$\ln\frac{(n_A/n_A^0)(n_B/n_B^0)}{n_{AB}/n_{AB}^0} = \ln\frac{n_A n_B}{n_{AB}} - \ln\frac{n_A^0 n_B^0}{n_{AB}^0}$$ (205)

$$= \ln\frac{P_A P_B}{P_{AB}} - \ln\frac{n_A^0 n_B^0}{n_{AB}^0}$$ (206)

$$= \ln\frac{P_A}{n_A^0} + \ln\frac{P_B}{n_B^0} - \ln\frac{P_{AB}}{n_{AB}^0}$$ (207)

From (187) in Sec. 82 we know that when a vessel contains n particles of a perfect gas,

$$-\frac{1}{kT}\left(\frac{\partial F}{\partial n}\right)_{v,T} = -\frac{1}{kT}\left(\frac{\partial G}{\partial n}\right)_{p,T} = \ln\frac{P}{n}$$ (208)

The first term on the right-hand side of (207) is therefore equal to the value that $-\dfrac{1}{kT}\left(\dfrac{\partial G_A}{\partial n_A}\right)_{p,T}$ will have when there happen to be n_A^0 particles of species A in the vessel, that is, when this species is in its arbitrarily chosen standard state. Similarly for the other two terms on the right-hand side of (207). Because the chemist prefers to deal with moles rather than with particles, the numerator and denominator of (208) may each be multiplied by Avogadro's constant L, thereby converting kT to RT.

If, for each species, p and p^0 denote the pressures when n and n^0 particles of the perfect gas, respectively, occupy the given volume, we have $p/p^0 = n/n^0$ for each species, and consequently

$$\ln\frac{(p_A/p_A^0)(p_B/p_B^0)}{p_{AB}/p_{AB}^0} = \ln\frac{(n_A/n_A^0)(n_B/n_B^0)}{n_{AB}/n_{AB}^0}$$

$$= -\frac{1}{RT}\left(L\frac{\partial F_A}{\partial n_A} + L\frac{\partial F_B}{\partial n_B} + L\frac{\partial F_{AB}}{\partial n_{AB}}\right)_{v,T}$$ (209)

$$= -\frac{1}{RT}\left(L\frac{\partial G_A}{\partial n_A} + L\frac{\partial G_B}{\partial n_B} + L\frac{\partial G_{AB}}{\partial n_{AB}}\right)_{p,T}$$ (210)

where each term in the parentheses is L times the change in the free energy per particle, when the species is in its standard state at temperature T. A notation such as ΔG^0 is sometimes used for the whole parenthetical expression in (210).[1] At the same time the standard pressures p_A^0, p_B^0, and p_{AB}^0 are sometimes set equal to unity and are omitted. This omission has the disadvantage that it removes from the expression on the left-hand side the arbitrary factors while the terms on the right-hand side still refer to arbitrarily chosen standard reference states. For imperfect gases see Secs. 90 and 142.

88. We saw that any change in volume usually distorts the set of energy levels and causes a change in the population of these levels. An adiabatic process, however, has the special property that this change in population is not accompanied by any change in the value of W. In an isothermal process, on the other hand, there will be a change in W; we can obtain an expression for this from (109). The first step is to differentiate (109) with respect to the temperature; using (78), we obtain

$$\frac{\partial p}{\partial T} = nk\,\frac{\partial \ln P}{\partial v} + nkT\,\frac{\partial^2 \ln P}{\partial T\,\partial v}$$

$$= k\left[\frac{\partial}{\partial v}\left(n \ln P + \frac{E}{kT}\right)\right] \tag{211}$$

Now, whether we take the expression (116) for a gas or the expression (115) for a solid, in either case, on differentiating with respect to the volume at constant temperature, we obtain the bracketed expression in (211). Thus we have

$$\left(\frac{\partial \ln W}{\partial v}\right)_T = \frac{1}{k}\left(\frac{\partial p}{\partial T}\right)_v \tag{212}$$

In the same way we can find an expression for the change in W that accompanies a change in pressure p at constant temperature

$$\left(\frac{\partial \ln W}{\partial p}\right)_T = \left(\frac{\partial \ln W}{\partial v}\right)_T\left(\frac{\partial v}{\partial p}\right)_T = \frac{1}{k}\left(\frac{\partial p}{\partial T}\right)_v\left(\frac{\partial v}{\partial p}\right)_T$$

$$= -\frac{1}{k}\left(\frac{\partial v}{\partial T}\right)_p \tag{213}$$

If we differentiate F with respect to the pressure, at constant T, we have

$$\left(\frac{\partial F}{\partial p}\right)_T = -nkT\left(\frac{\partial \ln P}{\partial v}\right)\left(\frac{\partial v}{\partial p}\right)_T$$

$$= -p\left(\frac{\partial v}{\partial p}\right)_T \tag{214}$$

[1] L. E. Steiner, "Introduction to Chemical Thermodynamics," Chapter 13, McGraw-Hill, 1941.

Hence, if we do the same for the Gibbs free energy, we obtain

$$\left(\frac{\partial G}{\partial p}\right)_T = \left[\frac{\partial}{\partial p}(F + pv)\right]_T$$
$$= v \tag{215}$$

We shall conclude this chapter with some expressions for an isothermal process carried out at constant pressure. If ΔH_0 denotes the change in the value of $(E + pv)$ at some standard temperatures T_0, then the value for the same process at any other temperature T will be

$$\Delta H = \Delta H_0 + \int_{T_0}^{T} C_p \, dT$$

Similarly

$$\Delta S = \Delta S_0 + \int_{T_0}^{T} \frac{C_p}{T} \, dT$$

Hence

$$\Delta G = \Delta H_0 - T\Delta S_0 + \int_{T_0}^{T} C_p \, dT - T \int_{T_0}^{T} \frac{C_p}{T} \, dT \tag{216}$$

Now

$$\frac{d}{dT}\frac{1}{T}\int C_p \, dT = \frac{C_p}{T} - \frac{1}{T^2}\int C_p \, dT$$

Hence, integrating

$$\Delta G = \Delta H_0 - T\Delta S_0 - T\int_{T_0}^{T}\frac{dT}{T^2}\int_{T_0}^{T_1} C_p \, dT_1 \tag{217}$$

Problems

1. When an evacuated vessel containing a little metallic sodium is heated, it becomes filled with sodium vapor, which consists of Na atoms, together with some diatomic molecules Na_2 in equilibrium with the free atoms. Derive an expression for the conditions for the equilibrium $2Na \rightleftarrows Na_2$ in terms of the partition functions of the atoms and molecules, assuming that the sodium consists of a single isotope.

2. A certain vessel contains n particles of a gas at low pressure. A thin dividing wall is now inserted, to separate the vessel into two unequal compartments. If $P_1 = Bv_1$ denotes the partition function for a particle in one of these compartments, and $P_2 = Bv_2$ for a particle in the other compartment, compare the Helmholtz free energy of the n particles before and after the introduction of the dividing wall, and discuss the result.

3. When a piece of ice is subjected to a sufficiently high external pressure, it melts. Let v_s and v_l denote the volumes occupied by a given mass of H_2O in the solid and liquid states, at the same temperature. Use (215) to find an expression for the lowering of the freezing point as a function of the applied pressure.

CHAPTER 6

Conditions of Equilibrium for a Partially Dissociated Diatomic Gas—For a Saturated Vapor—For Alternative Modifications of a Solid

89. Molecular Dissociation. We obtained in Sec. 86 an expression (203) for prescribing the equilibrium between the atoms and molecules of a partially dissociated gas. Consider a diatomic molecule AB in a vacuum; a certain amount of work is required to break up the molecule into its component atoms A and B. When the molecule is in its lowest vibration-rotational state, the work required to separate the two atoms from each other and to leave them at rest in the vacuum is called the "dissociation

TABLE 1. DISSOCIATION ENERGIES OF DIATOMIC MOLECULES

Molecule	D, electron-volts	D, kcal/mole
H$_2$......	4.455	102.7
HD.....	4.491	103.5
D$_2$......	4.533	104.5
N$_2$......	7.35	169.4
O$_2$......	5.05	148.8
Na$_2$.....	0.76	17.5
K$_2$......	0.51	11.8
Cs$_2$.....	0.45	10.4
LiH.....	2.54	58.5
Cl$_2$......	2.47	57
Br$_2$.....	1.96	46
I$_2$......	1.56	36

energy" of the molecule. This is likewise the amount of mutual potential energy that will be lost when the atoms unite to form a molecule in its ground state. If the distance between the atomic nuclei is taken as abscissa and their mutual potential energy is plotted, the curve has the form shown in Fig. 30. For large separations the curve is a horizontal straight line, but as the separation is diminished there is an attraction that changes over, at small distances, to an intense repulsion. The length of the vertical arrow in Fig. 30 corresponds to the dissociation energy, which will be denoted by D; this will have a characteristic value for each species of diatomic molecule. Some values are given in Table 1.

115

We can now discuss the expression that was obtained in the last chapter for a partially dissociated gas, namely,

$$\frac{n_A n_B}{n_{AB}} = \frac{P_A P_B}{P_{AB}}$$

Here the three partition functions are to be referred to the same zero of energy, and the expression is correct whatever choice is made for this zero. As mentioned in Sec. 75, we shall use the symbol $\mathbf{P}$ to denote the partition function for any set of levels, referred to the ground level of the set. Thus we shall use $\mathbf{P}_{AB}$ for the partition function of AB at the temperature T considered, referred to the energy of an AB molecule at rest in a vacuum and without internal energy. If we insert the mass of the atom A or the atom B in (142) in Sec. 71, we obtain the values of $\mathbf{P}_A$ or $\mathbf{P}_B$. Suppose that we have an atom of A and a distant atom of B at rest in a vacuum and that we choose this state as our zero of energy. The ground state of the molecule AB lies lower than this by an amount D; hence the partition function $\mathbf{P}_{AB}$ referred to the chosen zero of energy will be given, in accordance with (76), by

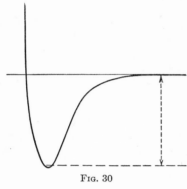

Fig. 30

$$P_{AB} = \mathbf{P}_{AB} e^{D/kT} \tag{218}$$

We find then that (203) takes the form

$$\frac{n_A n_B}{n_{AB}} = \frac{\mathbf{P}_A \mathbf{P}_B}{\mathbf{P}_{AB}} e^{-D/kT} \tag{219}$$

In comparing different diatomic gases, since D occurs in the exponent, the degree of dissociation will be very sensitive to the value of the dissociation energy. It is convenient to remember that at room temperature the value of kT is $\frac{1}{40}$ electron-volt; if then, for example, for a certain molecule D is 1 electron-volt, the value of the exponential factor is $e^{-40} = 10^{-17}$. Although the values of the partition functions in (219) do not vary rapidly with temperature, the degree of dissociation is sensitive to temperature through the exponential factor.

90. The expression (219) can be put into terms of concentrations. If for each species we divide n by Avogadro's number L, we obtain the number of moles of each species in the vessel; if further we divide each by the volume v, we obtain the number of moles per cubic centimeter.

$$\frac{(n_A'/v)(n_B'/v)}{n_{AB}'/v} = \frac{1}{L} \frac{\mathbf{P}_A \mathbf{P}_B}{v \mathbf{P}_{AB}} e^{-D/kT} \tag{220}$$

According to (142) in Sec. 71 and (159) in Sec. 75, $\mathbf{P}_A$, $\mathbf{P}_B$, and $\mathbf{P}_{AB}$ are each proportional to the volume of the vessel; hence the quantity $\mathbf{P}_A\mathbf{P}_B/v\mathbf{P}_{AB}$ is independent of the volume of the vessel. If, for each species, n is further multiplied by 1000, we obtain the ratio of the concentrations in moles per liter

$$\frac{c_A c_B}{c_{AB}} = \frac{1000}{L} \frac{\mathbf{P}_A \mathbf{P}_B}{v \mathbf{P}_{AB}} e^{-D/kT} \tag{221}$$

This quantity, independent of the volume of the vessel, has the dimensions of a concentration, that is, $(\text{length})^{-3}$; this concentration, characteristic of the gas AB at temperature T, is usually denoted by the letter K.

In deriving (221) it was supposed that each of the species A, B, and AB behaves as a perfect gas. For imperfect gases the quantity $c_A c_B/c_{AB}$ at a given temperature will not be independent of the volume of the vessel. In physical chemistry the method of dealing with this situation is to multiply each concentration by a numerical factor; thus in (221), for example, c_A will be replaced by $f_A c_A$, while c_B will be replaced by $f_B c_B$, and c_{AB} by $f_{AB} c_{AB}$. The product $f_A c_A$ is known as the "activity of A when at the concentration c_A" and may be denoted by a_A, while the activity of B and AB may be written a_B and a_{AB}. In an imperfect gas, the free energy bears the same relation to the activity that it bears to the concentration in a perfect gas. In a partially dissociated gas the quantity $a_A a_B/a_{AB}$ will be independent of the volume of the vessel, by definition since the coefficients f_A, f_B, and f_{AB} are functions of the concentration chosen for the purpose. At sufficiently low concentrations the behavior of an imperfect gas becomes indistinguishable from that of a perfect gas; thus any activity coefficient f tends to unity as a concentration tends to zero; at sufficiently low pressures the quantity $a_A a_B/a_{AB}$, for example, will become indistinguishable from (221).

91. Saturated Vapor Pressure. In discussing a monatomic vapor, we obtained in Secs. 62 and 64 an expression for the value of n_v at saturation, in terms of the ratio between the translational partition function (142) and the quantity (68) that we provisionally adopted as the partition function of a solid. In Chapter 11 we shall discuss the details of vapor pressures, both for monatomic and diatomic vapors. In this section we shall briefly consider how the expression $n_v = P_v/P_s$ leads to widely different values for the different elements, in agreement with experiment. According to (142) the partition function for a monatomic vapor depends somewhat on the mass of the particle; let us then compare two elements of nearly the same atomic weight—neon (with isotopes 20, 21, and 22) and magnesium (with isotopes 24, 25, and 26). The vapor pressure of solid magnesium has been measured at temperatures above 430°C, that is to say, above 703°K. The vapor pressure of solid neon, on the other hand, has been measured within 15 degrees of the absolute zero of temperature;

at this temperature the vapor pressure is greater than that of magnesium at 700°K.

In the familiar concept of evaporation, it is held that an atom can leave the surface of a solid only when it happens to acquire an unusually large amount of thermal energy. In order to remove a particle from the surface of the solid, a certain amount of work must be done against the

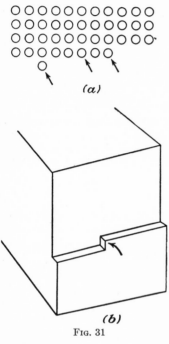

(a)

(b)

Fig. 31

forces of attraction that hold it in place. We have two sets of energy levels, like those of Fig. 20, the solid possessing levels lower than those of the vapor. It was pointed out in the footnote to Sec. 46 that for a particle on the surface of a solid we cannot expect the energy levels to be the same as for a particle in the interior. When a particle is transferred from the vapor to the solid, it will take up a position on the surface; at the same time, however, it will convert a surface atom into an interior atom. If on one surface an additional monatomic layer of n atoms is built up, the result will be that the number of internal atoms is increased by n while the number of surface atoms is (almost) unchanged. Therefore the set of levels with which we are concerned is the set of levels belonging to a particle in the interior. The work per atom required to break up the crystal into its constituent atoms will play a role similar to that played in Sec. 89 by D, the work required to break up a molecule.

In Fig. 31a the three arrows point to three surface atoms; these atoms are in different situations and the amount of work required for removal from the crystal will have a different value for each of the three. We wish to know the amount of work to remove a *representative* atom, so that the work done will be equal to the work per particle required to break up the crystal. For this purpose we consider one of the crystal faces and imagine one layer of atoms stripped off systematically, row by row and atom by atom. Figure 31b is intended to illustrate a stage in the process; from the upper half of the crystal face the rows of atoms have been removed, and the left-hand half of the next row. The position of the atom that is due for removal is indicated by the arrow. The important point is that when this atom has been taken away, the next atom will find itself in a precisely similar situation, that is, with the same number of adjacent atoms, in the same relative positions; and when this next atom has been removed, it in turn will leave still another atom in the same situation. The work to remove each of these atoms is thus the same until we get to the end of the row. The atoms at the ends of the rows are so few in number that they may be neglected. For each of the other atoms, the amount of work will be the same; this is likewise the amount of potential energy lost by an atom that in the reverse process approaches and adheres to the surface at the appropriate point. When this potential energy is plotted against the distance from the surface, the curve has the same form as that of Fig. 30 above; the horizontal part of the curve corresponds to an atom at rest in the vacuum; as the atom approaches the surface, the curve falls, but finally the attraction gives place to an intense repulsion and the curve rises steeply. The depth of the potential minimum will have a characteristic value for each substance.

In the expression $n_v = P_v/P_s$, the two partition functions must be referred to the same zero of energy. Introducing partition functions, each referred to its own ground level, and making use of (142), we may write, in accordance with (76),

$$n_v = \frac{\mathbf{P}_{tr}}{\mathbf{P}_s} e^{-s/kT} \tag{222}$$

where s is the difference in energy between the two ground levels.

The work per particle required to break up a solid at the absolute zero of temperature and to leave the separate particles at rest in a vacuum is known as the "sublimation energy" of the solid (see also Sec. 144). Some values for different elements are given in Table 2; the majority have been taken from Landolt and Bornstein's tables.

TABLE 2. SUBLIMATION ENERGIES

Element	Electron-volts	Cal/mole	Element	Electron-volts	Cal/mole
Li......	1.56	35.96	Kr......	0.110	2.54
Ne......	0.0194	0.446*	Rb.....	0.893	20.58
Na......	1.14	26.3	Ag.....	3.01	69.38
Mg......	1.49	34.44	Cd.....	1.17	27.01
Al......	2.93	67.58	Xe.....	0.167	3.85
A.......	0.0816	1.88	Cs.....	0.813	18.74
K.......	0.948	21.85	W......	8.81	202.90
Cr.....	3.88	89.44	Pt.....	5.41	124.70
Fe.....	4.19	96.52	Au.....	3.94	90.74
Ni.....	4.26	98.13	Hg.....	0.671	15.45
Cu.....	3.55	81.73	Tl......	1.87	43.05
Zn.....	1.36	31.39	Pb.....	2.03	46.72

*W. H. Keesom and J. Haantjes, *Physica*, **2**, 462 (1935).

92. The mass of the hydrogen atom being 1.67×10^{-24} gram, we can evaluate $\mathbf{P}_{tr}$ for any gas of molecular weight M as follows:

$$\mathbf{P}_{tr} = \left[\frac{2\pi \times 1.67 \times 10^{-24} \times 1.38 \times 10^{-16}}{(6.62 \times 10^{-27})^2} \right]^{\frac{3}{2}} (MT)^{\frac{3}{2}} gv$$

$$= 1.96 \times 10^{20} (MT)^{\frac{3}{2}} gv \tag{223}$$

At 273°K for a volume of 1 cubic centimeter, this takes the form

$$\mathbf{P}_{tr} = 8.7 \times 10^{23} M^{\frac{3}{2}} g$$

Thus at room temperature in a vessel having a volume of a few cubic centimeters, we have for most gases and vapors values ranging between 10^{25} and 10^{28}. This is the value of $\Sigma e^{-\epsilon_r/kT}$ taken over the enormous number of energy states available to a particle of the gas or vapor.

At normal temperature and pressure, 1 cubic centimeter of a gas or vapor contains 2.7×10^{19} molecules. Thus, to obtain a pressure of, for example, $\frac{1}{1000}$ atmosphere, which is equivalent to 0.76 millimeters of mercury, we need at this temperature 2.7×10^{16} molecules per cubic centimeter. From (223) we can see now under what circumstances the expression (218) will, in a volume of 1 cubic centimeter, give values of n_v corresponding to measurable pressures. When, for example, the value of P_v/P_s is 10^{23}, the value of the sublimation energy $\mathbf{s}$ could be as large as $15kT$, for in this case we should have $n_v = 10^{23}e^{-15} = 10^{23}10^{-7} = 10^{16}$ molecules per cubic centimeter. Similar estimates at other temperatures, made with the various values of $\mathbf{s}$ given in Table 2, will show that it is, for example, reasonable that the vapor pressure of neon should be easily measurable within 20 degrees of the absolute zero, while that of magnesium has similar values above 700°K.

Making use of (143) in Sec. 71, we obtain from Boyle's law

$$p = \frac{nkT}{v} = \frac{kTB}{\mathbf{P}_s} e^{-s/kT} \tag{224}$$

In (222) and (224) the sublimation energy plays a role similar to that played by the dissociation energy in (219). However, a small difference may be pointed out. If we consider a diatomic molecule in a vacuum, the ground level of this molecule is strictly independent of temperature. Consider, however, an atom in a crystal at room temperature; we say that this atom vibrates in a little volume in which it has a set of levels, of which the lowest is denoted by ϵ_0. The quantity ϵ_0 is not strictly independent of temperature. If we start with the crystal at the absolute zero and raise its temperature, the lattice spacing of the crystal increases slightly; in the process a small amount of energy goes into the form of potential energy as the distance between adjacent atoms increases (see Secs. 130 and 153). There is no need to discuss this question here, since we shall treat the vapor pressure in detail, for both monatomic and diatomic vapors, in Chapter 11. In the treatment given there the partition function will be referred unambiguously to the state of the crystal at the absolute zero of temperature.

93. High- and Low-temperature Modifications of a Solid. It was mentioned in Sec. 60 that many pure substances in solid form can exist in two different modifications; we gave a preliminary discussion to the equilibrium between two such forms A and B. The lowest level ϵ_0 of one set of levels will be lower than the ground level of the other set of levels; let us denote the former set of levels by A and the other by B; and let us take the ground level of A as our zero of energy. The partition functions P_A and P_B, which occur in (122) and (132), will both be measured from this zero of energy. Now let us denote by $\mathbf{P}_B$ the partition function of B referred to its own ground level. From (76) we have $P_B = \mathbf{P}_B e^{-u/kT}$, if u is the amount by which the ground level of B lies higher than the ground level of A. From (122) we find that the condition for equilibrium between the two modifications of the solid is

$$\mathbf{P}_A = \mathbf{P}_B e^{-u/kT} \qquad (225)$$

We notice that this expression, in contrast to (219), does not contain either n_A or n_B; the equilibrium is of a different kind. Whereas in (219) equilibrium was possible at every temperature, here equilibrium is possible only at that temperature which makes the right-hand side of (225) equal to the left-hand side, namely,

$$T = \frac{u}{k \ln (\mathbf{P}_B/\mathbf{P}_A)} \qquad (226)$$

This is the sharp transition temperature; below this temperature one modification is stable, above it the other. The modification for which ϵ_0 is the lower is obviously the low-temperature modification, since at the absolute zero all the particles will congregate in this level.

It will be noticed also that if u in (225) is positive, (226) can only be satisfied if $\mathbf{P}_B$ is greater than $\mathbf{P}_A$; otherwise a transition from one modification to the other will not occur.

94. Diagrams Illustrating Nature of Equilibrium. The various types of equilibrium may be illustrated in greater detail by means of diagrams. Let us take first the case of a solid in contact with its monatomic vapor, which fills a fixed volume v. Let P_v denote, as usual, the partition function for a particle of vapor in this volume. Let the distance OO' in Fig. 32 represent the total number of particles considered and let abscissas, measured from O, represent n_s, the number of these atoms that are in the solid. Then, at the same time, reading from right to left, from O' toward O, abscissas will represent the number of atoms in the vapor, since $n_v = n - n_s$. If against n_s we plot

$$F_s = - n_s kT \ln P_s$$

we obtain a straight line, such as OQ in Fig. 32. If against n_v we plot

$$F_v = - n_v kT\left(\ln \frac{P_v}{n_v} + 1\right)$$

we obtain, falling from O', a line which is curved, becoming less steep as the value of n_v increases, as shown in Fig. 32. For very small values of n the slope will be steeper than that of the straight line OQ. Thus, when the ordinates are added, there are two possibilities; either the resultant curve has a minimum, as in Fig. 32a, or it has no minimum, as in Fig. 32b.

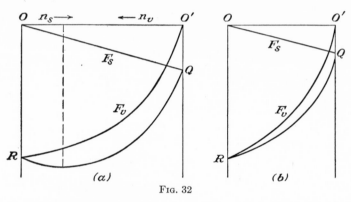

FIG. 32

A vertical line drawn through the minimum in Fig. 32a divides the line OO' into two parts, the left-hand part representing the equilibrium value of n_s, the number of atoms that remain in the solid state, and the right-hand part representing n_v, the number of atoms that are sufficient to fill the given vessel with saturated vapor at the temperature considered.

In Fig. 32b the total number of particles is so small that at the same temperature they are insufficient to fill the vessel with saturated vapor; we have then the vessel filled with unsaturated vapor, and no solid present. If, however, we consider a sufficiently small vessel, we would again obtain a curve with a minimum.

Fig. 32a shows that the value of the saturated vapor pressure is independent of n. If we had a larger number of particles, we should draw a wider diagram, with O' lying farther from O. The diagram shows that in this case the minimum would correspond to a larger value of n_s but the value of n_v would be the same.

In the same way we can illustrate the problem of the two alternative modifications of a solid substance. As before, we take the line OO' of Fig. 33a to represent the total number of particles and we take abscissas measured from the left to represent n_1, the number of particles belonging to the solid in its first modification, and abscissas measured from the right to represent n_2, the number of particles belonging to that part of the substance which is in its second modification. If now against n_1 we plot $n_1 \ln P_1$ and against n_2 plot $n_2 \ln P_2$, we obtain two straight lines $O'R$ and OQ, of which the relative slopes will depend on the temperature. On adding the ordinates, the resulting curve is the straight line RQ. In Fig. 33a the point R represents the state of lowest free energy. In Fig. 33b, on the other hand, corresponding to a higher temperature, the point Q represents the state of lowest free energy and the second modification is the stable form. At some intermediate temperature the line PQ will be horizontal, as shown in Fig. 33c. At this transition temperature both forms can be present together, no matter how the n atoms are divided among n_1 and n_2.

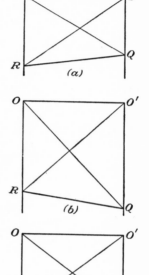

FIG. 33

If the values of the partition function of the two modifications were plotted against the temperature, we would obtain curves rising with increasing slope. If the values plotted are for the two partition functions referred to the same zero of energy, the curves will intersect at a temperature that is the transition temperature. In this region the curve for the low-temperature modification has the steeper slope.

A diagram analogous to Figs. 32 and 33 can be constructed to illustrate the partial dissociation of a diatomic gas of the type $A_2 \rightleftarrows 2A$. In this case, since both components are gaseous, the lines OQ and $O'R$ will both be curved and will resemble the curve $O'R$ in Fig. 32 above. The resultant curve, obtained by adding the ordinates, will possess a minimum under all circumstances. The higher the temperature, the more will the minimum be shifted in the direction of greater dissociation.

95. We saw in Sec. 11 that when we deal with an exponential population, we are really interested in all those distributions which show a close approximation to the strictly exponential population. When dealing with the way in which particles distribute themselves between two alternative sets of levels, an analogous question arises. In Fig. 32a, for example, points on the lower curve RQ correspond to various possible values of n_v. The position of the minimum of this curve, we have said, corresponds to the value of n_v required for the saturated vapor. Yet the curve does not show at all a sharp minimum.

In the line RQ obtained in Fig. 33c, there is no minimum at all; points on this horizontal line correspond, of course, to situations where the n particles share different values of E. Suppose that we have n particles of such a solid at its transition temperature, a certain portion being in the form of the low-temperature modification A and, in contact with this, a portion in the high-temperature modification B, the whole possessing a total energy E. This state of affairs, according to (225), is stable so long as E remains constant. If we allow additional energy to enter, the boundary between A and B will move so that some of the low-temperature modification is converted into the other form; or rather, we should say that after the admission of the heat the state with the greatest value of w will be one in which there is more of the high and less of the low-temperature modification. Conversely, if we allow some heat to flow out, we can say that the state corresponding to w_{max} will be one in which there is more of the low and less of the high-temperature modification. States with w less than w_{max} will certainly occur, but we have not yet investigated this question either for the case of thermal isolation or for contact with a thermal reservoir.

In the following discussion we shall anticipate some results that will be obtained in Chapters 9 and 10. Some solids that have very high melting points undergo a phase transition at a high temperature. It will be convenient to discuss such a case, since at high temperatures we may with sufficient accuracy take the two partition functions to be of the form

$$\ln \mathbf{P}_A = 3 \ln \alpha kT \qquad \ln \mathbf{P}_B = 3 \ln \beta kT \qquad (227)$$

where α and β are constants; see Secs. 152 and 154. Let us take the ground level of the low-temperature modification A as the zero of energy for both partition functions. Then we have, in accordance with (76) and (227),

$$\ln P_B = 3 \ln \beta kT - \frac{u}{kT}$$

If the transition temperature is denoted by T_0, the total energy at this temperature, according to (78), will be

$$E = 3(n_A + n_B)kT_0 + n_B u \qquad (228)$$

Suppose now that the whole is thermally isolated and that we transfer m additional particles from A to B. In doing so we use up a certain amount of the thermal energy, namely, an amount equal to mu. The temperature therefore falls from T_0 to a slightly lower value T, and the total energy is

$$E = 3(n_A + n_B)kT + (n_B + m)u$$

Equating this to (228), we find

$$\frac{T}{T_0} = 1 - \frac{mu}{3nkT_0} \tag{229}$$

Further, from (226) and (227), we have

$$T_0 = \frac{u}{3k \, \ln(\beta/\alpha)} \tag{230}$$

We can now write down the expressions for w before and after the particles are transferred. Initially we have

$$\ln w_{max} = n_A \ln \mathbf{P}_A + n_B \ln \mathbf{P}_B + \frac{E}{kT_0}$$

$$= 3n_A \ln \alpha kT_0 + 3n_B \ln \beta kT_0 - \frac{n_B u}{kT_0} + \frac{E}{kT_0}$$

$$= 3n_A \ln \alpha kT_0 + 3n_B \ln \beta kT_0 + 3n \tag{231}$$

After the transfer of m particles we shall have

$$\ln w = 3(n_A - m) \ln \alpha kT + 3(n_B + m) \ln \beta kT + 3n \tag{232}$$

Subtracting (231) from (232),

$$\ln \frac{w}{w_{max}} = 3n \ln \frac{T}{T_0} + 3m \ln \frac{\beta}{\alpha} \tag{233}$$

Making use of (229) and (230) and expanding the logarithm as in (30), we obtain

$$\ln \frac{w}{w_{max}} = 3n \left(-\frac{mu}{3nkT_0} - \frac{m^2 u^2}{18n^2 k^2 T_0^2} + \cdots \right) + \frac{mu}{kT_0}$$

We see that the first term in the bracket will be canceled by the last term. Hence for values of m comparable with $\sqrt{n}$, we finally obtain

$$\frac{w}{w_{max}} = e^{-\gamma m^2/n} \tag{234}$$

where

$$\gamma = \frac{u^2}{6k^2 T_0^2} \tag{235}$$

We may expect γ to have a value comparable with unity. We have thus reached a result quite similar to the expression (32) that we obtained for deviations from an exponential population. If, for example, we are discussing 10^{20} particles, thermally isolated, a spontaneous transfer of more than 10^{10} particles in either direction may frequently occur, but this is much smaller than could be detected.

In the problem of vapor pressure, a similar discussion may be given for a solid or liquid in contact with its own saturated vapor and thermally isolated. If we ask what is the total number of different states available to the particles, this evidently includes not only the most probable state corresponding to w_{max}, but also states where the particles in the vapor are more or less numerous than the n_v given by (222). To obtain the value of Z, we must sum over all possible values of n_v. But the difference between the numerical value of $\ln Z$ and that of $\ln(w_{max})$ will be negligible when n is large.

96. A Chemical Reaction. As a further example, let us examine a chemical gaseous equilibrium of the type

$$A_2 + B_2 \rightleftarrows 2AB \tag{236}$$

Let D_{AA}, D_{BB}, and D_{AB} be the dissociation energies of the three diatomic molecules, and let the quantity $(D_{AA} + D_{BB}) - 2D_{AB}$ be denoted by D. This is the work required to form two AB molecules each in its lowest state by the process (236); it may have a positive or negative value. If we consider a range of temperature such that kT is small compared with any of the three dissociation energies, the diatomic molecules will not be accompanied by an appreciable number of free atoms. The free energy F of the mixture will then be given by

$$-\frac{F}{kT} = n_{AA}\left(\ln\frac{P_{AA}}{n_{AA}} + 1\right) + n_{BB}\left(\ln\frac{P_{BB}}{n_{BB}} + 1\right) + 2n_{AB}\left(\ln\frac{P_{AB}}{n_{AB}} + 1\right) \tag{237}$$

Since the dissociation of one AA molecule and one BB molecule yields two AB molecules, the condition for equilibrium is

$$-\ln\frac{P_{AA}}{n_{AA}} - \ln\frac{P_{BB}}{n_{BB}} + 2\ln\frac{P_{AB}}{n_{AB}} = 0 \tag{238}$$

Or

$$\frac{n_{AB}^2}{n_{AA}n_{BB}} = \frac{P_{AB}^2}{P_{AA}P_{BB}} \tag{239}$$

In (239) we may introduce the factor $e^{-D/kT}$ in the usual way.

For comparison with a problem to be treated later, we may express (239) in terms of n_A and n_B, the number of *atoms* of A and B. Since $n_A = n_{AB} + 2n_{AA}$, we have $n_{AA} = \frac{1}{2}(n_A - n_{AB})$, and similarly $n_{BB} = \frac{1}{2}(n_B - n_{AB})$. Denoting n_{AB} by ν, (239) takes the form

$$\frac{4\nu^2}{(n_A - \nu)(n_B - \nu)} = \frac{P_{AB}^2}{P_{AA}P_{BB}}e^{-D/kT} \tag{240}$$

As mentioned above, the quantity D may be positive or negative. In either case, with rise of temperature the equilibrium moves toward that state which would arise from a random distribution of the atoms among the three types of molecules. At lower temperatures, the quantity D is important, since the characteristic interatomic forces prevent the equilibrium from resembling a random distribution.

Problems

1. From a modified form of (201), plot diagrams analogous to Fig. 32 to illustrate the degree of dissociation of a homonuclear gas at various temperatures and pressures.

2. The following table gives the observed saturated vapor pressure of solid neon at liquid hydrogen temperatures. Plotting $\log p$ against $1/T$ and setting the multiplicity g in (223) equal to unity, deduce from (224) the value of $\mathbf{P}_s$ for neon at 15°K.

T, °K	p, cm.
15	0.039
17	0.292
19	1.44
20.4	3.67

CHAPTER 7

Solid and Liquid Solutions—Alloys—Solid Solutions in Alpha and Gamma Iron

97. Solutions. In recent years, with the development of metallurgy, solid solutions have become as important as the more familiar liquid solutions. At the same time, it has come to be recognized that at temperatures near its freezing point the internal character of a liquid has a much greater resemblance to that of a solid than had previously been supposed; in the liquid the relation between a particle and its immediate neighbors is very similar to that in the solid state; each particle vibrates in a little volume that is determined by the positions occupied by the adjacent particles at the moment. In most liquids near the freezing point the volume available to a particle is only a little larger than in the solid; the principal difference between a liquid and the corresponding solid is that there is no long-range order.

At its critical point, on the other hand, there is no distinction between a liquid and a dense vapor. There are thus two lines of approach to the study of liquids, according as we are more interested in the liquid near its critical point or near its freezing point. Near the critical point one might attempt to describe the liquid as a very imperfect gas, but the density is very great. Near the critical point of water, for example, both the vapor and liquid water have a density greater than 0.3 gram per cubic centimeter, which is comparable with the density at room temperature. It is recognized that in a gas or vapor of high density a particle is to be regarded as confined for most of the time in a small volume between its neighbors and that the average environment of each particle is not very different from that in a solid.[1] In this chapter, however, for comparison with solid solutions, we shall discuss only liquids near the freezing point, recognizing that here the liquid differs little from the corresponding solid. For a particle in the liquid the spacing of the energy levels will be somewhat narrower than in the solid, since the volume in which the particle vibrates is a little larger. As a result of this narrower spacing, the value of the partition function for a particle in the liquid will be a little greater than it would be in the solid at the same temperature. Near the freezing point,

---

[1] J. E. Lennard Jones and A. F. Devonshire, *Proc. Roy. Soc. A.*, **163**, 54 (1937).

the relation between a liquid and its solid is similar to the relation between the two modifications of a solid. The liquid will correspond, of course, to the high-temperature modification.[1] If we introduce the partition functions P_s and P_l into (226), we find that the solid and the liquid can be in equilibrium only at a certain temperature given by

$$T = \frac{u}{k \ln (\mathbf{P}_l / \mathbf{P}_s)} \qquad (241)$$

This is the normal melting point of the solid and the freezing point of the liquid. Under a high pressure the melting point of the solid will be altered; this is because the values of the quantities on the right-hand side of (241) are changed.

98. When two pure substances A and B are placed in contact with each other, there is a tendency for particles of B to enter substance A, and at the same time a tendency for particles of A to enter substance B. Although from a theoretical point of view both tendencies are present, it happens that in very many cases one of these is quite negligible in comparison with the other; we then call one substance the "solute" and the other the "solvent." In such cases we shall in this chapter use the letter A to refer to the particles that are behaving as solvent, and the letters B and C, and so on, to refer to the species that are behaving as solutes. In the study of simple dilute solutions the problems of first interest are problems of equilibrium between the solution and one of its components in the pure state. It is well known, for example, that when an aqueous solution is cooled, pure ice begins to crystallize out. In this problem we are interested in the equilibrium between ice and the solution, that is, between the solution and the solvent in its pure form. We must discuss the problem by considering the transfer of dm_A particles from solvent to solution, or vice versa. Again, when we wish to know the solubility of some solid in a liquid at temperature T, we are asking what the condition is for equilibrium between the pure solid and its saturated solution. Here we shall consider the transfer of dm_B particles from pure solute to the solution, or vice versa. In the case of a liquid solution, we may fix attention on a temperature that is a little above the melting point of either component; we are then discussing the mixture of two liquids, which may or may not be completely miscible. We may fix attention on a temperature that lies between the melting point of one component and the melting point of the other; in this case we have the familiar solution of a solid solute in a liquid solvent. Alternatively, if we fix attention on a temperature that is sufficiently far below the melting point of either component, the resulting solution will be solid.

---

[1] For a discussion of melting, see F. Seitz, "The Modern Theory of Solids," Chapter 14, McGraw-Hill, 1940; A. F. Devonshire, *Proc. Roy. Soc. A.*, **170**, 464 (1939).

The simplest kind of solution will be a mixture of two isotopes. For example, ordinary water or ice contains a small number of deuterons, which replace protons to form HDO molecules instead of H_2O molecules. The structure of the ice or water is the same whether HDO molecules are present or not. It will be useful to introduce a terminology that is applicable to both solid and liquid solutions. Consider a mixture of two isotopes A and A^* of any element. Since the two particles differ only in the mass of the nucleus, the structure of the solid or liquid will be the same for A and A^* and for any mixture of A with A^*; the number of sites per unit volume will be the same, and likewise the relative positions of these sites. If there are altogether N particles, there are for each particle N possible sites. In counting the possible positions for the particles of either species, the procedure is the same as that used in Sec. 65, namely, there will be N choices for the position of the first, $(N - 1)$ choices for the second, and so on. The total number of possible arrangements is quite independent of the amount of energy E shared by the particles; it is a configurational W and will be denoted by W_{cf}, as in Sec. 67. Both in a solid and in a liquid each particle will vibrate in a little volume, or cage, determined by the positions of its neighbors. In the solid, these positions occur at fixed points in space, the lattice points. When the solid melts, the number of particles is unchanged and the answer is again N choices for the first solute particle, $(N - 1)$ choices for the second, and so on, although in the liquid the possible positions no longer occupy fixed positions in space. We are interested in the number of alternative positions available at any moment in an instantaneous sample of the liquid. In the solid the possible sites are at lattice points, in the liquid they are not; but it will be convenient to use the term *site* in both cases.

We turn next to solutions containing atoms of different elements. X-ray measurements show that in many alloys and mixed crystals the solution is of the kind just described, that is, each solute particle occupies a site that would normally be occupied by a particle of the original crystal; the solution is formed by a process of simple one-for-one substitution. Such a solution is known as a "substitutional solution." The other principal type of solution is one in which the solute particles occupy positions in the interstices between the particles of the original substance. Only relatively small solute particles can be accommodated in this way. The most important examples of interstitial solutions are the solutions of carbon atoms in metallic iron; these form the basis of steel and are discussed in Sec. 119. In a solution of this kind, the number of interstitial sites will of course be proportional to the number of particles of the solvent, in contrast to substitutional solutions, where the number of available sites is equal to the total number of particles, including both solvent and solute.

99. We have mentioned in Sec. 98 some of the equilibrium problems that we shall wish to solve. Before discussing the methods of approach to these problems, since W_{cf}, the number of alternative configurations of the particles, is independent of the amount of energy E that they share, it will be convenient to obtain first the appropriate expressions for W_{cf} for the principal types of solutions. We shall postpone until Sec. 101 inquiry as to how W_{cf} is to be combined with the other relevant factors in order to prescribe conditions of equilibrium.

Taking a solvent consisting of n_A particles of species A, let us first discuss the situation when this solute contains *only two* solute particles. If in the solution there are altogether N sites, we have N choices for the position of the first and $(N-1)$ choices for the position of the second. There are two cases to be considered: (1) where the two solute particles are of the same species, and (2) where they are of different species. Consider a solution where one particle momentarily occupies a site at a point P while the other particle occupies a site at a point Q. If the particles are of different species, this situation is distinguishable from that where the former occupies the site at the point Q and the latter occupies the site at the point P. On the other hand, if the two solute particles are of the same species, we cannot distinguish the two situations. Since this is true for every pair of points P and Q, the value of W_{cf} for a solution containing two similar particles is just half the value for a solution containing two dissimilar particles; the value is, in fact, $\frac{1}{2}N(N-1)$. In a solution containing three similar particles we shall have the product of three factors, namely, $N(N-1)(N-2)$ to be divided by 3!. In general, for a solution containing n similar solute particles, we shall have the product of n factors to be divided by $n!$. These considerations can be applied both to substitutional and interstitial solutions.

Let the solvent consist of n_A particles of species A and let it contain a single solute, namely, n_B particles of species B. In a substitutional solution the total number of sites available to each solute particle is $N = (n_A + n_B)$. We require the product of n_B factors divided by $n_B!$, thus

$$(n_A + n_B)(n_A + n_B - 1) \cdots (n_A + 1) \div n_B! = \frac{(n_A + n_B)!}{n_A!} \div n_B! \quad (242)$$

$$= \frac{(n_A + n_B)!}{n_A! \, n_B!} \quad (243)$$

This is the number of different ways in which the n_B solute particles can be distributed among the available sites, leaving n_A sites vacant to accommodate the n_A solvent particles. Since the allocation of these solvent particles to the vacant sites can be made in only one way, this adds nothing to the value of W. Consequently, (243) gives the number of different ways in which the solvent and solute particles can be assigned to the sites available in the substitutional solution. We shall now generalize (243) to cover any number of solute species.

It was pointed out in Sec. 7 that the $n!$ which occurs in the numerator of (1) may be taken to refer either to the number of particles or to the number of sites. In the latter case n_0 of these sites are destined to be occupied by particles that are momentarily in the level ϵ_0, and so on. We use the same approach here to deal with a mixed crystal containing several species of particles, $A, B, C \ldots$. The total number of sites is $(n_A + n_B + n_C + \cdots)$; and of these sites n_A are destined to be occupied momentarily by particles of the species A, and likewise n_B by particles of the species B, and so on. The correct expression for W_{cf} has the same form as (1), namely,

$$W_{cf} = \frac{(n_A + n_B + n_C + \cdots)!}{n_A! \, n_B! \, n_C! \cdots} \qquad (244)$$

Using Stirling's approximation,

$$\ln W_{cf} = (n_A + n_B + n_C + \cdots) \ln(n_A + n_B + n_C + \cdots) - n_A \ln n_A - n_B \ln n_B - \cdots$$

$$= -\left(n_A \ln \frac{n_A}{n_A + n_B + n_C + \cdots} + n_B \ln \frac{n_B}{n_A + n_B + n_C + \cdots} + \cdots \right) \qquad (245)$$

Now the quantity $n_A/(n_A + n_B + n_C + \cdots)$ is the mole fraction of the component A, and in the next term occurs the mole fraction of the component B, and so on.

If we denote the mole fraction of A by x_A and the other mole fractions by $x_B, x_C \ldots$ we obtain

$$\ln W_{cf} = - n_A \ln x_A - n_B \ln x_B - \cdots \qquad (246)$$

As each mole fraction is less than unity, each of the logarithms is a negative quantity, which makes $\ln W_{cf}$ positive.

In investigating conditions for equilibrium, we shall need to know how the value of $\ln W_{cf}$ will vary with the concentration of each component. For the rth component, we find

$$\frac{\partial}{\partial n_r} (\ln W_{cf}) = - \ln x_r - 1 + (x_A + x_B + \cdots)$$

$$= - \ln x_r \qquad (247)$$

Since x_r is less than unity, the value of (247) is positive.

100. Interstitial Solutions. It was pointed out at the end of Sec. 98 that the number of interstitial sites provided by a crystal will be proportional to the number of particles forming the crystal. Let us consider a solution of B in A; let n_A be the number of particles in the original crystal and let N be the total number of interstitial sites that they provide for particles of B. Then we may write $N = b n_A$. If n_B is the number of particles dissolved in A, the number of interstitial sites remaining vacant is $(N - n_B)$. In writing down the expression for W_{cf}, this number of sites must be allocated to remain vacant, just as if they were to be occupied by another species of particle; the value of W_{cf} is thus $N!/n_B!(N - n_B)!$.

If various solutes are present, namely, n_B particles of the species B, n_C particles of the species C, and so on, and if each of the N interstitial sites can accommodate one particle of any of these solute species, the number of sites assigned to remain empty will be

$$n_e = N - n_B - n_C - \cdots$$

We obtain then an expression of the usual form

$$W_{cf} = \frac{N!}{n_e! \, n_B! \, n_C! \cdots} \tag{248}$$

For the rth interstitial component we find then

$$\frac{\partial}{\partial n_r} (\ln W_{cf}) = -\ln \frac{n_r}{n_e} \tag{249}$$

In a dilute solution n_r is less than n_e and the logarithm is negative, which gives a positive value to (249).

Turning now to the solvent, we have

$$\frac{\partial}{\partial n_A} (\ln W_{cf}) = \frac{\partial}{\partial N} (\ln W_{cf}) \frac{\partial N}{\partial n_A} = b \frac{\partial}{\partial N} (\ln W_{cf}) \tag{250}$$

$$= -b \ln \left(1 - \frac{\Sigma n_r}{b n_A} \right) \tag{251}$$

101. Now that we have obtained expressions for W_{cf}, we may begin to discuss the simplest kinds of solution. When particles of a solid dissolve either in a liquid or in another solid, the process is very similar to the evaporation of the solid. When a solid begins to evaporate, each particle with excess energy leaves the surface and enters a large region (vacuum) through which it can wander at random. When a solid dissolves, each particle with excess energy leaves the surface and enters a large region (solvent) through which it wanders at random. From this point of view, one substance tends to dissolve in another because each solute particle, instead of being confined at a particular lattice site, finds in the solvent an enormous number of equivalent sites available to it. But the process of solution does not continue indefinitely. In the case of a sparingly soluble substance, an equilibrium is reached when the solvent contains few solute particles; we then have a saturated solution, quite analogous to a saturated vapor. In Chapter 6 we saw that when a substance has an unusually low saturation vapor pressure, this is because the value of the sublimation energy **s** is unusually large compared with kT. So here, when a substance is sparingly soluble in a certain solvent, this is because the work required to take a particle from the surface into this solvent is large compared with kT. To account for the difference between the process of evaporation and the process of solution, we have to describe the role played by the solvent. There are two ways of doing this; we shall introduce one method here, and later in Sec. 126 we shall describe an alternative method.

In the problem of vapor pressure, we saw in (126) and (222) that the equilibrium depends on the character of the two sets of energy levels, the set of energy levels for a particle of the solid, and the set of energy levels for a particle of the vapor. In the vapor the environment of a particle is so completely different from that in the solid that nothing is to be gained by making a direct comparison. On the other hand, when a particle of a solid dissolves in a liquid or in another solid, no great change of environment is involved. In the original solid, each particle is closely surrounded by other particles. When a particle has gone into solution, it is again closely surrounded by other particles; the solute particle will vibrate in this small volume and will have a set of energy levels not so very different from those which it had in the pure solid. At the same time the presence of a solute particle will modify to some extent the energy levels of those *solvent* particles with which it is in contact. When a solute particle is electrically charged, as in an ionic solution, many solvent particles not in contact with the ion will also be affected. When, however, the solute particle is electrically neutral, those solvent molecules which, at any moment, are immediate neighbors of a solute particle will be chiefly affected. We may begin by discussing those solutions where the effect on more distant particles may be neglected. The energy levels of some solvent particles will be modified by the presence of solute particles. One method of procedure, then, is to describe a solution in terms of environments, by paying attention to the environment of every solvent particle and every solute particle that the solution contains.

Using the notation W_{th}, let us recall the expression derived in Sec. 27 for localized particles

$$\ln W_{th} = n \ln P + \frac{E}{kT} \tag{252}$$

which refers to n similar particles sharing an energy E and populating the set of levels to which P refers. Hitherto we have thought of these n particles as being in contact with each other and as forming a continuous homogeneous solid, or else a liquid near its freezing point. But we may now recognize that it is not necessary that any of the n similar particles should be in contact with each other. The expression is applicable to n similar particles that have no connection with each other. It is only necessary that each particle should have the same set of energy levels— the set of levels to which P refers. We may therefore use (252) for any n

particles that happen to have the same environment, E being the total energy that these n particles possess when the temperature of the solution has the value T. The expression (252) gives, for an exponential population, the number of different ways in which this energy E may be distributed among the n particles. We see now how to write down an expression for $\ln W$ for the whole solution. There will be, as described below in Sec. 102, a term of the form $\ln W_{th}$ contributed by each environment present in the solution; and the expression for $\ln W$ for the whole solution will be the sum of these terms together with $\ln W_{cf}$.

We found in Chapter 5 that for any group of particles the most convenient quantity for prescribing conditions of equilibrium is $(E - kT \ln W)$. When we write down this expression for a solution, W_{cf} contributes the term $- kT \ln W_{cf}$. This term is contributed jointly by the various species of particles that comprise the solution; it cannot be split in separate terms for the separate species, hence the free energy of the solution cannot be expressed as a sum of the free energies of solvent and solute. On the other hand, the thermal contributions of the form $(E - kT \ln W_{th})$ are additive, provided that the energy levels in the various environments are measured from a common zero of energy.

102. Consider a solvent A containing n_B solute particles of species B. In a sufficiently dilute solution it is unlikely that two solute particles will be found in contact with each other; hence each solute particle may be treated as having the same environment, namely, complete enclosure by solvent particles. Each solute particle has the same set of energy levels. According to (184) if P_B denotes the sum $\Sigma e^{-\epsilon_r/kT}$ taken over this set of levels, the contribution that the solute particles make to the free energy of the solution, in virtue of their thermal energy E_B, will be $- n_B kT \ln P_B$.

Consider next the *solvent* particles in this dilute solution at any moment. These must be divided into two classes, those which are completely surrounded by other solvent molecules, and those which are in contact with a solute particle. Since we must suppose that contact with a solute particle is likely to modify the set of levels of the solvent molecule, these two classes must be treated separately. Let there be n_0 solvent particles in the former class and n_1 in the latter class. Let P_0 be the partition function characteristic of the pure solvent and let P_1 be the value of $\Sigma e^{-\epsilon_r/kT}$ taken over the set of levels modified by the presence on one adjacent solute particle of species B. In a sufficiently dilute solution we may suppose that no solvent molecule is simultaneously in contact with two solute particles, so that $n_0 + n_1 = n_A$. Then, so far as the solvent is concerned, (70) is to be replaced by

$$\ln W_{th} = n_0 \ln P_0 + \frac{E_0}{kT} + n_1 \ln P_1 + \frac{E_1}{kT} \tag{253}$$

We may make use of (253) in a more convenient form, by saying that the contribution to the Helmholtz free energy of the solution, made by the solvent in virtue of its thermal energy E_A, amounts to

$$- n_0 kT \ln P_0 - n_1 kT \ln P_1 \tag{254}$$

The expression for the free energy of the whole solution is thus obtained by adding to (254) the term $- kT \ln W_{cf}$ and the term $- n_B kT \ln P_B$ for the solute. This result applies to very dilute solutions of both the substitutional and interstitial types. Before making use of (254), however, let us briefly discuss the environments of particles in a less dilute solution.

103. Consider two substances A and B, with particles of nearly the same size, which mix by the process of one-for-one substitution. In the pure substance A let the structure be such that each particle has z similar particles in contact with it, and let us suppose that in pure B the structure is such that each particle likewise has the same number of nearest neighbors. In order to discuss the various environments that will be present in the solution, let us fix attention on a particular A-particle in the interior of the pure substance A, and let us suppose that, one by one, we replace the neighbors by B-particles. Let us consider how the energy levels of this A-particle will be affected by the replacement of successive neighbors.[1] If the first substitution shifts and alters the spacing between the energy levels, the next substitution will cause a further change, and so on, until all the z neighboring sites are occupied by B-particles. Such a progressive distortion of the set of energy levels will cause a progressive change in the value of the partition function of the particle considered. In (253) we used P_0 to denote the partition function characteristic of the pure substance A at the temperature considered, when none of the z neighboring sites is occupied by a B-particle; and we used P_1 to denote the partition function for the set of energy levels belonging to a particle when *one* adjacent particle has been replaced by a B-particle. Now let $P_2 \ldots P_r \ldots P_z$ denote the values when two, or r, or z neighbors have been replaced by B-particles. We are concerned with a progressive change from P_0 to P_z consisting of z steps.

At the temperature considered, let the value of P_1 be α times that of P_0, where α has a value not very different from unity. The simplest plausible way to deal with the progressive change from P_0 to P_z is to assume that the z steps are similar, that is, to assume that $P_2 = \alpha P_1$, and that $P_3 = \alpha P_2$, and so on. In this case we shall have $P_2 = \alpha^2 P_0$ and $P_z = \alpha^z P_0$. In general $P_r = \alpha^r P_0$, where r is to take the values $0, 1, 2 \ldots z$. Turning next to the energy levels of a B-particle in the solution, we introduce a factor β similar

---

[1] At the same time, other A-particles are affected by the presence of the B-particles that we introduce; but at the moment we discuss the effect on only the one A-particle.

to α; and we suppose that the energy levels are modified in an analogous way, with β replacing α.

Let us consider now all the A-particles in a certain solution. In (253) we denoted by n_1 the number of A-particles that have *one* B-neighbor and $(z - 1)$ A-neighbors. Since $P_1 = \alpha P_0$, we have

$$n_1 \ln P_1 = n_1(\ln P_0 + \ln \alpha) \tag{255}$$

In the same way let n_r denote the number of A-particles that have r B-neighbors and $(z - r)$ A-neighbors. Then we have for any value of r

$$- n_r kT \ln P_r = - n_r kT(\ln P_0 + r \ln \alpha) \tag{256}$$

The free energy of all the A-particles is to be obtained by summation over all values of r from zero to z, which gives

$$- kT(\Sigma n_r \ln P_0 + \Sigma r n_r \ln \alpha) \tag{257}$$

Now Σn_r is simply the total number of A-particles n_A, while the sum $\Sigma r n_r$ is simply the total number of A-B contacts in the whole of the solution; let this number be denoted by ν.

We are attempting to calculate the quantity that must be introduced, in addition to the quantity W_{cf}, to take into account the different environments in which the A-particles find themselves. If, for example, $z = 12$, there are 13 possible environments. We have just said that the first term in (257) is simply $- n_A kT \ln P_0$, which is the normal free energy of n_A particles of species A when their set of energy levels is not distorted or displaced by the presence of B-particles. The change in the free energy of the solution arising from the ν A-B contacts is given by the second term, which is to be written

$$- \nu kT \ln \alpha \tag{258}$$

When a similar treatment is given to the various environments in which the B-particles find themselves, we have a basis for beginning to discuss mutually soluble substances over the whole range of composition from 100 per cent of A to 100 per cent of B. There are, however, many problems in very dilute solutions that can be discussed without making use of (258). We shall discuss these first and shall return to (258) in Sec. 109.

104. Before attacking any problem, we may take this opportunity to recall what was said in Sec. 56 about the difference between one set of levels and another, namely, that there is usually a difference in spacing as well as a difference in the energy of the ground level. For the sake of illustration, Fig. 20d depicted two sets of levels between which the only difference was a shift in energy. According to (76), if this shift is η, the ratio between the two partition functions will be $P'/P = e^{-\eta/kT}$.

We may notice that the quantity α, which was introduced in (255), will usually imply a change in spacing as well as a change in ϵ_0; and we may make the same remark with regard to the difference between the quantities P_1 and P_0 in (253). A small change of environment will be accompanied by only a small change in the spacing of the levels. In these solid and liquid solutions the total change in spacing may cause the value of P to change by 40 or 50 per cent, and in some cases perhaps by a greater factor. But such a change in P is small compared with that which may result from a shift in energy. Suppose that we are dealing with a temperature T such that the value of kT is equal to, say, one-third of the shift η. Then the factor $e^{-\eta/kT}$ gives us $P'/P = e^{-3} = \frac{1}{20}$. No change in P as great as this could arise from the change in spacing alone.

Bearing this in mind, consider a very dilute solution of a solute B in a solvent A. If the number of B-B contacts is small enough to be neglected, we shall have, as pointed out in Sec. 102, instead of $(z + 1)$ possible environments, only one environment for a solute particle, namely, complete enclosure by solvent particles. We shall likewise have only two environments for a solvent molecule, namely, one characteristic of the pure solvent, and secondly the situation where one neighbor is a B-particle. The number of A-particles in the latter class is z times the number of solute particles, that is, zn_B; hence the number of A-particles in the former class is $(n_A - zn_B)$. We have then in the solution only three partition functions to deal with, corresponding to the sets of energy levels in the three environments, one of which is the same as that characteristic of pure solvent. We may therefore use a much simpler notation than that of Sec. 103, writing simply P_A, P_A', and P_B', reserving P_B to denote the partition function for a particle in the pure solute, when required. Proceeding as in (254), we find that the Helmholtz free energy of the solution will amount to

$$- kT[(n_A - zn_B)\ln P_A + zn_B \ln P_A' + n_B \ln P_B' + \ln W_{cf}] \qquad (259)$$

where W_{cf} is to be taken from either (243) or (248) according to the type of solution.

We can use this expression to find the conditions for various equilibria, such as the solubility of B in A, the lowering of the freezing point of A, the change in the vapor pressure of A due to the presence of B, and so on. For example, to find the solubility of B in A, we add to (259) an expression for the free energy of a certain amount of pure B, and we differentiate the whole expression with respect to n_B. In the same way, if we wish to study the equilibrium between the solution and pure A we add to (259) an expression for the free energy of a certain amount of pure A, differentiate the whole with respect to n_A, and set the result equal to zero;[1] in this we

[1] It may be pointed out here that in a systematic study of these equilibria there are two alternative methods of procedure. One, which has just been described, is to have available the expressions for the free energy of each of the various substances that we wish to put in contact. Let us denote these by F_I, F_{II}, F_{III}, and so on. From these we choose the two required for the particular equilibrium to be studied. We write down

may use the partition function for pure A either in the solid form or in the vapor state, as required.

105. The expression (259) enables us to deal with the solubility of A in B provided that the saturated solution is very dilute. If P_B denotes the partition function for pure solid B, the change in the free energy of the solid for each particle removed from and transferred to the solution will be $+ kT \ln P_B$. We shall deal here with a substitutional solution and in Sec. 106 with an interstitial solution. Using (243), we find for the equilibrium between pure B and the solution of B in A, the condition

$$\frac{\partial F}{\partial n_B} = - kT\left(\ln \frac{P_B'}{P_B} + z \ln \frac{P_A'}{P_A} - \ln x_B\right) = 0 \tag{260}$$

Here P_A, P_A', P_B, and P_B' denote, of course, the values at the same temperature T; the values depend only on the species A and B that make up the solution; on the right-hand side, only the quantity x_B depends upon the concentration. From (260) we obtain

$$x_B = \frac{n_B}{n_A + n_B} = \frac{P_B'}{P_B}\left(\frac{P_A'}{P_A}\right)^z \tag{261}$$

This expression states that, at the temperature considered, there can only be equilibrium between the pure solute B and the solution of B in A, when the concentration of the latter has the particular value prescribed; this is the concentration of the saturated solution at this temperature.

If each solute particle of species B is slightly larger in size than a solvent particle, it will be somewhat cramped when introduced into the lattice of A and it will at the same time somewhat restrict the vibration of the z solvent particles in contact with it. As a result, the spacing of the energy levels is likely to be somewhat wider than in pure A and pure B. In other cases the spacing may become narrower. This change of spacing

---

the expression for the total free energy, say, for example $(F_I + F_{III})$, and we consider the transfer of dm particles of the required species from one set of levels to the other; that is, we differentiate with respect to either n_A or n_B, whichever is appropriate. In one set of levels the number of particles is increased, in the other set the number is diminished; this introduces a minus sign, for example,

$$\frac{\partial F}{\partial m} = \frac{\partial}{\partial m}(F_I + F_{III}) = \frac{\partial}{\partial n_B}(F_I - F_{III}) = 0$$

An alternative procedure for systematic study is as follows: instead of having available the expression for the free energy of each substance, we may tabulate the expressions for $\dfrac{\partial F_I}{\partial n_A}$, $\dfrac{\partial F_I}{\partial n_B}$, $\dfrac{\partial F_{II}}{\partial n_A}$, and so on. When we wish to consider the equilibrium between any two populations, it will be unnecessary to write down the free energy of the whole system; we merely choose from these tabulated expressions the two that are required and equate them. In the example above, we would take

$$\frac{\partial F_I}{\partial n_B} = \frac{\partial F_{III}}{\partial n_B}$$

will alone ensure that the values of both P_B'/P_B and P_A'/P_A will differ from unity. But, as pointed out at the beginning of Sec. 104, a small change in spacing cannot lead to a value differing much from unity; a shifting of the whole set of levels, up or down, gives a more pronounced effect. We know from (76) that if the set of levels were raised without distortion by an amount η, the partition function would thereby be multiplied by the factor $e^{-\eta/kT}$. It is only in this way that the solute B in (261) can be sparingly soluble, the condition for which (261) is valid. We therefore find it convenient to use a notation that separates the alteration in spacing of the levels from the amount by which the set of levels is raised. In (260) the four partition functions are, of course, all referred to the same zero of energy. We shall follow the method of Chapter 6 and refer each partition function to its own ground level. Consider first the ground level of a particle in pure solute. Let η_B be the amount by which the lowest level of the solute particle is raised when this particle is dissolved in the solvent, and let $\mathbf{P}_B'$ be the partition function for the modified set of levels when their energies are measured from this lowest level. Then the P_B' of (259) is equal to $\mathbf{P}_B' e^{-\eta_B/kT}$. Similarly, we may write $P_A' = \mathbf{P}_A' e^{-\eta_A/kT}$. Then, if we denote an energy s by

$$s = \eta_B + \eta_A \tag{262}$$

the expression for equilibrium, (261), takes the form

$$x_B = \frac{n_B}{n_A + n_B} = \frac{\mathbf{P}_B'}{\mathbf{P}_B}\left(\frac{\mathbf{P}_A'}{\mathbf{P}_A}\right)^z e^{-s/kT} \tag{263}$$

This expression is a good approximation provided that the value of s is large enough to ensure that the saturated solution at the temperature considered is extremely dilute. At room temperature kT is equal to $\frac{1}{40}$ electron-volt per particle; hence, if s amounts to $\frac{1}{4}$ electron-volt per solute particle, or 5750 cal/mole, this will be sufficient.

106. Dilute Interstitial Solution. Using (248), let us consider a solution containing only a single solute B. The original crystal consisting of n_A particles provides altogether bn_A interstitial sites for the n_B solute particles. It does not matter how many neighbors each solvent particle has in the original lattice. Let z denote the number of solvent particles with which one solute particle makes contact. Then we obtain an expression that is identical with (259). The number of sites that are to remain empty is $(bn_A - n_B)$. Hence, combining (249) with (259), we can prescribe the condition for equilibrium between pure B and the dilute solution of B in A:

$$kT\left(\ln \frac{P_B'}{P_B} + z \ln \frac{P_A'}{P_A} - \ln \frac{n_B}{bn_A - n_B}\right) = 0 \tag{264}$$

Defining s as before, we obtain

$$\frac{n_B}{bn_A - n_B} = \frac{\mathbf{P}_B'}{\mathbf{P}_B}\left(\frac{\mathbf{P}_A'}{\mathbf{P}_A}\right)^z e^{-s/kT} \tag{265}$$

107. We have discussed the equilibrium between the solution and pure solute. We did this by adding to (259) an expression for the free energy of a certain amount of pure solute and differentiating with respect to n_B. Let us now consider the possibility of equilibrium between the solute and pure solvent. We shall add to (259) an expression for the free energy of a certain amount of solvent, which may be in either vapor or solid form, according to the problem we wish to discuss. On the other hand, if we consider a range of temperature where both solvent and solution are liquids or where both are simple solids, no equilibrium with pure solvent is possible. When the solution is put into contact with the solvent, the solute will merely diffuse into the solvent, to form a solution at a lower concentration. If, however, there is a range of temperature in which the solution is liquid while the pure solvent is solid, equilibrium between the two is possible. The familiar "lowering of the freezing point of the solvent" by the presence of a solute provides such a situation. For example, when the temperature of an aqueous solution is reduced, a point is reached at which pure ice crystallizes out.

There are thus two problems to be discussed, the vapor pressure of the solvent, and the lowering of the freezing point. In both cases, for a dilute substitutional solution, we shall have to differentiate (259) with respect to n_A. A very simple expression is obtained, namely,

$$-kT \ln \frac{P_A}{x_A} \tag{266}$$

The simplicity of this expression arises from the fact that in the very dilute solution there are at any moment $n_B z$ solvent particles in contact with solute particles, and this number is unchanged when we transfer δn_A additional solvent particles to the solution.

Let us first discuss the vapor pressure of the solvent in a dilute substitutional solution. In (224) we had an expression for the vapor pressure of a pure substance; we can now use (266) to find how (224) will be modified by the presence of a small quantity of another species dissolved in the solid or liquid under consideration. Taking a vessel of a certain size, let us first pay attention to the number of particles of A that will form a saturated vapor in equilibrium with pure A (liquid or solid) at the temperature considered, when no B is present; this number may be denoted by n_{vA}^0. Its value is found, as in (190), by setting the following expression equal to zero:

$$kT \ln \frac{P_{vA}}{n_{vA}} - kT \ln P_A \tag{267}$$

Let us take next a dilute solution containing n_B solute particles of species B, n_C solute particles of species C, and so on. We have to transfer δn_A particles from the solution to the vapor, or vice versa. Using (266), we see that the value of n_{vA} is to be found by setting the following expression equal to zero:

$$kT \ln \frac{P_{vA}}{n_{vA}} - kT \ln \frac{P_A}{x_A} \qquad (268)$$

Comparing (268) with (267), we find

$$\frac{p_A}{p_A^0} = \frac{n_{vA}}{n_{vA}^0} = x_A = \frac{n_A}{n_A + n_B + \cdots} \qquad (269)$$

The vapor pressure of the substance A will be lowered by the presence of one or more solutes dissolved in it; in sufficiently dilute solution the vapor pressure of the solvent at any temperature will be diminished in proportion to its mole fraction.

A similar expression may be found for the vapor pressure of each component of the solution, assuming as before that the vapor behaves as a perfect gas.

108. We shall next make use of (259) to study the lowering of the freezing point of a liquid solvent. The expression (259) was intended to apply to either a dilute solid solution or a dilute liquid solution. The symbol P_A stood for the quantity $\Sigma e^{-\epsilon_r/kT}$ for a particle either in pure solid solvent or in pure liquid solvent. That is to say, it referred to the energy levels of a particle in a solid in which some solute particles were to be dissolved to form a solid solution, or alternatively it referred to the energy levels of a particle in a liquid in which some solute particles were to be dissolved to form a liquid solution. We have not yet had to use a notation to distinguish between the levels in liquid and those in solid solvent, but we must do so here. Let P_s denote the value of $\Sigma e^{-\epsilon_r/kT}$ summed over the levels of a particle in pure solid A and let P_l be the same quantity for a particle in pure liquid A at the same temperature. The latter is likewise the value for any solvent particle in the dilute solution that is not in contact with a solute particle; since this is the quantity that occurs in (266), we shall write here P_l/x_A. The condition for equilibrium between the dilute solution and pure solid A is obtained by setting the following expression equal to zero:

$$kT \ln P_s - kT \ln \frac{P_l}{x_A} \qquad (270)$$

This is correct for a very dilute solution containing any number of solutes. When the solution contains one solute species B, we have from (270)

$$-\ln x_A = \ln \left(1 + \frac{n_B}{n_A}\right) = \ln P_s - \ln P_l \qquad (271)$$

Since x_A is necessarily less than unity, this expression will represent an equilibrium state, provided that the right-hand side is positive, that is to say, at temperatures below the normal freezing point.

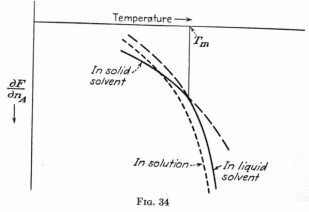

Fig. 34

The values of P_s and P_l are equal at the normal freezing point; let these values be denoted by P_s^0 and P_l^0; then at a temperature slightly below the normal freezing point, using (78), we obtain

$$\ln P_s = \ln P_s^0 + \frac{\partial \ln P_s}{\partial T} \delta T$$

$$= \ln P_s^0 + \frac{E_s}{kT^2} \delta T \qquad (272)$$

$$\ln P_l = \ln P_l^0 + \frac{E_l}{kT^2} \delta T \qquad (273)$$

Subtracting (273) from (272) and substituting in (271), we find that the lowering of the freezing point of A, when a small number of solute particles is dissolved in it, is given by

$$\delta T = -\frac{kT^2}{E_l - E_s} \frac{\delta n_B}{n_A} \qquad (274)$$

When the equilibrium temperature is plotted against the concentration of the solution, we shall find a straight line for very dilute solutions if the quantity $(E_l - E_s)$ is independent of temperature.

The lowering of the freezing point is illustrated in Fig. 34, in terms of the free energy. Let abscissas be the temperature and ordinates the free energy per particle of the solvent, or $\partial F/\partial n_A$. We have already seen in Fig. 28 that, for particles populating alternative sets of levels, there is the possibility of the curves crossing. Here the curve for liquid solvent intersects the curve for solid solvent at the melting temperature T_m, the liquid having the lower free energy at temperatures greater than T_m. If some solute is added to the liquid, the value of $\partial F/\partial n_A$ for the solvent has a greater negative value at any temperature, as shown schematically by the dotted curve in Fig. 34. This curve intersects the curve for the solid solvent at a temperature lower than the normal melting point T_m.

109. The examples given in Secs. 107 and 108 have illustrated how the simple expression (259) may be used to derive the conditions for various cases of equilibrium in very dilute solution. We shall now return to the original problem outlined in Sec. 103, attempting to carry the treatment to high concentrations.

We saw that this problem will not be simple except in cases where the particles A and B are not too different in size [1] and where the quantity z has the same value for the pure substance A, for pure B, and for all intermediate mixtures. In Sec. 104 we discussed the solution of a sparingly soluble substance B; in the very dilute solution each solute particle was surrounded by z solvent particles; the total number of A-B contacts in the solution was taken to be zn_B, and this number was independent of temperature. As soon as we go to high concentrations, however, we must be prepared to find that the number of A-B contacts depends on the temperature. Before we can consider an external equilibrium between the solution and pure B (or pure A), we have an internal equilibrium problem to dispose of.

If there are n sites occupied by particles, the total number of contacts between particles is $\frac{1}{2}zn$, the factor $\frac{1}{2}$ being introduced to ensure that each contact is not counted twice; in the mixture the total number is thus $\frac{1}{2}z(n_A + n_B)$. In Sec. 103 we denoted the total number of A-B contacts by ν. The number of A contacts that are not of the type A-B is thus $\frac{1}{2}(zn_A - \nu)$; these are the A-A contacts. Similarly the number of B-B contacts is $\frac{1}{2}(zn_B - \nu)$.

110. If from any site in the solution, we take at random an A-particle and at the same time take from a distant site a B-particle and interchange them, by so doing we usually bring about a change in the number of A-B contacts. For every *pair* of A-B contacts that is created, one A-A and one B-B contact disappear. This reminds us of the gaseous equilibrium that was briefly studied in Sec. 96. It was pointed out there that in equilibrium at low temperatures the characteristic interatomic forces cause a sorting of the atoms into the more stable diatomic forms, but that with rise of temperature the equilibrium tends to approach a more random distribution. The same tendencies will be present here in the solution, and we are led to ask the following preliminary question. Given n_A particles of type A and n_B of type B, how many A-B contacts would be expected in a perfectly random arrangement?

---

[1] For particulars as to the conditions under which a rigorous discussion of a liquid solution is possible, see R. H. Fowler and E. A. Guggenheim, "Statistical Thermodynamics," Chapter 8, Cambridge, 1939.

Suppose that we have $(n_A + n_B)$ empty sites and that we fill these sites with the particles at our disposal. Consider a site adjacent to an A-particle (which has already been placed); this site is to be occupied either by another A-particle or by a B-particle, chosen at random. If the number of A-particles and B-particles at our disposal were equal, the choice of an A-particle or a B-particle for this particular site would be equal. Since, however, there are n_A/n_B times as many A-particles at our disposal as there are B-particles, the probability of choosing an A must be n_A/n_B times as great as the probability of choosing a B. Since the sum of these two probabilities must be unity, their values are $n_A/(n_A + n_B)$ and $n_B/(n_A + n_B)$, the former providing the A-particle with an A-neighbor, and the latter providing the A-particle with a B-neighbor. Since there are n_A particles of type A to be provided with neighbors, it appears that the number of A-A contacts formed in this way will be proportional to n_A times $n_A/(n_A + n_B)$, while the number of A-B contacts formed in this way will be n_A times $n_B/(n_A + n_B)$.

In the same way, if we consider a site adjacent to a B-particle, this site is to be occupied either by another B-particle or by an A-particle. The total number of B-B contacts will be proportional to $n_B^2/(n_A + n_B)$, while the number of B-A contacts formed in this way will be proportional to $n_A n_B/(n_A + n_B)$; of course B-A contacts are the same as A-B contacts. We know that in an extremely dilute solution of B in A the number of A-B contacts must tend to the value $\nu = z n_B$, while in an extremely dilute solution of A in B the value must tend to $\nu = z n_A$. The required expression for ν in a completely random mixture is

$$\nu = z \frac{n_A n_B}{(n_A + n_B)} \tag{275}$$

For a random mixture of fifty-fifty per cent composition, for example, setting $n_A = n_B$, we find that the number of A-B contacts is equal to half the total number of contacts in the solution. In practice, the number will usually be somewhat greater or smaller than this value for a random arrangement, according as the interatomic forces favor one type of contact or another. For the same reason, in a solution of any composition, the number will usually be somewhat greater or less than the value given by (275). The lower the temperature, the more will the interatomic forces cause the equilibrium to deviate from a random mixture, as in the equilibrium discussed in Sec. 96. The two problems, however, are not precisely the same; the expression (275) is not consistent with (240) but with a slightly different expression. By analogy with (240), the assumption[1] is made that ν will be given an expression of the form

$$\frac{\nu^2}{(z n_A - \nu)(z n_B - \nu)} = \frac{\mathbf{P}^2_{AB}}{\mathbf{P}_A \mathbf{P}_B} e^{-\eta/kT} \tag{276}$$

[1] A. R. Miller, *J. Chem. Phys.*, **15**, 513 (1947).

With rise of temperature the value of the right-hand side tends to unity. It may easily be verified that when the right-hand side is equal to unity, ν is given by (275).

111. It will now be shown that we can obtain an insight into the behavior of partially miscible and completely miscible substances, if we use (275) as a first approximation. In problems of solubility and vapor pressure, we need to know what happens when we add either dn_A particles or else dn_B particles to the solution. The value of ν is changed by the following amounts, obtained from (275):

$$\frac{\partial \nu}{\partial n_A} = z\left(\frac{n_B}{n_A + n_B}\right)^2 \qquad \frac{\partial \nu}{\partial n_B} = z\left(\frac{n_A}{n_A + n_B}\right)^2 \qquad (277)$$

Writing P_A and P_B instead of P_0, we find from (257) and (258) for the free energy of the solution

$$F = kT(- n_A \ln P_A - n_B \ln P_B + n_A \ln x_A + n_B \ln x_B - \nu \ln \lambda) \quad (278)$$

where $\ln \lambda$ has been written for $\ln(\alpha\beta) = \ln \alpha + \ln \beta$. If we divide through by $(n_A + n_B)kT$, we find, since $x_B = 1 - x_A$, that (278) takes the form

$$[ax + b(1 - x)] - [x \ln x + (1 - x) \ln(1 - x)] + gx(1 - x) \quad (279)$$

where $g = z \ln \alpha\beta$. The value of $\alpha\beta$ may be greater or less than unity. We shall consider first cases where g is positive. In Fig. 35 are sketched the forms of the three parts of (279), plotted against x. The last term, representing the work to form A-B contacts, has a maximum at $x_A = x_B = \frac{1}{2}$, where the number of A-B contacts is greatest. The middle term of (279), representing the decrease in free energy on mixing the two substances, has a minimum at $x_A = x_B = \frac{1}{2}$. Consider now the addition of the ordinates of curves II and III. For small values of g the resultant curve will still have a minimum at the center. For larger values of g there is, however, the possibility that the resultant curve will have a maximum instead of a minimum at the center. We have

$$\frac{d^2}{dx^2} [gx(1 - x)] = - 2g \quad (280)$$

and from curve II

$$\frac{d^2}{dx^2} [x \ln x + (1 - x)\ln(1 - x)] = \frac{1}{x} + \frac{1}{1 - x} \quad (281)$$

which has the value 4 when $x = \frac{1}{2}$. Adding (280) and (281), we find then that d^2F/dx^2 will be negative when $(4 - 2g)$ is negative, that is, when the value of g is greater than 2.

For mixtures of many substances g does not exceed 2 at any accessible temperature. In Sec. 112 we shall study the nature of the equilibrium for cases where g is greater than 2, and in Sec. 113 the discussion will include mixtures with g less than 2.

112. We have seen that, on adding the ordinates of the three curves of Fig. 35, the resultant curve will have a minimum when $g = z \ln \lambda$ has a value greater than 2. In Fig. 36 is sketched the form that the free energy will have when P_B is greater than P_A and when g has a value in the neighborhood of $2\frac{1}{2}$.

Consider now a straight line drawn to touch the curve at two points; the line QRS touches the curve at Q and S; the point Q corresponds to

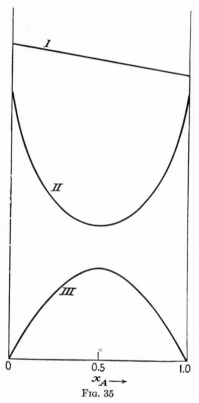

a solution of composition $x_A = OY$ and $x_B = O'Y$, while the point S corresponds to a composition $x_A = OZ$ and $x_B = O'Z$. Since the curve is a plot of F against x, the slope of the curve at any point represents $\dfrac{dF}{dx_A} = -\dfrac{dF}{dx_B}$. We see that this quantity has the same value for solutions of the compositions corresponding to Y and Z on the diagram. If any amount of one of these solutions is put into contact with any

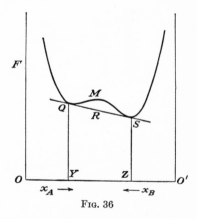

FIG. 35

FIG. 36

amount of the other, they will not tend to mix; they will be in equilibrium since the transfer of dm particles of A or of B from one solution to the other will not be accompanied by any change in the free energy. They will not mix, because, at the temperature considered, the work required to form the additional A-B contacts compensates for the increase in $\ln W_{cf}$. At a different temperature, or for a pair of substances with a smaller value of g, additional A-B contacts can still be formed and the points Q and S will lie nearer together, until for $g = 2$ they will coincide and the two substances will be miscible in all proportions. The effect of change of temperature on the value of λ and of g will be considered in Sec. 114.

At the beginning of this chapter it was pointed out that when two substances are put into contact, there is a tendency for each to diffuse into the other. In many cases this is merely an academic point, since one of these tendencies is negligibly small compared with the other. The kind of mutual solubility discussed here, however, is common among alloys and in mixtures of organic liquids; no equilibrium is possible between the solution and pure A or pure B; the equilibrium is between A containing a limited amount of B, and B containing a limited amount of A. The portion of the curve QMS between Q and S corresponds to compositions that are unstable at the temperature considered and that will break up into two phases with compositions given by Y and Z. The free energy represented by a point such as M on the curve is greater than the free energy of the two phases into which the mixture will break up, which is represented by a point on the straight line QS below.

The pairs of metals mentioned in Table 3 are miscible in all proportions when molten, but on solidifying they separate into A containing a certain amount of B, and B containing a certain amount of A, according to the percentages given in the table.

Table 3. Limited Mutual Solubility of Metals (Solid)*

Pb dissolves 4.5% of Sb and Sb dissolves   5% of Pb
Cu dissolves 8.0% of Ag and Ag dissolves 8.8% of Cu
Pb dissolves 19.5% of Sn and Sn dissolves 2.6% of Pb
Ni dissolves 47.0% of Cr and Cr dissolves 37.0% of Ni

*H. Carpenter and J. M. Robertson, "Metals," Oxford, 1939.

In connection with (275), we mentioned the value that ν would take in a very dilute solution of B and A. If this value is substituted in (278), and at the same time the appropriate values of α and β from Sec. 103 are introduced, the reader may easily verify that (278) reduces to precisely (259) for the dilute solution, as it should. Resuming the discussion of (278), we shall now derive the vapor pressure of the components of the mixture.

113. To study the equilibrium between the solution and the vapor of A, we add the free energy of n_{vA} particles of vapor, differentiate the whole with respect to n_A, and divide through by kT, obtaining

$$\ln \frac{P_A}{x_A} + (\ln \alpha + \ln \beta)\frac{\partial \nu}{\partial n_A} - \ln \frac{P_{vA}}{n_{vA}} = \ln \frac{P_A}{x_A} + z\left(\frac{n_B}{n_A + n_B}\right)^2 \ln \lambda$$
$$- \ln \frac{P_{vA}}{n_{vA}} \quad (282)$$

To replace (269), we find

$$\frac{p_A}{p_A^0} = \frac{n_{vA}}{n_{vA}^0} = \frac{n_A}{n_A + n_B} \exp\left[\left(\frac{n_B}{n_A + n_B}\right)^2 z \ln \lambda\right] \quad (283)$$

When n_B is small compared with n_A, the exponential term in (283) will differ little from unity but will deviate more from unity as the concentration of B is increased.

For the partial pressure of the B component we find the corresponding expression, with n_A and n_B interchanged.

Before discussing this expression in detail, we may deal with a special case, namely, a mixture of two substances A and B for which the value of the product $\alpha\beta$ happens to be unity; ln λ is zero, and the exponential term in (283) is unity. We obtain

$$\frac{p_A}{p_A^0} = \frac{n_A}{n_A + n_B} \qquad \frac{p_B}{p_B^0} = \frac{n_B}{n_A + n_B} \tag{284}$$

The vapor pressure of each component is proportional to its mole fraction over the whole range of concentration from zero to 100 per cent; a mixture that shows this behavior is said to obey Raoult's law.[1]

In the nineteenth century it was found by van't Hoff that in dilute aqueous solutions the solute obeyed laws very similar to the gas laws, and the concept of an ideal solution was introduced, analogous to the concept of a perfect gas. A liquid solution obeying Raoult's law was called an "ideal solution." Just as an imperfect gas behaves like a perfect gas at sufficiently low pressures, so a non-ideal solution will become indistinguishable from an ideal solution at sufficiently low concentrations. In (283) when x_B is sufficiently small, the exponential term does not differ appreciably from unity; thus, at sufficiently low concentrations, (284) may be used instead of (283)—a result already obtained in (269) above.

Consider the various terms on the right-hand side of (278). The first two terms in the large bracket together comprise the free energy of the pure components *before* mixing; the remaining terms therefore comprise the change ΔF in the free energy on mixing the components. When λ is unity the last term in (278) drops out and we obtain

$$F' - F = (n_A \ln x_A + n_B \ln x_B)kT \tag{285}$$

On comparing this with (198) in Sec. 85, it will be seen that (285) is identical with the expression for the change in free energy on mixing two perfect gases under certain conditions. The thermodynamic relations are the same, although the structural basis is entirely different.

Formerly it was not suspected that behind the thermodynamic resemblance there lay a wide structural dissimilarity; liquids and gases were classed together as fluids and there was a persistent idea that structurally a liquid was much more like a gas than like a solid, even near the freezing point of the liquid. The expressions (278) and (285) have, how-

---

[1] J. H. Hildebrand, "Solubility of Non-electrolytes," Chapter 2, Reinhold, 1936; for partially miscible liquids see *ibid.*, Chapter 9.

ever, been derived for a structure that is as applicable to a solid as to a liquid. The expression (285) applies to a mixture of localized particles in which the occupation of the sites has been arranged by one-for-one substitution; this bears no resemblance to a mixture of two perfect gases in which the molecules move freely throughout the vessel without interaction.

In an ideal solution at any concentration we obtain from (278), with λ equal to unity,

$$\left(\frac{\partial F}{\partial n_B}\right)_{T,v} = \left(\frac{\partial G}{\partial n_B}\right)_{T,p} = -kT \ln P_B + kT \ln x_B$$

This may be put in the form

$$\mathbf{\mu} = \mathbf{\mu}_0 + kT \ln x_B \tag{286}$$

where the term $\mathbf{\mu}_0$ is independent of the concentration (but varies with temperature). In physical chemistry the usual way of dealing with a solute whose behavior is not in accordance with (286), that is, with a non-ideal solution, is to introduce an activity coefficient f, which is a function of the concentration, like that mentioned in Sec. 91 for an imperfect gas. We can replace (286) by[1]

$$\mathbf{\mu} = \mathbf{\mu}_0 + kT \ln f_B x_B \tag{287}$$

obtaining from (278) an expression for the activity coefficient f_B if the solution is of the kind to which (278) applies. We may verify that at low concentrations the value of f_B tends to unity as the solution approaches infinite dilution.

In general there are two principal factors which will give to f a value different from unity, that is, which will make the solution differ from an ideal solution. One we have just discussed—the modification of the energy levels of the particles when the quantity λ occurring in (278) is different from unity. In Sec. 122 we shall show that when the solution is not formed by the process of one-for-one substitution, this fact alone is sufficient to give f a value different from unity, even when $\lambda = 1$.

114. In discussing the environments of solute particles, it was emphasized in Sec. 104 that whereas a small change in the partition function can arise from the change in spacing, a large change can only be due to the shift of the set of levels by an amount comparable with or greater than kT. In using the factors α and β, we have not yet asked to what extent the modification of the levels has been a shift or a change in spacing. One could easily write α and β in a form that would express the presence of both kinds of modification. Here it will be sufficient to ask what form (283) takes when the change in spacing has an effect that is negligible

[1] L. E. Steiner, "Introduction to Chemical Thermodynamics," p. 411, McGraw-Hill, 1941.

in comparison with the shift of the whole set of levels. In this case, in accordance with (76), we may write

$$\alpha = e^{-\eta_A/kT} \qquad \beta = e^{-\eta_B/kT}$$

and   (288)

$$\ln(\alpha\beta) = -\frac{(\eta_A + \eta_B)}{kT}$$

Suppose now that we start with the pure substances A and B, and we take one particle from the interior of A and one from the interior of B, and interchange them. The A-particle acquires as neighbors z B-particles, each of which acquire one A-neighbor, namely, the transferred particle. At the same time the transferred B-particle acquires as neighbors z A-particles, each of which acquires one B-neighbor. The total work done, or the increase in potential energy is thus

$$- 2zkT(\ln\alpha + \ln\beta) = 2z(\eta_A + \eta_B) \tag{289}$$

If this quantity is denoted by $2U$, we may replace the factor $z \ln(\alpha\beta)$ in (283) by U/kT when the change in the spacing of the levels is unimportant compared with the shift in energy.

115. We will consider next a sparingly soluble substance BC, whose molecules are completely dissociated into separate particles B and C when it is dissolved in a solvent A, forming a very dilute substitutional solution

$$BC \rightarrow B + C$$

In Sec. 96 we supposed that the solution was so dilute that the chance of finding two solute particles in contact with each other was negligible; we shall make the same assumption here. In the solution we have altogether $(n_A + n_B + n_C)$ sites; the value of W_{cf} is given by (244), and the values of $\partial \ln W_{cf}/\partial n_B$ and $\partial \ln W_{cf}/\partial n_C$ are given by (247).

Using the same notation as in (259), let the partition functions be denoted as follows: P_A with the summation taken over the energy levels of a solvent molecule surrounded by other solvent molecules; P_B and P_C taken, respectively, over the levels of B and of C in the pure solid; P_B^* over the levels of a dissolved B particle completely surrounded by solvent molecules, and similarly P_C^* for a dissolved particle of C; finally P_{AB} over the levels of a solvent molecule that is in contact with a dissolved B particle, and P_{AC} for one that is in contact with a dissolved C particle. Let us define quantities Q_B, Q_C, and s as follows:

$$\ln Q_B = \ln\frac{P_B^*}{P_B} + z \ln\frac{P_{AB}}{P_A} \tag{290}$$

$$\ln Q_C = \ln\frac{P_C^*}{P_C} + z \ln\frac{P_{AC}}{P_A} \tag{291}$$

$$s = s_B + s_C = \eta_B + z\eta_{AB} + \eta_C + z\eta_{AC} \tag{292}$$

Every B-particle that goes into solution is accompanied by one C-particle (moving to a distant site); thus $\partial/\partial n_B = \partial/\partial n_C$. From (291), proceeding as in Sec. 105, we obtain

$$\frac{dF}{dn_B} = -kT(\ln Q_B + \ln Q_C - \ln x_B - \ln x_C) \tag{293}$$

Setting this equal to zero, we obtain for the saturated solution of the sparingly soluble substance BC

$$x_B x_C = Q_B Q_C = \mathbf{Q}_B \mathbf{Q}_C e^{-s/kT} \tag{294}$$

For a substance whose saturated solution is less dilute, the product $x_B x_C$ must be replaced by the product $f_B x_B f_C x_C$, where f_B and f_C are activity coefficients of the kind introduced in Sec. 113, which tend to unity at extreme dilution. The quantity $f_B x_B f_C x_C$ is known as the "solubility product" of the substance BC.

When the solution is formed by dissolving BC only, the number of B-particles in the solution is necessarily equal to the number of C-particles. If, however, we introduce into the solvent some B-particles or else some C-particles from another source, the number of B-particles can be unequal to the number of C-particles. In deriving (294) nothing was said about x_B being equal to x_C. The expression (294) gives the composition of solutions that can be in equilibrium with the pure substance BC at the temperature considered; the condition is that the solubility product must have the specified value. If, for example, we add to the saturated solution some C-particles from any source, the number of B-particles must be reduced; that is, some B will be precipitated and vice versa. This method may readily be extended to find the form of the solubility product for substances, such as BC_2 or B_2C, which yield three particles when they dissolve and dissociate; or in general for a substance $B_p C_q$ which dissociates into $(p + q)$ particles. The general expression for a sparingly soluble substance is of the form

$$x_B{}^p x_C{}^q = \mathbf{Q}_B{}^p \mathbf{Q}_C{}^q e^{-s/kT} \tag{295}$$

116. We discussed in Sec. 115 a solute that dissociates yielding two particles B and C, both of which are of a different species from the particles A of the solvent. We can likewise study a solute where one of the particles is of the same species as the solvent in which it dissolves, that is, we consider a definite compound BA that dissolves to form a solution of B in A. The solution may be either a solid or a liquid solution. In either case, when some of the compound BA dissolves, each pair of particles that goes into solution yields one solute particle B and at the same time adds one A-particle to the solvent. Examples of dilute solid solutions of this kind occur in metallurgy (see Sec. 121), while a familiar example of a liquid solution is the solution of a monohydrate $(B.H_2O)$ in water.

In such cases the character of the equilibrium is interesting at high concentrations. We have seen in Sec. 113 that concentrated solutions may be divided into two classes, solutions where the free energy is sensitive to the number of A-B contacts present at a given concentration in the solution, and solutions where it is insensitive. For the former, the treatment of Sec. 111 would have to be used but we shall not consider that case here. We shall briefly consider what will be the character of the solution of BA in A if the free energy is insensitive to the number of A-B contacts present at a given concentration. Defining suitable quantities Q_A and Q_B analogous to those of (291), we find, as in (294), that the character of the equilibrium between the solution and the solid is given by

$$x_A x_B = \frac{n_A n_B}{n_A{}^2 + 2n_A n_B + n_B{}^2}$$

$$= Q_A Q_B = \mathbf{Q}_A \mathbf{Q}_B e^{-s/kT} \tag{296}$$

When the value of the right-hand side is greater than $\frac{1}{4}$, the equation has no real solution. The existence of a limiting temperature is to be expected, since no equilibrium between solid and liquid is possible above the melting point of the solid AB. Since the sum of the mole fractions has constant value (unity), their product has its greatest value when they are equal; their product is then equal to $\frac{1}{4}$. A liquid of this composition has the same composition as the solid AB; it is, in fact, molten AB and can be in equilibrium with solid AB when in contact with the solid at its melting temperature T_m. Setting (296) equal to $\frac{1}{4}$, we obtain for T_m the expression

$$T_m = \frac{s}{k \ln (4/\mathbf{Q}_A \mathbf{Q}_B)} \tag{297}$$

Returning to (296), let the right-hand side of (296) be denoted by $f(T)$. For values of $f(T)$ less than 0.25, the equation has two solutions. When, for example, $f(T)$ is equal to 0.24, we have the solution $x_A = 0.6$, $x_B = 0.4$, and also the solution $x_A = 0.4$, $x_B = 0.6$. Thus at a temperature below T_m the solid AB may be in equilibrium with a solution when the composition of the latter has either of the two values appropriate to this temperature. Clearly we may regard this as a lowering of the freezing point of molten AB. In the molten AB we may dissolve either a certain amount of B or a certain amount of A; in either case the temperature for equilibrium with the solid is lower than the normal freezing point T_m and continues to fall as the excess of B or of A in the solution is increased.

The same treatment may be given for a solid that has the composition AB_2 or A_2B or A_3B, and so on (compare Sec. 121 below). It should be noted that the expression (274) obtained for small quantities of a simple solute does not apply to any of these cases. According to (274), the lowering of the freezing point is proportional to the amount of solute and this proportionality continues to hold as the concentration of solute tends to zero.

117. We studied in Sec. 93 a solid that could exist in two different modifications, with a transition temperature below which one form is stable and above which the other is stable. Denoting the low-temperature modification by A_l and the high temperature modification by A_h, let us consider the interesting question that arises when another substance B is soluble in A_l or A_h, or in both. This problem is important in steel metallurgy, since iron can exist in the alpha and gamma modifications, in which carbon and many other elements are soluble.

Let us first consider the case where B is soluble in the form A_h but is not appreciably soluble in the low-temperature form A_l. This problem will be very similar to that discussed in Sec. 108. When, for example, we freeze an aqueous solution, we are dealing with a solute that is not appreciably soluble in ice (which corresponds to the low-temperature modification) but is soluble in water (which corresponds to A_h). We saw that there could be a state of equilibrium between ice and the aqueous solution. So here we can consider a dilute solution of B in A_h, at any temperature at which A_l is stable, and we can ask whether there can be equilibrium when this solution is placed in contact with A_l. For this purpose we have to consider the transference of δn_A particles from pure A_l to the solution of A_h containing n_B dissolved particles of B.

The difference between A_h and A_l will play the same role as the difference between solid and liquid solvent in Sec. 108. The diagram for the free energies will be similar to Fig. 34; the presence of solute in A_h will cause a "lowering of the transition temperature"; that is, the high-temperature modification, containing solute particles, will be stable at temperatures below the normal transition temperature. If we denote the partition functions for a particle of pure solvent by P_l and P_h, the expression (271) will apply for a substitutional solution if an appropriate change is made in the subscripts; and the expression (274) will apply to the interstitial solutions as well.

We have discussed the case where the substance B is soluble in the high-temperature form of A only. Conversely, when B is soluble only in the low-temperature form A, this leads to a *raising* of the transition temperature; that is, the low-temperature modification, containing solute particles, will be stable at temperatures above the normal transition temperature for the pure substance A. This effect is analogous to the raising of the boiling point of a liquid when a substance is dissolved in it.

118. Let us pass on now to the situation that commonly occurs, where the solute is appreciably soluble in both the high- and low-temperature forms. There are four cases, all of which are important in the alloys of iron that form the basis of steel: there are (1) interstitial and

(2) substitutional solutions in which the solute is more soluble in the high-temperature form A_h than in A_l; and there are (3) interstitial and (4) substitutional solutions, in which the solute is more soluble in the low-temperature form A_l than in A_h.

We may begin by giving a discussion that is applicable to both (1) and (2). Consider a temperature just *above* the normal transition temperature of the pure substance A and consider separately the free energy of a

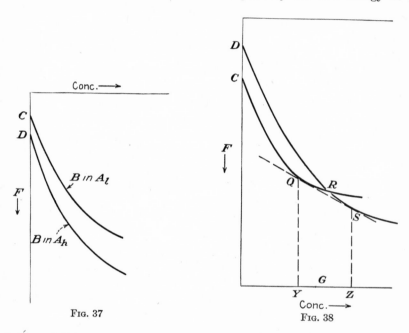

FIG. 37   FIG. 38

solution of B in A_h and the free energy of a solution of B in A_l. If the free energy is plotted against the concentration of the solute B, we obtain for each solution a curve, as in Fig. 37. At this temperature the curves must reach the axis at neighboring points C and D, of which the lower belongs to A_h, since at zero concentration we are dealing with pure solvent A and at this temperature the form A_h, being the more stable, must have the lower free energy. If we consider progressively lower temperatures, the points C and D must approach each other, must coincide at the normal transition temperature, and must reverse their positions, as in Fig. 38, when A_l becomes the stable form.

When the solute is more soluble in A_h than in A_l, the curves will have the character sketched in Fig. 38. The curves intersect at a point R, depending on the temperature; the point R corresponds to the concentration given by the point G. At this concentration the free energy of the solution of B in A_h has the same value as the free energy of the solution of B in A_l at the same temperature. In Fig. 34 the intersection of the free-energy curves denoted a state of stable equilibrium, but not so here. In Fig. 34 the curves were a plot of the free energy per particle against the temperature, but here they are a plot against the concentration. At the point of intersection R, the curves differ in slope, the curve for the solution in A_h being the steeper. If the two solutions at the same concentration are put into contact, particles will spontaneously be transferred from A_l to A_h, that is to say, the boundary between A_l and A_h will move in such a way that A_h grows at the expense of A_l, since thereby the free energy of the whole can fall to a lower value. During this process the free energy of one solution is given by a point that moves from R toward Q, while the free energy of the other solution is given by a point that moves along the curve from R toward S. This process will continue until points are reached where the slopes of the curves are equal. In Fig. 38 the state of equilibrium can be found, as was done in Fig. 36, by drawing the straight line that will touch the two curves. The points of contact in Fig. 38 correspond to a solution of B in A_l with the concentration given by the point Y, and a solution of B in A_h with the concentration given by the point Z.

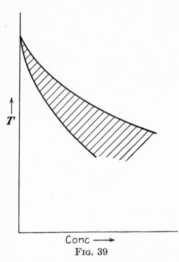

Conc ⟶

FIG. 39

If we consider temperatures intermediate between those of Fig. 37 and Fig. 38, it is clear that in Fig. 38 the point of intersection R, which lies on the axis at the normal transition temperature, moves away from the axis as the temperature is reduced. At the same time the points of contact and the corresponding points Y and Z move to the right and become more widely separated. If we take the temperature as ordinates and the concentration, as before, as abscissas, we may obtain two diverging curves, as in Fig. 39, where one curve corresponds to the concentration Y while the other curve corresponds to the concentration Z. Any point lying between the two curves corresponds to an unstable composition that will break up into a solution of B in A_h and a weaker solution of B in A_l; in this range of temperature a horizontal line will cut both curves, and the points of intersection will give the concentrations of the two solutions that can be in equilibrium with each other at this temperature.

119. Solutions in Alpha and Gamma Iron. Below 910°C the crystal structure of iron that is stable is body-centered cubic; this is known as "alpha iron." At 910° this undergoes a transition to a face-centered

cubic structure, known as "gamma iron." Solutions of carbon and many
other elements in iron are important as the basis of steel. In Secs. 119–121
we give a discussion of these solutions, according to Zener.[1] When nickel,
copper, zinc, or manganese are dissolved in iron, a diagram like Fig. 39
is obtained for temperatures below 910°C. These are substitutional solutions. Experimental results for solutions of manganese[2] in iron are
shown by the circles in Fig. 40.

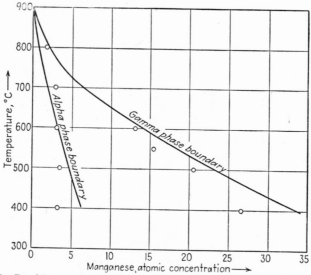

FIG. 40. Boundaries of the alpha and gamma phases in an iron-manganese alloy.

A diagram like Fig. 40 is also obtained for solutions of carbon in iron;
these are interstitial solutions. In the face-centered gamma phase the
interstitial positions for the carbon atoms are at the center of the unit
cube and at the centers of the cube edges. There are therefore four interstitial positions per unit cell, or one per iron atom. In the body-centered
alpha phase the interstitial positions are at the face centers and at the
centers of the edges, which are crystallographically equivalent to the face
centers. There are therefore six per unit cube, or three per iron atom.

Using the equations of Sec. 105 or Sec. 106, we may easily write down
the conditions of equilibrium for either dilute substitutional or dilute
interstitial solutions. We have to consider the transference of δm_B solute
particles from the solution in A_h to the solution in A_l, or vice versa, and
likewise the transference of δm_A solvent particles from one solution to the
other. For interstitial solutions we must use (249) and (250). Let b_h
and b_l be the values of b for the solute in A_h and A_l, respectively. We

[1] C. Zener, *Metals Technology*, **13** (1946).
[2] A. Troiano and F. McGuire, *Trans. Amer. Soc. Metals*, **31**, 340 (1943).

have seen that for carbon in iron below 910°C the value of b_h/b_l is $\frac{1}{3}$. From (251), writing $n_B/n_A = c$, we find that when solvent particles are transferred from A_l to A_h, the change in $\ln W_{cf}$ is equal to

$$\left[b_l \ln\left(1 - \frac{c_l}{b_l}\right) - b_h \ln\left(1 - \frac{c_h}{b_h}\right) \right] \delta m_A \tag{298}$$

In very dilute solution this reduces to $(c_h - c_l)\,\delta m_A$. Writing down the change in the free energy as in (260) and equating to zero, we find that this leads to

$$c_h - c_l = \ln \frac{P_A}{P_{A_h}} \tag{299}$$

In a very dilute solution the number of empty lattice sites n_e in (249) does not differ appreciably from bn_A. We find then that, when solute particles are transferred, the change in $\ln W_{cf}$ is equal to

$$\left(\ln \frac{c_l}{b_l} - \ln \frac{c_h}{b_h}\right) \delta m_B \tag{300}$$

which leads to the second condition for equilibrium, of the form

$$\frac{c_h}{c_l} = \frac{b_h}{b_l}\, Q e^{-s/kT} \tag{301}$$

where Q depends on the energy levels of the solute.

This expression together with (299) determines the forms of the curves of Fig. 39 in dilute solution. The quantity $(c_h - c_l)$ given by (299) is the horizontal distance between the two curves at the temperature considered. In this range of temperature A_l is the stable form, and hence the value of P_{A_l}' is greater than P_{A_h}. The right-hand side of (299) is therefore positive, which is consistent with the situation discussed in which the solute is more soluble in the high-temperature form. The same would be found if we wrote down the expressions for substitutional solutions.

Many substances, such as tin, tungsten, and silicon, are more soluble in the body-centered alpha structure than in the face-centered gamma iron. In these cases there is no lowering of the transition temperature below 910°C; instead the diagram replacing Fig. 39 consists of a pair of curves rising from 910°C. As before, any point lying between the two curves corresponds to an unstable composition, which breaks up; but in this case, at each temperature, c_l is greater than c_h. For each solute the slopes of the curves will be different, since each solute has its own characteristic solubility in iron. Furthermore, the form of the curves can only be predicted at very low concentrations; at higher concentrations each solute is likely to show its own deviations.

120. In discussing two modifications of a solid, it was pointed out in Sec. 94 that if the partition functions, plotted against the temperature, give two curves that intersect, the point of intersection corresponds to the transition temperature. Usually, above the transition temperature, the curves after intersecting continue to diverge. The partition functions for body-centered and face-centered iron, however, are peculiar. After intersecting at 910°C, the curves do not continue to diverge but intersect again at about 1400°C. That is to say, between 910 and 1400° the gamma face-centered structure is the more stable, but if the temperature is raised beyond 1400°, it is once more converted into the body-centered form.

In Sec. 119 we discussed the alloys of iron in the neighborhood of 910°C only. Precisely the same considerations apply to the solutions of the same substances in iron in the neighborhood of 1400°, except that the roles of the body-centered and face-centered structures have been exchanged, the former now playing the part of A_h. The substances that are more soluble in the body-centered form, namely, tin, tungsten, silicon, and so on, cause a lowering of the transition temperature below 1400°, providing a pair of curves (like those of Fig. 39), which, falling from 1400°, join the other pair of curves that rise from 910°, so that the complete diagram for the iron alloys of tin, tungsten, silicon, titanium, vanadium, molybdenum, and aluminum has a form resembling that shown schematically in Fig. 41a.

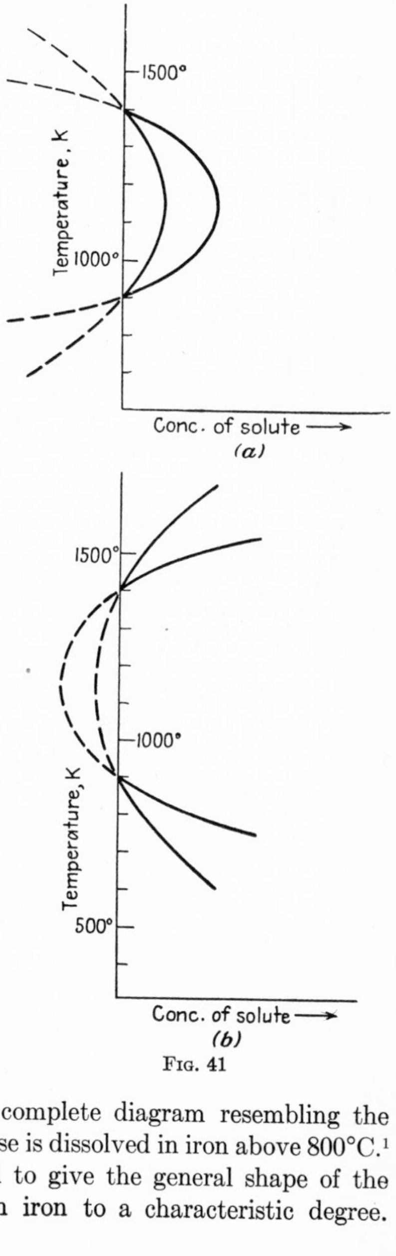

On the other hand, the substances that are more soluble in the face-centered form, namely, carbon, nickel, copper, zinc, and manganese, give a complete diagram resembling the form shown in Fig. 41b, when one of these is dissolved in iron above 800°C.[1] Figures 41a and 41b are only intended to give the general shape of the curves; each solute will be soluble in iron to a characteristic degree.

[1] Zener, *op. cit.*

Temperature, K

—1500°

1000°

Conc. of solute ⟶
(a)

1500°

—1000°

Temperature, K

500°

Conc. of solute ⟶
(b)

FIG. 41

Further, the symmetry of Fig. 41 is not to be expected except at the lowest concentrations, since each curve is likely to exhibit characteristic behavior of the solute, as already pointed out in Sec. 119.

121. In addition to dissolving in the alpha and gamma phases of iron, carbon also forms a definite compound, a carbide with the composition Fe_3C; this is known as "cementite." A problem important in steel metallurgy between 800 and 1200°C is the equilibrium between cementite, on the one hand, and the solution of carbon in gamma iron, on the other.

In Sec. 116 the equilibrium between a compound AB and a solution of B in A was considered, and it was stated that the results could be extended to compounds such as AB_2 or A_3B. Here we have to deal with the equilibrium between the compound Fe_3C and the saturated solution of carbon in gamma iron, in which the carbon atoms are scattered at random through the available interstitial sites. We are not interested in the structure of the solid Fe_3C, but only in the fact that, when some Fe_3C dissolves, each carbon atom is accompanied by three iron atoms. Each carbon atom will occupy an interstitial site, while the iron atoms, occupying lattice sites, will build up additional solvent; by doing so, the iron atoms provide thereby additional interstitial sites and this must be taken into account. The problem is to find the concentration of the saturated solution of carbon in gamma iron that can be in equilibrium with cementite, as a function of temperature.

If we denote the compound by A_mB, the value of m will be 3 in the case of cementite. In any case when δn_B particles of B are transferred from the compound to the solution, we have $\delta n_A = m\, \delta n_B$, and the expression for equilibrium will have the form

$$\left(\ln Q_A + b \ln \frac{bn_A}{bn_A - n_B}\right) m\, \delta n_B + \ln\left(Q_B \frac{bn_A - n_B}{n_B}\right) \delta n_B = 0 \tag{302}$$

Hence

$$\left(\frac{n_B}{bn_A - n_B}\right)\left(\frac{bn_A - n_B}{bn_A}\right)^{bm} = Q_A{}^m Q_B \tag{303}$$

$$\frac{n_B}{bn_A}\left(1 - \frac{n_B}{bn_A}\right)^{bm-1} = \mathbf{Q}_A{}^m \mathbf{Q}_B e^{-s/kT} \tag{304}$$

At temperatures above 910°C, the stable structure of iron, as mentioned in Sec. 120, is a face-centered structure, in which the number of interstitial positions that may be occupied by a carbon atom is one-fourth the number of lattice sites, that is, $b = \frac{1}{4}$. The value of $(bm - 1)$ in (304) will therefore be $(\frac{3}{4} - 1) = -\frac{1}{4}$. The solubility of carbon in gamma iron is small; n_B/n_A is small compared with unity and may be omitted from the bracket. Thus (304) reduces to

$$\frac{n_B}{n_A} = \frac{1}{4}\mathbf{Q}_A{}^3\mathbf{Q}_B e^{-s/kT} \tag{305}$$

This gives the composition of the interstitial solution that may be in equilibrium with cementite. Figure 42 shows the experimental results, which may be represented by the formula

$$\frac{n_B}{n_A} = 0.54e^{-2670/T} \tag{306}$$

In Fig. 42 the line AB is a plot of (306), forming one boundary for gamma iron in the phase diagram. The pair of curves diverging from 910°C and the other pair of curves diverging from 1400°C will be recognized as corresponding to the four theoretical curves shown schematically in Fig. 41*b*.

In discussing the dilute interstitial solutions of carbon in either alpha or in gamma iron, we have been supposing that the few carbon atoms will be distributed at random among the many interstitial positions. Under normal circumstances this will be the case. But if the piece of iron is stretched in one direction, say the *x*-direction, the volume available to a carbon atom is no longer the same at all sites in a unit cell of the lattice. At any temperature where the carbon atoms have an appreciable chance of jumping from one site to another, a redistribution of the carbon atoms will take place; when the stress is removed, they will again adopt a random distribution. Snoek[1] has suggested that the elastic aftereffect, which is observed at room temperature in alpha iron containing carbon, is to be explained in this way; more than 1 second is required for the majority of the relevant carbon atoms to move to a neighboring interstitial site.

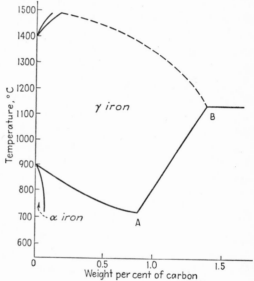

FIG. 42. Phase diagram of the iron-carbon system.

122. In dealing with substitutional solutions, we have so far discussed only cases where the solute and solvent particles are of nearly the same size, so that the solution is formed by a process of one-for-one substitution. We can likewise discuss cases where the solute particle is the larger, for example, where it has the same size as *two* solvent particles and consequently occupies sites which, in the pure solvent, would be occupied by

[1] J. L. Snoek, *Physica*, **8**, 731 (1941); **9**, 862 (1942).

two solvent particles. A simpler problem is the case where the solute particle has nearly the same size as $(z + 1)$ solvent particles, where z is the coordination number of the solvent, as used in Sec. 103. Consider as solvent a solid or liquid whose structure is such that each particle has z similar particles as nearest neighbors in contact with it and symmetrically placed. In ice, for example, each H_2O has four molecules in contact with it, placed approximately at the corners of a tetrahedron. We can consider a solute particle that has the same size and shape as five of these particles, namely, a central particle and its four neighbors, and we can suppose that in the solution each solute particle occupies sites that, in pure solvent, would be occupied by five solvent particles. We can suppose that the solute particle is similar to the molecule of carbon tetrafluoride, CF_4, that is to say, when the central particle has been placed on a site, no new configurations can be obtained by rotating the whole, as would be the case if any of the four fluorine particles were distinguishable from the other.

In general we discuss a solute particle with approximately the same size and shape as $(z + 1)$ solvent particles. We shall use the word *sites* to refer to sites that can be occupied by a solvent particle; in the solution the number of such sites will be

$$N = n_A + (z + 1)n_B \tag{307}$$

We proceed to ask in how many different ways the n_B solute particles can be distributed among the available sites. When the solute particles have been placed, the remaining n_A sites are to be filled in with solvent particles.

In the problem of Sec. 98 where we were dealing with one-for-one substitution, we had N choices for the position of the first particle and $(N - 1)$ choices for the position of the second particle, since this second particle could occupy any vacant site, including those immediately adjacent to the first particle. In the problem considered here, we fix our attention on the site that the center of each solute particle is to occupy, bearing in mind the footnote to Sec. 46. For the center of the first particle there are N sites available; but the center of the second particle cannot occupy a site adjacent to that occupied by the center of the first particle, nor can it occupy a site that is the next-nearest neighbor of the first site. Thus, instead of $(N - 1)$ choices, there will be $(N - r)$ choices for the second particle, where the value of r depends on the value of z. If we consider a sufficiently dilute solution, it is unlikely that three solute particles will be in contact; there will thus be $(N - 2r)$ choices for the third particle, $(N - 3r)$ for the fourth, and so on. The product of these n_B terms must, as usual, be divided by $n_B!$ to remove duplicate configurations. We have then

$$W_{cf} = \frac{(r)^{n_B}(N/r)!}{(N/r - n_B)!\, n_B!} \tag{308}$$

In the quartz or ice structure, for example, r appears to be 17. Every molecule has four neighbors; each of these has four neighbors, namely, the central molecule and three others, none of which are duplicates; thus

$$r = (1 + 4 + 12) = 17 \tag{309}$$

The solution contains altogether n_A sites occupied by solvent particles and $(z + 1)n_B$ sites occupied by the n_B solute particles; thus, writing p for $(z + 1)$, we have $N = n_A + pn_B$; from (308) we obtain

$$\frac{\partial \ln W_{cf}}{\partial n_B} = -\ln\left[\frac{n_B}{n_A - rn_B + pn_B}\left(\frac{n_A - rn_B + pn_B}{n_A + pn_B}\right)^{p/r}\right] + \ln r \tag{310}$$

It may be easily verified that this expression reduces to (247) in the normal case, where p and r are both unity. The term $\ln r$ is small and may be neglected. We are interested in the degree to which the right-hand side of (310) differs from $-\ln x_B$. For direct comparison with (237) we may write (310) in the form

$$\frac{\partial \ln W_{cf}}{\partial n_B} = -\ln\left[\frac{n_A + n_B}{(n_A - rn_B + pn_B)^{(r-p)/r}(n_A + pn_B)^{p/r}}\right]\left(\frac{n_B}{n_A + n_B}\right) \tag{311}$$

where the last bracketed expression is the mole fraction of the solute, x_B.

It will be recalled that the expression (259) was derived from (244) and (247). In the present problem (244) and (247) must be replaced by (308) and (310); we could proceed as in (256) by introducing quantities α and β. If, however, we assume α and β equal to unity, we obtain from (311)

$$\frac{\partial F}{\partial n_B} = \mathbf{v}_B = \mathbf{v}_B^0 + kT \ln f_B x_B \tag{312}$$

where $-\ln f_B x_B$ is the right-hand side of (311). The fact that the solution under discussion is not obtained by one-for-one substitution is, in itself, sufficient to make the solution non-ideal; that is to say, it provides an activity coefficient f whose value is different from unity.

The expression (311), as pointed out above, is valid only when n_B is very small compared with n_A; the expression for f_B in (311) may therefore be simplified by using the usual approximation for the logarithm of each factor. We find in this way for very dilute solutions

$$\ln f_B = (1 + r - 2p)\frac{n_B}{n_A} \tag{313}$$

In the numerical example we had $r = 17$ and $p = 5$; hence in this case we obtain

$$f = 1 + \frac{8n_B}{n_A} \tag{314}$$

Consider, for example, water as the solvent; 1 liter of water at room temperature contains 55.5 moles. If 0.1 mole of solute is added to 1 mole of water, the expression (314) gives $f = 1 + \frac{8}{555} = 1.014$ at this concentration.

123. We were able in Sec. 122 to fix attention on the position of the *center* of the large solute particle and to disregard different orientations owing to the high degree of symmetry. This is no longer true if we consider a simple diatomic molecule, which has roughly the same size and shape as *two* solvent particles. Let us denote the solute molecule by BC and the solvent particle as usual by A; we can discuss later the case where the diatomic molecule is homonuclear, of the type B_2, both halves of the molecule being identical. In either case let us denote the number of solute diatomic molecules by n_B. In the whole solution the total number of sites is $N = (n_A + 2n_B)$.

When a particular site is occupied by the B half of a BC molecule, there are z adjacent sites, any one of which may be occupied by its C half. To obtain an expression for W_{cf} we have to decide what is to replace the usual formula "N choices for the position of the first particle, $(N - 1)$ choices for the second, and so on." We have N choices for the position of the B half of the first molecule, together with z choices for the position of its C half. We have $(N - 2)$ choices for the position of the B half of the second molecule, with again (in very dilute solution) z choices for the position of its C half. These lead to the expression

$$[N(N - 2)(N - 4) \cdots (N - 2n_B)]z^{n_B} \tag{315}$$

from which we have to remove duplicate configurations. When the molecule is of the heteronuclear type BC, we have only to remove permutations of the n_B molecules by dividing by $n_B!$. When the solute molecule is homonuclear, of the type B_2, we have also to remove redundant orientations of the molecule by dividing by 2^{n_B}. We may therefore introduce a symmetry factor σ (which will be used again in Sec. 160), having the value 2 for a homonuclear and unity for a heteronuclear molecule. Thus in extremely dilute solution we find the expression

$$W_{cf} = \left(\frac{2z}{\sigma}\right)^{n_B} \frac{(\frac{1}{2}n_A + n_B)!}{(\frac{1}{2}n_A)!\, n_B!} \tag{316}$$

This expression will be a good approximation only if the solution is so dilute that it is a rare event for two of these solute molecules to be in contact. If the B half of one molecule is in contact with the B half of another molecule, it is evident that the number of sites that can be occupied by the C half is less than z for each molecule; thus the value of W_{cf} falls below that given by (316) as the concentration increases. This and cognate problems have been investigated by Fowler and Rushbrooke[1] and others.

[1] R. H. Fowler and G. S. Rushbrooke, *Trans. Faraday Soc.*, **33**, 1272 (1937).

124. The atoms B and C of the solute molecule BC discussed in Sec. 123 remain united to form a diatomic molecule in the solution, because it requires a certain amount of work to pull the two atoms apart and leave them in the solution. We may imagine the dissociation of the molecule carried out by a series of steps, in which the B atom is not moved. When the two halves of the molecule occupy adjacent sites in the solution, if we interchange the C atom with an adjacent solvent particle that is not in contact with B, this is the first step and requires a certain amount of work. If we next interchange the C atom with an adjacent solvent particle that lies still farther from B, we may have to do an additional amount of work, smaller than the previous amount; and so on for succeeding steps. If the forces of attraction between B and C are short-range forces, the work done in the third and fourth steps will be small or even negligible. We regard the dissociation of the molecule as complete when no further work is required, that is, when the energy is independent of the distance between the particles (as in the horizontal portion of the curve in Fig. 30). If the forces of attraction are long-range forces, the dissociation will not be complete until the distance between B and C amounts to many atomic diameters; this question will be discussed in Sec. 125.

In (294) we had an expression for a solution that contained two species of solute particles B and C in addition to the solvent A. By combining (316) with (294), we may derive an expression for an extremely dilute solution containing the solute species B, C, and BC in addition to the solvent A, that is, we can deal with the problem of a partially dissociated solute

$$BC \rightleftarrows B + C \tag{317}$$

similar to the problem of a partially dissociated gas.

Let us discuss first a large amount of solvent A containing only one solute molecule. We shall regard the dissociation of this molecule complete when the particle C has been removed to a distance greater than some value r' from the particle B. Imagine a small sphere of radius r' described around the site occupied by the B particle; this sphere will contain a number of sites N', small compared with the total number of sites N in the solution. To break up the molecule BC and leave the particle C at any site outside this sphere requires a certain amount of work (which we shall denote by D) that is the same for any site outside the sphere. For the C particle there are thus $(N - N')$ sites of equal energy, whereas when the C particle was adjacent to the B particle, there were only z sites of equal energy. The value of W_{cf} has thus been increased in the ratio $(N - N')/z$. In practice, this will not differ appreciably from N/z. In the same way, when the solvent contains more than one solute molecule of the species BC, we can derive an expression for the change in ln W_{cf} per particle dissociated. The solute BC will be either feebly or highly dissociated, according to the magnitude of the work D required to dissociate the molecule in this solvent at the temperature considered.

125. In this connection, for comparison with Fig. 30, let us consider the mutual potential energy of two particles in a liquid at temperature T (or in a gas at temperature T). Perhaps the most familiar example of this is where the two particles are electrically charged and the strength of their mutual attraction (or repulsion) depends on the dielectric constant of the liquid (or the gas). To say that between a particle bearing a positive charge q and a particle bearing a negative charge $-q$ there is a Coulomb attraction equal to $q^2/\epsilon r^2$ is equivalent to saying that their mutual electrostatic potential energy varies as $-q^2/\epsilon r$, where ϵ is the dielectric constant of the medium at the temperature considered. For a gas at ordinary pressures the value of ϵ is not much greater than unity, while for a liquid it may be several times greater than unity. If the distance between the particles is increased from r_1 to r_2, the work done is

$$\frac{q^2}{\epsilon}\left(\frac{1}{r_1} - \frac{1}{r_2}\right) \tag{318}$$

When in Fig. 30 we dealt with the mutual potential energy of two particles in a vacuum, the question of temperature did not arise. Here, however, each charged particle is supposed to be in thermal equilibrium with the particles of the liquid (or gas) at temperature T; and the ϵ in (318) denotes the value of the dielectric constant at this temperature. That is to say, (318) gives the amount of work done in isothermal separation of the particles; in other words, it is a change in the free energy. If we could allow the particles to come together under their mutual attraction, isothermally and reversibly, the potential energy could be recovered in the form of useful work.

126. The method that we have used in Sec. 124 for discussing the dissociation of a molecule in solution may likewise be used for the solution of a solid in a solvent. Suppose that the crystal depicted in Fig. 31b in Sec. 91 is at temperature T and is in contact with a pure solvent (either solid or liquid) at the same temperature, in which it is sparingly soluble; and suppose that the particle indicated in Fig. 31b by an arrow is in contact with a solvent particle. If we interchange these two particles, we begin to remove the particle from the solid; in this step we have to do a certain amount of work. If next we interchange the solute particle with a solvent particle that occupies a site still farther from the surface of the solid, we may have to do an additional amount of work, smaller than the previous amount. Whether the forces of attraction between the particle and the surface are short- or long-range forces, the energy may be regarded as independent of the distance as soon as the distance x from the surface exceeds a certain value x'; that is to say, if the potential energy of the particle in the solvent at temperature T is plotted against x, the curve becomes horizontal, as in Fig. 30 in Sec. 89. We can say that in the solvent there are $(N - N')$ sites of equal energy for the particle, that is, sites that lie at a distance greater than x' from the surface. The important quantity is the amount of work per particle to take particles from the solid to such distance sites in the solvent.

We pointed out in Sec. 101 the resemblance between a saturated vapor and a saturated solution. In (222) the value of the saturated vapor pressure is very sensitive to the amount of work required to remove a particle from the solid. Here, likewise, the solubility of a substance in a solvent will be very sensitive to the amount of work required to take a particle to a distant site in the solvent. When long-range forces are present, it is convenient to plot a curve for the potential energy of a solute particle in the solvent at temperature T near the

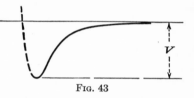

FIG. 43

surface of the solid; in the case of a sparingly soluble substance we know that the shape of the curve must be like that shown in Fig. 43, similar to that of Fig. 30. The slope of the curve in Fig. 43 represents the force of attraction between the solute particle and the surface.

It is clear that the length of the vertical arrow in Fig. 43 corresponds to the work required to take a particle to a distant site in the solvent at temperature T. Let this amount of work be denoted by V; it will evidently play a role similar to that of the sublimation energy in Sec. 92. In comparing different solutes, the greater the value of V, the smaller will be the solubility of the solute at the temperature considered. This is similar to the conclusion of Sec. 92 that the greater the value of s, the smaller would be the saturated vapor pressure. The work s, however, was simply work done against the interatomic forces of attraction and the question of the temperature of the environment did not arise.

127. It was pointed out in Sec. 47 and elsewhere that when the volume available to particles is increased so that the spacing of their energy levels becomes narrower, the number of different ways W in which the total energy can be distributed among the particles is thereby increased; in other words, the amount of entropy will be larger. In the case of a solid the effect is not determined directly by the change in the total volume v of the solid but indirectly by the increase or decrease in the little volume available to each particle of the solid. We may notice that it does not matter whether the n particles are in contact with each other or not; the same ideas may be applied to n solute particles occupying separate sites in a dilute solution. The volume available to each of these solute particles could, for example, be reduced, either by compressing the whole dilute solution or by other processes that are of more interest to us here. If the n_B solute particles in a solution are, for example, transferred to a different solvent, which provides for them the same number of sites, the value of W_{cf} will be unchanged; but if at each site the spacing of the energy levels for a solute particle is different, there will be a change of entropy.

It is of greater interest to apply these ideas to the solution of a solid in a liquid solvent. Most solids have a compact structure so that when a particle goes into solution in a liquid, it finds at each site a greater freedom of vibration and consequently a set of levels with narrower spacing. This leads to an increase in entropy, which must not be confused with the increase in entropy arising from W_{cf}; the latter depends on the amount of solvent but the former, being a change in W_{th}, does not depend on the number of sites available to a particle. When we go on to consider the free energy, we shall have to draw the corresponding distinction between the contribution from $-kT \ln W_{cf}$ and the contribution from $-kT \ln W_{th}$.

With this in view, let us examine the character of the potential energy V depicted for a particle of a sparingly soluble substance in Fig. 43. Let us consider a particle taken either into pure solvent or into a solvent that contains few other solute particles. The quantity V is the change in the free energy when the particle is taken to a particular distant site; we may say that it is the change in F', where F' denotes the free energy *excluding* the contribution from $-kT \ln W_{cf}$. Further, if x denotes the distance of the particle from the surface, the slope of the curve in Fig. 43, representing the force of attraction between the particle and the surface, is $\left(\dfrac{\partial F'}{\partial x}\right)_T$, where F' is once again the free energy excluding the contribution from W_{cf}.

Now this exclusion of W_{cf} does not imply that no change in entropy has been included. Usually, as we have seen, there is for each particle a change in entropy that is included in

$$V = \Delta E - T \, \Delta S'$$

At the same time, we see that the force of attraction between the particle and the surface is partly determined by the rate of change of entropy

$$\frac{\partial V}{\partial x} = \frac{\partial E}{\partial x} - T \, \frac{\partial S'}{\partial x} \tag{319}$$

128. The species of solute particle studied in Sec. 104 was one that had a negligible effect on all solvent particles except those which were its immediate neighbors. On the other hand, when long-range forces are present, we have to take into account a greater number of different environments, to include those of solvent particles not in contact with any solute particle. We have to use, even in very dilute solution, a method similar to that used in Sec. 103 for concentrated solutions. Supposing that we have labeled the various environments for both solvent and solute particles, let n_i denote the number of particles that at any moment are in the ith environment, to which the partition function P_i belongs. The free energy of the solution is

$$F = F' - kT \ln W_{cf}$$
$$= - kT\Sigma n_i \ln P_i - kT \ln W_{cf} \qquad (320)$$

If a very dilute solution contains solute particles at a mole fraction x_B and we add an additional dn_B particles, we have

$$\frac{\partial F}{\partial n_B} = \frac{\partial F'}{\partial n_B} - kT \frac{\partial}{\partial n_B} \ln W_{cf} \qquad (321)$$

$$= V + kT \ln x_B \qquad (322)$$

The expression (259) is a special case of (320), in which the summation happens to contain only three terms, and we may, in conclusion, discuss the other expressions that were derived from (259). In (263) and elsewhere occur the ratios $\mathbf{P}_A'/\mathbf{P}_A$ and $\mathbf{P}_B'/\mathbf{P}_B$. Since each of these four partition functions is referred to its own ground level, the values of the ratios are determined by the change in spacing of the energy levels. The expression (260) is a special case of (321); using (263), we may put (260) into the form

$$\frac{\partial F}{\partial n_B} = s - kT \ln\left[\frac{\mathbf{P}_B'}{\mathbf{P}_B}\left(\frac{\mathbf{P}_A'}{\mathbf{P}_A}\right)^z\right] + kT \ln x_B \qquad (323)$$

Comparing this with (322), we see that the first two terms on the right-hand side of (323) are together equal to the depth V of the potential minimum in Fig. 43.

129. Adsorption. When particles of a species B have been adsorbed onto the surface of a crystal A, the state of affairs closely resembles the formation of an interstitial solution of B in the interior of A. The treatment will be so similar that a brief discussion of adsorption may be included in this chapter.

When a solid is in contact with its own vapor, particles of the vapor that adhere to the solid are incorporated into the solid. On the other hand, when a gas or vapor B is in contact with a solid A that is a different chemical substance, particles of the gas or vapor that adhere to the surface of the solid form an adsorbed film, which partially or completely covers the surface. We shall be interested here only in cases where the surface is partially covered.

Let us consider a monatomic gas B and a crystalline solid A. Unit area of the solid surface provides a definite array of sites at which particles of the gas can be adsorbed; let there be N such sites per unit area. The problem is very similar to the solutions discussed in Sec. 100, for when particles are to be adsorbed, we have N choices for the first, $(N - 1)$ choices for the second, and so on. It will be recalled that in the substitutional solution of Sec. 99, the number of sites increased when solute particles were added to the solution but that in an interstitial solution a fixed number of sites was given in advance, as it is here. In Sec. 100 in dealing with an interstitial solution, we thought of the available sites as being distributed throughout a certain volume. In deriving (249) and (250), however, nothing was said about the sites having a three-dimensional distribution. These expressions apply equally well to the array of sites over the surface of the solid that we are discussing.

Let us examine the adsorption of a monatomic gas. When adsorbed at one of these sites, each atom has a set of vibrational levels; let the partition function be P_{ad}, measured from the same zero as the partition function for the gas. Writing down the free energy and differentiating with respect to n, we find, from (249),

$$\ln P_{ad} - \ln \frac{n}{n_e} - \ln \frac{P_v}{n_v} \tag{324}$$

It is customary to denote by θ the fraction of the surface that is covered by the adsorbed particles, $(1 - \theta)$ being the area left uncovered. We may substitute $\theta/(1 - \theta)$ for n/n_e. Setting (324) equal to zero, we find

$$n_v = \frac{P_v}{P_{ad}} \frac{\theta}{(1 - \theta)} \tag{325}$$

If, for the ratio P_v/P_{ad} we write n_v^0, (325) takes the form

$$\frac{p}{p^0} = \frac{n_v}{n_v^0} = \frac{\theta}{(1 - \theta)} \tag{326}$$

$$\theta = \frac{p}{p^0 + p} \tag{327}$$

which is known as "Langmuir's isotherm."

In this treatment it has been assumed that the set of levels for an adsorbed particle is the same, whether an adjacent site is occupied or vacant; a better treatment must take into account the fact that the set of levels will be modified.[1]

Problems

1. Discuss the lowering of the freezing point of a solvent due to the presence of unequal quantities of two solute species.

2. Figure 32 illustrates the equilibrium for a saturated vapor; construct similar diagrams to show the equilibrium for a saturated solution of a sparingly soluble substance at various temperatures.

---

[1] A. F. Devonshire, *Proc. Roy. Soc. A.*, **163**, 132 (1937); W. Band, *J. Chem. Phys.*, **8**, 178 (1940); T. L. Hill, *J. Chem. Phys.*, **14**, 263 (1946).

3. Verify that for a very dilute solution of B in A the expression (278) reduces to (259).

4. Taking abscissas to represent the mole fraction $x_A = (1 - x_B)$, construct three diagrams, using (283) to plot values of p/p_0 for the components A and B, for the following three values of $\ln \lambda$, namely, -1, $+1$, and $+2.5$, showing in the third case to what extent the observed vapor pressures will differ from the theoretical curves.

5. Two solid substances BC and BD are sparingly soluble in a solvent A, and BD is at all temperatures less soluble than BC. When BC dissolves in A it is completely dissociated into particles B and C; and likewise BD is completely dissociated into B and D. Obtain expressions for the various possible states of equilibrium between the mixed solution and the pure components.

CHAPTER 8

The Total Energy Shared by Interacting Particles—Quantization of the Total Energy—A Group of Samples

130. Thermal Expansion of a Solid. In discussing the internal energy of a diatomic molecule in Sec. 75, energies were not ascribed to the separate atoms of the molecule. The mutual potential energy of the two atoms cannot be split into two parts. The energy must be quantized but there is not a separate set of energy levels for each atom. Neither in a diatomic nor in a polyatomic molecule can a set of energy levels be ascribed to one of its component atoms. Nor, strictly, can this be done when a vessel contains two or more atoms that do not combine to form a molecule. Consider, for example, an evacuated vessel containing only two argon atoms, between which there are van der Waals's forces of attraction and repulsion. It is the total energy of the pair of atoms that should be quantized. When the vessel contains n particles of any imperfect gas, their mutual potential energy cannot be split into separate parts; consequently, it is the total energy of the n particles that should be quantized. A so-called "perfect gas" is a group of particles between which there are supposed to be no intermolecular forces and no mutual potential energy; only on this assumption is it correct to ascribe quantized energies to the individual particles. To do so for an imperfect gas is only an approximation. For a liquid or a solid it is a still rougher approximation.

In this chapter we shall pay less attention to the energies of individual particles and more attention to the total energy E shared by the group. As a beginning, let us discuss the free energy of a solid, as determined by the mutual interaction of the particles. Consider a simple crystal at the absolute zero of temperature. The distance between the atoms in the lattice is determined by the forces of attraction and repulsion between the atoms; the crystal adopts that value of the interatomic distance for which the total potential energy is a minimum. If the interatomic distance in the lattice were taken as abscissa and the energy of the crystal as ordinate, a curve like Fig. 30 in Sec. 89 would be obtained. At this temperature the energy of the crystal containing n atoms is $n\epsilon_0$; thus ϵ_0, referred to a fixed zero of energy, has a minimum value at a certain value of the lattice

172

interval, that is, at that distance at which the interatomic forces of attraction and repulsion are in equilibrium with each other, let this minimum value of ϵ_0 be denoted by ϵ_{00}.

At higher temperatures the particles of the crystal adopt a progressively wider separation. (In this section we shall always discuss solids subjected to a pressure that has a negligible effect on the volume, that is, 1 atmosphere or less.) We shall find that this thermal expansion takes place because it enables the value of W to reach higher values. For each particle the expansion provides a slightly larger volume in which to vibrate. If we use the simple model discussed in Chapters 1 and 2, this means that the spacing of the energy levels for each particle is slightly narrower.

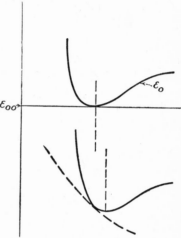

We must now ask what determines the value of the volume adopted by the crystal at any temperature T. The answer that we must give is that at each temperature T the crystal adopts that volume which gives to the partition function P its maximum value at this temperature. At any temperature T we must imagine the interatomic distance as capable of variation; this variation will be accompanied by changes in the values of $\epsilon_0, \epsilon_1 \ldots \epsilon_r \ldots$ and con-

FIG. 44.   Abscissas are the interatomic distance.

sequently will be accompanied by a change in the partition function $\Sigma e^{-\epsilon_r/kT}$, referred to a fixed zero of energy. Let **P** denote, as usual, the same partition function referred to the level ϵ_0, which is now taken as variable. From (76), we may write

$$P = \mathbf{P} e^{-(\epsilon_0 - \epsilon_{00}/kT)} \tag{328}$$

Taking ϵ_{00} as our fixed zero of energy, we have

$$-kT \ln P = -kT \ln \mathbf{P} + \epsilon_0 \tag{329}$$

We are interested in how these terms vary with the volume of the crystal. A plot of ϵ_0 against the interatomic distance (lattice spacing) will, as already mentioned, have the form of Fig. 30 in Sec. 89. A curve of this form has been drawn in Fig. 44 (the upper curve); its minimum corresponds to the lattice spacing adopted at the absolute zero of temperature.

Consider now the value of **P** at some higher temperature T. An increase in volume will be accompanied by a narrower spacing of the energy levels, as described in Sec. 28. Hence the value of **P** increases with volume at constant temperature. If the broken line in Fig. 44 is taken to be a plot of $- kT \ln \mathbf{P}$ at temperature T, it is clear that, on adding the ordinates to the ordinates of the upper curve, the resultant curve (which will represent the free energy of the crystal) will have a minimum, and that this minimum must lie slightly to the right of the minimum at the absolute zero of temperature, indicating a certain thermal expansion of the crystal.[1]

When the solid, or liquid, at temperature T is subject to a negligible external pressure, the familiar tendency for the entropy to increase with increasing volume is in this case exactly compensated by the tendency for E to increase owing to the work done against the forces of interatomic attraction:

$$\frac{\partial E}{\partial v} - \frac{T}{\partial v}\frac{\partial S}{\partial v} = 0$$

131. Fluctuations in Energy. In Chapter 1 we considered two bodies in thermal contact and asked what the condition was that gives the product $Z_A Z_B$ its maximum value. We found that strict equality of μ_A and μ_B in the exponential term $e^{-\mu\epsilon}$ was the required condition. In the case of a single body we had previously found that it is the strictly exponential form for the population that gives w its maximum value, and that deviations from the strictly exponential form cause w to fall below w_{max}. Small deviations of this kind occur all the time and their frequency of occurrence was discussed in connection with Fig. 10. In the same way a deviation from strict equality of μ_A and μ_B will cause the value of $Z_A Z_B$ to fall below its maximum value, and a curve depicting this relation would closely resemble that of Fig. 10. For large groups of particles we shall expect the fluctuations to be exceedingly small, and we shall inquire now whether this fact can be verified. For this purpose we may ask how great a deviation from strict equality of μ_A and μ_B is sufficient to cause the product $Z_A Z_B$ to fall to, say, one-thousandth of its maximum value.

For simplicity let us consider two equal quantities of the same chemical substance, occupying equal volumes, that is, containing the same number of particles and possessing the same set of energy levels. Let the initial temperature of each body be T_0 and let the heat capacity of each body at this temperature be C_v. If an amount of heat dQ is transferred from one body to the other, we may write for each body $dQ = C_v \, dT$. Now let an amount of heat be transferred sufficient to bring the temperature of the body A to a value T_A, appreciably different from T_0. For this body we find from (110)

$$\ln W_A^* - \ln W_A = \frac{1}{k}\int_{T_0}^{T_A}\frac{dQ}{T} = \frac{C_v}{k}\int_{T_0}^{T_A}\frac{dT}{T} = \frac{C_v}{k}\ln\frac{T_A}{T_0} \qquad (330)$$

---

[1] For a detailed discussion of metallic sodium, see J. C. Slater, "Introduction to Chemical Physics," Chapter 13, McGraw-Hill, 1939; for solid argon see O. K. Rice, *J. Chem. Phys.*, **12**, 290 (1944).

Before going further it will be convenient to notice the numerical magnitude of the quantity C_v/k. We see from (150) that for a gas C_v/k will be greater than n and this will likewise be true for a solid. This is because C_v is the heat capacity of the whole body, while the heat capacity of a single particle has a value in the neighborhood of k.

The transfer of heat that brings the temperature of the body A from T_0 to T_A brings at the same time the body B from T_0 to T_B. When the change in $\ln W_A$ is given by (328) there is at the same time a change in $\ln W_B$ for which we obtain a similar expression containing $\ln(T_B/T_0)$. We now write

$$T_A = T_0 + \Delta T = T_0\left(1 + \frac{\Delta T}{T_0}\right)$$

$$T_B = T_0 - \Delta T = T_0\left(1 - \frac{\Delta T}{T_0}\right)$$

To (330) we add the analogous expression for the body B and use the expansion $\ln(1 + x) = x - \frac{1}{2}x^2 + \cdots$; we obtain

$$\ln(W_A W_B)^* - \ln(W_A W_B) = \frac{C_v}{k}\ln\frac{T_A}{T_B}$$

$$= \frac{C_v}{k}\left[\frac{\Delta T}{T_0} - \frac{1}{2}\left(\frac{\Delta T}{T_0}\right)^2 - \frac{\Delta T}{T_0} - \frac{1}{2}\left(\frac{\Delta T}{T_0}\right)^2 + \cdots\right]$$

$$= -\frac{C_v}{k}\left(\frac{\Delta T}{T_0}\right)^2 + \cdots \tag{331}$$

Writing $\Delta T = x$ and $C_v/kT_0^2 = \gamma$, we obtain

$$\frac{(Z_A Z_B)^*}{Z_A Z_B} = \frac{(W_A W_B)^*}{W_A W_B} = e^{-\gamma x^2} \tag{332}$$

The result is similar to (32) in Sec. 19; hence, if we take the temperature as abscissa, we shall obtain a diagram similar to Fig. 10. We wish to know the width of this diagram, that is, to find the value of T that is sufficient to reduce $Z_A Z_B$, say, to one-thousandth of its maximum value. If, for example, we consider a group containing between 10^{21} and 10^{22} particles, setting C_v/k equal to 10^{22} and T_0 equal to $300°$, since $\log_e 1000 = 6.9$, we obtain

$$\Delta T = 300\sqrt{6.9 \times 10^{-22}}$$

$$= 8 \times 10^{-9} \text{ degree centigrade}$$

This value is extremely small, and fluctuations in temperature greater than this will be rare.

According to (145) in Sec. 72, E is proportional to T; hence for two vessels containing equal portions of a perfect monatomic gas in thermal contact with each other, we may substitute $\Delta E/E$ for $\Delta T/T$ in (331); the same will be approximately true for most solids and liquids at room temperature. We can plot $\ln(W_A W_B)$ against E and obtain the curve with the maximum mentioned in Sec. 69. Alternatively, using (332), we can plot $W_A W_B$ against E and obtain a curve like that of Fig. 10, which will show the probability that for either body the value of E will differ from the central value by the amount ΔE when the energy of the other similar body differs from the central value by the opposite amount $-\Delta E$. If the energy shared by the two bodies is $2E^0$, we have

$$\frac{Z_A Z_B}{(Z_A Z_B)_{\max}} = e^{-\gamma(E-E^0)^2}$$

where $\gamma = C_v/kE^{0^2}$. We see from (332) that if, for example, E^0 is 3 calories, the energy of either body will rarely differ from the central value by as much as 10^{-10} calorie, which is equivalent to 4×10^{-3} erg.

132. Quantization of the Energy of a Group of Particles. The above preliminary discussion of the total energy E will serve as an introduction to the problem that forms the main subject of this chapter. It was pointed out in Sec. 130 that, in treating a crystal, it is the total energy of the crystal that should be quantized. Throughout this book, on the other hand, in discussing a solid, we have assigned to each particle a set of allowed energies $\epsilon_1, \epsilon_2 \ldots \epsilon_r \ldots$. To use for a solid this simple model, in which each particle is treated as independent, is clearly to use a model that needs to be replaced by something nearer to the true state of affairs. In the foregoing chapters we have found the quantity $\Sigma e^{-\epsilon_r/kT}$ to be the most convenient instrument for handling the problems of a solid, and we have expressed the behavior of solids in terms of this quantity. To abandon the energies of individual particles $\epsilon_0, \epsilon_1 \ldots \epsilon_r$ means that we abandon the partition function whose summation was taken over these energies ϵ_r and that we render meaningless all the equations containing $\ln P$, unless a new interpretation can be found for these equations. But we shall find here, as so often happens in physical theories, that the replacement of a simple model by an improved and more complicated model is accompanied by an interpretation that allows one to use the old equations with little or no modification.

Quantizing the total energy of the solid, let us say that the total energy E can take only certain discrete values $E_0, E_1, E_2 \ldots E_r \ldots$, where E_0 is the energy of the solid at the absolute zero of temperature. Attention is now to be focused on the possible modes of vibration of the solid body, that is, in a crystal, on the modes of vibration of the crystal lattice. The different modes of vibration are very numerous, and the energy E_r can be shared among the various modes in a large number of alternative ways. If we denote the number of different ways by Z_r, we see that the relation between Z_r and E_r will be the same as the relation between Z and E in Chapter 1. There will, however, be only a discrete set of values

Z_0, Z_1, Z_2 ... Z_r, corresponding to the allowed values of E. We can now begin to speak of the energies E_0 ... E_r as forming a set of energy levels for the body, just as formerly we spoke of the energy levels ϵ_0 ... ϵ_r of a single particle. For any level E_r the multiplicity is Z_r. The multiplicity of the lowest level E_0 will be discussed in Chapter 10. When there is a unique state of the crystal for the energy E_0, we have $Z_0 = 1$. For the higher energy levels the values of Z_1, Z_2 ... increase rapidly.

Before considering the details of these energy levels, we may broaden the discussion. Although we have been speaking of a solid body, we should recognize that these concepts apply to all forms of matter. It is true that in a perfect gas the particles are treated as completely independent but in a real gas they are not independent. It is the energy of the whole gas, E, which ought to be quantized; in an imperfect gas one cannot ascribe allowed energies to the individual particles. Since this is also true of liquids, we have embarked on a discussion that is applicable to all forms of matter.

133. We come now to the problem that is to occupy the remainder of this chapter, a reconsideration of the whole basis of statistical mechanics. The treatment given in Chapter 2 was a quantized form of the classical treatment associated mainly with the names of Boltzmann and Maxwell. The discussion that we shall now give will be a quantized treatment nearer to the classical conceptions introduced by Gibbs. Although we shall often refer to the procedures followed and the results obtained in Chapter 2, it should be understood that such references are merely for the sake of illustration and that the development of statistical mechanics to be given here is self-contained and is independent of any results obtained in earlier chapters.

Let us consider the general problem of a large number of similar bodies all of the same size and composition, sharing a certain amount of energy. Although there is no need to restrict the problem to solid bodies, we may first think of them as N similar crystals, sharing a total energy E. We shall use the letter E, as usual, to denote the energy of any one crystal. When a uniform temperature T prevails, we may regard each of the N bodies as being in contact with a heat reservoir, consisting of the other (N − 1) bodies.[1] Let us suppose then that interchange of energy may take place freely between the N bodies, until any differences in temperature are equalized and a certain uniform temperature T prevails throughout. By a uniform temperature we mean that the sharing of energy among the bodies is as uniform as it ever will be. At any moment it is *possible* that each crystal in the group has exactly the same energy as every other crystal; but this is, of course, extremely improbable. It is

[1] See E. Schroedinger, "Statistical Thermodynamics," Chapter 2, Cambridge, 1941.

analogous to the case where every molecule in a gas has exactly the same energy as every other molecule. In both cases the state is so improbable that it does not occur; we have to inquire how the energy is likely to be distributed; in both cases we do this by asking what state can arise in the greatest number of ways. We can describe the problem by saying that we wish to find the distribution that has the greatest value of w consistent with the total energy E. If at any moment N_r is the number of crystals that have energy E_r, the total energy of the group is $\mathsf{E} = \Sigma N_r E_r$.

For each crystal the allowed energy states are extremely numerous and we may follow a procedure similar to that used in Sec. 40 for the particles of a gas. We divide the energy states into batches, and we number the batches, starting from the bottom, the 1st, 2d, 3d . . . rth . . . batch. Each batch is to include only a narrow range of energy. Let the rth batch include p_r different allowed values of the energy; by a slight change of notation, let E_r now denote the average energy of a level in this rth batch and let Z_r denote the average multiplicity of a level in this batch. The total number of energy states included in this batch is clearly given by the product $p_r Z_r$. If N_r denotes the number of crystals having an energy within this range when a uniform temperature prevails, we have to ask first how the N_r crystals may be distributed among the $p_r Z_r$ available states. This is not given by the expression (81) in Sec. 40 that was used for the particles of a gas. In the gas the particles were indistinguishable, whereas here we can distinguish the crystal at the point P from the crystal at the point Q. There will thus be $(p_r Z_r)^{N_r}$ different ways in which the N_r crystals may be distributed among the $p_r Z_r$ states. The same treatment is to be applied to the particles within each batch of levels.

The number of ways in which one batch of levels may be populated is independent of the other batches of levels; hence, for the whole population, the value of w will be given by the product

$$w = \mathsf{N}!\,\frac{(p_0 Z_0)^{N_0}}{N_0!}\,\frac{(p_1 Z_1)^{N_1}}{N_1!}\cdots\frac{(p_r Z_r)^{N_r}}{N_r!}\cdots \tag{333}$$

To find the most probable distribution of energy among the crystals, we use the familiar requirement that any small rearrangement leaves the value of w unchanged. Suppose, for example, we fix attention on any two crystals in the group that happen to have energy E_j—two crystals both of which have energy lying within the jth batch of levels—and suppose we transfer a small quantity of energy η from one crystal to the other; after the transfer, instead of two crystals with energy E_j, we have one with energy $E_k = E_j + \eta$, and one with energy $E_i = E_j - \eta$. The three energies E_i, E_j, and E_k are "equally spaced," whatever the value of η. The whole problem is so similar to that of Sec. 41 that we may expect to obtain an exponential distribution of the energy. In fact, either by this procedure or by the method of undetermined multipliers, the reader can easily verify that we reach an expression analogous to (85), namely,

$$\frac{N_r}{p_r Z_r} = A e^{-\sigma E_r} \tag{334}$$

This is the most probable distribution of energy among the crystals. When (334) is substituted into (333), it gives the value of w_{max}, which will be denoted below by W. If initially the distribution of energy is different from (334), the value of w will be less than w_{max}; but if the interchange of energy is unrestricted, we may expect that a redistribution will take place, accompanied by an increase in w.

134. When the group of crystals is sharing a certain total energy, let us make an increment in this energy by giving an additional amount of energy η_1 to one of the crystals. We can show, as was done in Sec. 16, that the value of W is thereby multiplied by $e^{\sigma \eta_1}$. If then to various crystals in the group we give various amounts of energy η_1, η_2, $\eta_3 \ldots$, so that the group thereby receives an amount of heat δQ, we shall obtain the relation

$$\delta \ln \mathsf{W} = \sigma \, \delta Q \tag{335}$$

We can now consider a separate group of crystals belonging to a different chemical substance; in these crystals the relation between Z and E will be different from that in the first group. Denoting the two groups by A and B, let one group possess a total energy E_A and the other a total energy E_B. In general, if the two groups are placed in thermal contact with each other, the product $\mathsf{W}_A \mathsf{W}_B$ will not have its maximum value consistent with the energy $\mathsf{E}_A + \mathsf{E}_B$. If a quantity of heat is transferred from A to B, we have $\delta Q_B = - \delta Q_A$, and hence from (335)

$$\delta \ln \mathsf{W}_A \mathsf{W}_B = (\sigma_B - \sigma_A) \, \delta Q \tag{336}$$

There will be a spontaneous flow of heat from A to B if σ_A is less than σ_B, and vice versa. Thus the two groups of crystals (which may be different chemical substances) will be in equilibrium when they have the same value of σ.

The total volume of the crystals in the group A is the sum of the volumes of the individual crystals, a quantity that depends upon the external pressure to which they are subject. When we compare two groups A and B, the second group B need not be of a different chemical substance from A; the group may be a similar set of crystals, subjected to a different external pressure and having in consequence a different set of allowed energies $E_0 \ldots E_r \ldots$ When two such groups are compared, we can construct isothermal curves on a p-v diagram, since all points having a common value of σ correspond to thermal equilibrium; we can thus envisage an absolute scale for σ.

Instead of placing another group of crystals in thermal contact with group A, suppose that we place a vessel containing a large quantity of a certain perfect gas in contact with group A. Let the perfect gas possess a total energy E_g and let the particle population be exponential with the appropriate value of μ. We can now investigate the relation between μ for the particles of the gas and σ for the crystals of group A. When the gas has a total energy E, the number of states available to the particles is by definition Z. The product $\mathsf{W}_A\mathsf{W}_B$ in (336) is thus replaced by the product $\mathsf{W}_A Z_g$. From (99) and (336), we obtain at once that, on the thermal contact, if an amount of heat δQ flows into the gas thermometer,

$$\delta \ln(\mathsf{W}_A Z_g) = (\mu_g - \sigma_A)\, \delta Q \qquad (337)$$

Thus, the group of crystals is colder than the gas when σ_A is greater than μ_g, and vice versa; it is clear that the undetermined multiplier σ that was introduced into the equations leading to (334) has the same relation to temperature as the familiar quantity μ that determines the form of the particle population for a perfect gas. We may write $\sigma = \mu = 1/kT$.

In (57) and (97) the factor μ described the *internal* distribution of energy within any one portion of solid, gas, or vapor. The basis of σ is different. In Chapters 2 to 7 our idea of temperature was associated with the form of the exponential particle population. But (334) and (336) evidently give a concept of temperature that mentions only the energies $E_j,\, E_k \ldots E_r$ of the various groups. We may recall here that, although we have been referring to these groups of particles as crystals, the argument applies to samples of any form of matter—solid, liquid or gaseous; in the case of a gas, we must suppose that we have N similar samples contained in vessels of the same size.

135. Although the procedure followed in Sec. 133 was very similar to that of Sec. 38, a difference should be noted. In Sec. 38 we used p_r to denote the number of states in a batch; here p_r has been used for the number of allowed values of the energy in a batch of levels, each of which has a high multiplicity. In Sec. 38, when we let p_r take the value unity, n_r became the number of particles in a particular state, which had been given the label r. In (334), on the other hand, if we let p_r take the value unity, N_r will denote the average number of samples that occupy a multiple level, namely, the rth level that has multiplicity Z_r.

The device of dividing the allowed energies into batches was used in Sec. 133, in order that each of the quantities N_r should be large compared with unity. There is no longer any objection to N_r being less than unity. The quantity p_r, which was the number of allowed energies in the rth batch, has served its purpose. If p_r is set equal to unity, the notation reverts to the original form proposed at the beginning of this chapter, in which E_0, E_1, $E_2 \ldots E_r \ldots$ denote the successive allowed values of the energy. Remembering that $\Sigma N_r = \mathbf{N}$, we obtain with this notation

$$N_r = \frac{\mathbf{N} Z_r e^{-E_r/kT}}{\mathsf{P}} \tag{338}$$

where

$$\mathsf{P} = \Sigma Z_r e^{-E_r/kT} \tag{339}$$

The expression (338) gives the degree to which the levels are populated. N_r/Z_r is the average number of samples in any state that has energy E_r, when the uniform temperature T prevails throughout the group.

It will be noticed that from this discussion a quantity (339) had emerged, which has the same form as the partition functions of Chapter 2 except that it mentions only the allowed values of the total energy E. We shall show below that the quantity P is as useful in prescribing equilibrium conditions, and so on, as was the quantity P in earlier chapters. In the case of a perfect gas both the quantities P and P exist, and we can examine the relation between the two.

Let us first discuss the meaning of (338). When a number of bodies of the same size and composition share a total energy E and a uniform temperature prevails, we expect to find that each body has, so far as an ordinary calorimetric measurement can detect, the same energy as the others, namely, $\mathsf{E}/\mathbf{N}$. At the same time, it was pointed out previously that an equal sharing of energy is comparable to the improbable state of gas where every molecule has the same energy. In this connection, consider now the expression (338) in which r takes the values $0, 1, 2 \ldots r \ldots$; the expression states that when a uniform temperature T prevails, the number of bodies that have any allowed energy E_r is given by N_r; that is to say, (338) assigns values to N_r for every E_r, even down to the lowest energy E_0. If this is to be in agreement with observation, the truth must be that all values of N_r are negligibly small except in a narrow range of energy in the neighborhood of the value $\mathsf{E}/\mathbf{N}$, the value for equal sharing. The factor $e^{-E_r/kT}$ in (338) decreases very rapidly for all values of E. If then (338) is to show a sharp maximum, this must be due to a very rapid rise in the value of Z over a certain range of energy. The position of this sharp maximum must be correlated with the prevailing temperature T. In Sec. 131 we discussed the sharing of energy between two samples of the same size and composition and we found that only small deviations from equal sharing were probable. We shall show in Chapter 10 that this is also true in the case of $\mathbf{N}$ samples, and in the meantime we shall continue to discuss (338) as if this had already been proved.

In Chapter 1 we mentioned in Sec. 3 the concept of an ensemble of $\mathbf{N}$ independent systems. In the example discussed there, to each member was allotted the same fixed amount of energy E. We can also imagine an ensemble in which the total energy E is not distributed uniformly among the members; we can allot fixed amounts of energy to the independent members according to any chosen scheme. For example, if E_0, $E_1 \ldots E_r \ldots$ are the allowed energies for each member, we could allot energies in accordance with (338). Now the importance of this ensemble is that it apparently does not matter whether the members are independent or not. If we were to put the members into thermal contact with each other (as we supposed in Sec. 133), the distribution of energy among the members would not depart from (338) and a stable and uniform temperature would prevail. There is no distribution of E that has a greater value of w than (338), and consequently no tendency for a redistribution of the energy to take place.

136. The discussion above has been founded on the fact that substitution of (334) into (333) will give the maximum value of w consistent with the total energy E. Making this substitution and using (338), we obtain for $\ln w_{\max}$

$$\ln \mathsf{W} = \mathsf{N} \ln \mathsf{P} + \frac{\mathsf{E}}{kT} \tag{340}$$

which is quite analogous to (70).

It was shown in Sec. 58 that when the level ϵ_0 is chosen as the zero of energy, the term $n \ln P$ is n times the increment in $\ln W$ when a particle is added to the ground level. Here likewise we may imagine the addition of a sample to the group of samples. This may be carried out in two steps; we may first include an additional sample with energy E_0 and then add the requisite amount of energy. If we have taken E_0 as the zero of energy, it may be easily shown from (333) that the first of these two steps is accompanied by an increment in $\ln \mathsf{W}$ that is equal to $\ln \mathsf{P}$. Thus the interpretation of the two terms on the right-hand side of (340) is similar to that of the two terms in (70).

Both terms on the right-hand side are proportional to N, the number of samples. If we identify the quantity $k \ln \mathsf{W}$ with the entropy of the whole group of samples of equal size, then one Nth part of this will be the entropy of one sample. Dividing (340) by N, we obtain the expression

$$\frac{1}{\mathsf{N}} \ln \mathsf{W} = \ln \mathsf{P} + \frac{E}{kT} \tag{341}$$

where $E = \mathsf{E}/\mathsf{N}$.

Carrying the same process further, we can consider the subdivision of one sample and the entropy of the parts so obtained. Now we know from the study of Figs. 27a and 27b that when a vessel containing a gas is subdivided, the results are not simple because the unlocalized particles become localized to a greater degree. In a solid this effect does not enter; if a pure solid is divided into a few portions (the number of surface atoms in each portion being negligible in comparison with the internal atoms), the entropy of each portion is proportional to its size. If this is to be so in (341), not only the term E/kT but also the term $\ln \mathsf{P}$ must be proportional to n, the number of particles (all of the same species) that share the energy E in one sample. That is to say, the quantity $\ln \mathsf{P}$ must be of the form nx, where x is independent of n. In place of x we may define a number $\mathcal{P}$ such that

$$n \ln \mathcal{P} = \ln \mathsf{P} \tag{342}$$

From (341) we can now obtain the Helmholtz free energy $(E - TS)$ of one sample, in the form

$$E - \frac{kT}{\mathsf{N}} \ln \mathbb{W} = - kT \ln \mathsf{P} \tag{343}$$

$$= - nkT \ln \mathcal{P} \tag{344}$$

In earlier chapters we used for a solid the expression $- nkT \ln P$. Thus, the new quantity $\mathcal{P}$ will play the same role as P in all expressions involving the free energy of a solid.

In Fig. 44, for example, the upper curve can be taken to be a plot of E_0/n, while the lower curve represents $- kT \ln \mathsf{P}$.

137. In order to make use of (339), we have to know the allowed values of E_r to be inserted. The problem of an imperfect gas will be discussed in Chapter 9 and that of a solid in Chapter 10. Since in a perfect gas each particle has its own set of energy levels, it is legitimate to speak of the partition function $P = \Sigma e^{-\epsilon_r/kT}$ as well as of P; and we can examine the relation between P and P. As an approach to this problem, let us first consider a vessel containing only two gas molecules, one molecule of species A and the other of species B. The allowed values of E for the pair are the possible values of the sum of the energies of the two particles. The A-particle will have levels ϵ_r, while for the B-particle the set of levels may be denoted by $\epsilon'_0 \ldots \epsilon'_s$. The combination of any ϵ_r with any ϵ'_s gives a possible value of E. We find now that the required summation $\Sigma Z_r e^{-E_r/kT}$ can be simply obtained as a product of $\sum_r e^{-\epsilon_r/kT}$ and $\sum_s e^{-\epsilon'_s/kT}$. If we write down

$$(e^{-\epsilon_0/kT} + \cdots + e^{-\epsilon_r/kT} + \cdots)(e^{-\epsilon'_0/kT} + \cdots + e^{-\epsilon'_s/kT} + \cdots) \tag{345}$$

the resulting product will contain a term $e^{-(\epsilon_r + \epsilon'_s)/kT}$ for every possible combination of an ϵ_r with an ϵ'_s. For the pair of particles we thus find $\mathsf{P} = P_A P_B$. Let us consider next a pair of particles of the *same* species. If, in (345), we write $\epsilon_r = \epsilon'_r$ for each value of r, the energies occurring in the resultant product will again be the possible levels E_r for this pair of particles. The question arises as to the multiplicity of these levels. In discussing Fig. 15 we saw that for a pair of particles moving in the same volume, there is only one state for any value of $(\epsilon_r + \epsilon_s)$, whereas there would be two states for a similar pair of localized particles. Examining the quantity P^2, we find that this would give $\Sigma Z_r e^{-E_r/kT}$ correctly for a pair of localized particles; and, further, that P^n would give $\Sigma Z_r e^{-E_r/kT}$ for a group of n localized particles (for example, in the situation depicted in Fig. 27b). For n particles moving in the same vessel, as in the communal volume of Fig. 27a, the value of $\Sigma Z_r e^{-E_r/kT}$ will be considerably smaller than P^n, because many redundant terms in (345) must be discarded; that is to say, the multiplicity of the levels E_r will be smaller. In order that (341) and (343) shall agree with (185b), we must have

$$\ln \mathsf{P} = n\left(\ln \frac{P}{n} + 1\right) = \ln\left(\frac{eP}{n}\right)^n \tag{346}$$

$$= \ln P^n - \ln\left(\frac{n}{e}\right)^n \tag{347}$$

This quantity is smaller than $\ln P^n$ in agreement with expectation; the magnitude of the difference may be understood from Sec. 77.

138. We saw in Sec. 134 that, for the N samples, we could take N equal vessels each containing n particles in the form of vapor. We can likewise consider the case where each of the N vessels contains more than enough particles to form a saturated vapor at the prevailing temperature. In this group many vessels (but not necessarily all) will contain a certain amount of liquid or solid in equilibrium with the vapor, and (338) should provide a solution of the vapor pressure problem.

Each vessel contains the same total number of particles $n = n_v + n_s$, but we cannot expect the number of particles n_v in the form of vapor to be the same in the various vessels. We could not expect this, even if each sample possessed the same amount of energy E; and according to (338) different samples will possess different amounts of energy E_r. We should therefore have to take into account all possible values of n_v and n_s consistent with the total energy possessed by the sample.

This problem must be contrasted with the problem of a mixture of perfect gases, A and B; here not only is the total number of particles $(n_A + n_B)$ fixed, but also the separate values of n_A and n_B are to be the same in each sample; the value of $\Sigma Z_r e^{-E_r/kT}$ for the mixture is given by

$$\mathsf{P} = \left(\frac{eP_A}{n_A}\right)^{n_A}\left(\frac{eP_B}{n_B}\right)^{n_B} \tag{348}$$

We have, as a matter of fact, already made use of the relation contained in this expression, although we did not derive it in this way. In view of (343), the relation expressed in (348) is, in fact, the additivity of the free energies that we derived in Sec. 82 from the properties of $\ln W$. We made use of this additivity in Secs. 85 and 86, and for localized particles in Sec. 102.

There are still many different choices that we can make for the samples to which (338) refers. If, for example, N vessels contain N similar specimens of a gas, we do not have to decide in advance that the gas is a diatomic gas or that it is a monatomic gas. Each vessel may contain a partially dissociated gas, having an equilibrium $A_2 \rightleftarrows 2A$. Although the total number of atoms of A is to be the same in each sample, the number of atoms that remain unattached will be different in different vessels. This number would be different even if every sample possessed the same amount of energy E; and according to (338) different samples will possess different amounts of energy. The summation in $\Sigma Z_r e^{-E_r/kT}$ is to be taken over all possible states of the n atoms consistent with the energy possessed by the sample, that is to say, over all possible degrees of dissociation. The same will, of course, be true for the dissociation of the heteronuclear molecule AB studied in Sec. 91.

If $- kT \ln \mathsf{P}$ in these problems is identified with the free energy of thermodynamics, since this quantity involves a summation over all possible degrees of dissociation, it is not the same as that quantity which was identified with the free energy in Chapter 5. In Fig. 32a, for example, any point on the lower curve gives the value of $(E - kT \ln W)$ for that particular situation where a certain fraction of the n particles is in the form of vapor. The position of the lowest point on this curve is taken as giving the equilibrium value of n_v for the saturated vapor, and larger and smaller values of n_v are disregarded. We shall return to the discussion of (338) in Chapter 10.

Problems

1. Discuss the thermal expansion of a solid while it is subject to a constant high pressure, describing the state of equilibrium at different temperatures.

2. Derive (334) from (333) by each of the methods suggested in Sec. 133.

CHAPTER 9

Classical Mechanics—Phase Space—Imperfect Gases—The Condensation of a Vapor

139. Classical Mechanics. In the days before the introduction of the quantum theory, the description of a perfect gas differed in two respects from that outlined in Chapter 2: first, the energy of a particle could take any value, instead of a set of discrete values; and secondly, to describe the state of the gas at any moment it was thought to be necessary to assign to each particle a position and a velocity.[1] In the quantum description of a gas in equilibrium, values are assigned to the probabilities of finding a particle in the various energy states and no attempt is made to say anything further about the velocity or position. In the absence of any external field, for a particle of given energy the wave function has an amplitude that will be uniform throughout the volume of the containing vessel; hence there is an equal probability of finding the particle anywhere in the vessel. The fact that the gas fills the vessel uniformly follows from this.

In classical mechanics the argument is quite different.[2] Consider the whole volume as being the sum of a large number of equal portions labeled 1, 2, 3 . . . and at any moment let there be n_1, n_2, n_3 . . . particles in these several portions. If there are s such portions, the number of different ways in which this state of the gas can arise is taken to be

$$w = \left(\frac{1}{s}\right)^n \frac{n!}{n_1!\, n_2!\, n_3! \cdots n_s!}$$

Completely uniform distribution would correspond to $n_1 = n_2 = n_3$ and so on; in fact, it can easily be shown that this gives to w its greatest value. Other distributions will occur with a frequency depending on the value of w/w_{max}.

To describe the translational motion of a particle, we must assign values to six coordinates, namely, to x, y, and z for position, and to the

---

[1] In this chapter only a very brief discussion of classical mechanics will be given; for a thorough comparison between classical and quantum statistics, see R. C. Tolman, "The Principles of Statistical Mechanics," Chapter 9, Oxford, 1938.

[2] See, for example, K. T. Herzfeld, "Kinetische Theorie der Wärme," in Müller-Pouillet, "Lehrbuch der Physik," p. 122, Braunschweig, 1925.

three components of the velocity, u, v, and w. But first, as a simpler approach to the problem, we can imagine a one-dimensional monatomic gas in which each particle has only the x-coordinate and the x-component of the velocity, u; the volume of the "vessel" will be the length l of the line along which each particle moves. In Fig. 45 let u be taken as ordinate and x as abscissa; then the motion of a particle at any moment can be represented by a point on this diagram. It is more usual to take the momentum mu, instead of u, as one of the coordinates. In either case, a particle moving with uniform velocity will be represented in Fig. 45 by a point moving along a horizontal line, either from left to right or from right to left. When there are n particles, the condition of the gas at any moment will be represented by n points scattered over the diagram. Now consider the points that happen to fall within the little rectangle R in the diagram; the particles represented by these points have at the moment a position lying between x and $(x + dx)$ and a momentum lying between mu and $m(u + du)$.

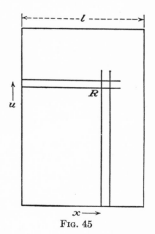

Fig. 45

If we go on to consider a two-dimensional gas, we shall need, instead of a rectangle of area $m \, dx \, du$, a volume $m^2 \, dx \, dy \, du \, dv$ in four-dimensional space. Finally, when we consider an ordinary three-dimensional monatomic gas, we shall need a volume

$$m^3 \, dx \, dy \, dz \, du \, dv \, dw \qquad (349)$$

in six-dimensional space; this space is known as the "phase space" for a single moving particle. The motion of a particle will be represented by the motion of a representative point in this phase space. The n particles of a gas will be represented by a swarm of n such points.

140. In order to make a comparison between these classical ideas and the quantum treatment, we may draw attention once more to the two forms of quantum statistics with which we have dealt, namely, that of Chapter 8, in which we consider only the values of the total energy E, and the earlier treatment of Chapter 2, in which we consider the energies of the individual particles. In Sec. 142 we shall discuss the classical phase space to which the states of Chapter 8 are the quantum analogue. Here we shall use (349) to discuss the individual particles of a perfect gas; the kinetic energy of any particle is

$$\tfrac{1}{2}m(u^2 + v^2 + w^2) \qquad (350)$$

We wish now to find the most probable state of the gas. In equation (1) the quantities n_1, n_2, $n_3 \ldots n_r \ldots$ in the denominator were the numbers of particles in the various quantized states. But in classical mechanics there are no discrete states on which we can fix our attention; for each particle an infinite number of values of u, v, and w are available. The postulate is introduced that equal portions of phase space have equal a priori probability. In Fig. 45, for example, we can imagine the entire surface ruled out into small rectangles of equal size and each rectangle labeled by means of a letter or number, such as 0, 1, 2 . . . r . . . . We have already referred to the n representative points lying scattered over the diagram; we can denote by n_r the number of representative points that at the moment lie within the rectangle that has been called the rth. In the same way, using (349), we can imagine the whole of phase space divided into equal volumes, each large enough to contain many representative points; these volumes are often called "cells" of phase space. In Chapter 1 we assigned a number to each quantized state, irrespective of whether there were other states of the same energy. So here, we shall assign a number or a letter to each cell of phase space, disregarding the fact that there are other cells corresponding to the same energy. Let the number of particles in the various cells at any moment be n_0, n_1, n_2 . . . n_r . . . ; then the assumption is made that this condition of the gas can arise in w different ways, given by the familiar expression

$$w = \frac{n!}{n_0! \, n_1! \, n_2! \cdots}$$

Let us consider now n particles of a monatomic gas, sharing a total energy E. When the cells are small, all the points in a cell will have sensibly the same energy. Let us consider a cell where each particle has an energy ϵ_j; let there be n_j representative points in this cell, representing n_j particles in the gas. If we take two of these particles and allow one to communicate a certain amount η of its energy to the other, we shall now have one particle with energy $\epsilon_j + \eta$ and the other with energy $\epsilon_j - \eta$; let us denote these resulting amounts of energy by ϵ_k and ϵ_i, respectively. The number of representative points in the jth cell has been diminished from n_j to $(n_j - 2)$. At the same time the number of representative points in the ith cell has been increased from n_i to $(n_i + 1)$, and in the kth cell the number has been increased from n_k to $(n_k + 1)$. The question is whether, as a result of this change, the value of w for the gas has been changed. The argument is evidently the same as was used in Chapter 1 except that the particles are now populating cells of phase space instead of quantized states. Alternatively, by the method of undetermined multipliers, we would arrive at the expression for the rth cell

$$\ln n_r - \lambda - \mu \epsilon_r = 0$$

By either method, we reach the expression

$$\frac{n_r}{n} = \frac{e^{-\mu \epsilon_r}}{\Sigma e^{-\mu \epsilon_r}} \tag{351}$$

This does not give the total number of particles which have energy ϵ_r, but only those whose representative points lie in the rth cell.

In classical mechanics there is no reason why the cells of phase space should be allotted any particular size. When we allow the cells to become sufficiently small, the summation in the denominator of (351) may be replaced by an integral and we may write

$$\frac{dn}{n} = \frac{m^3 e^{-\mu\epsilon}\, dx\, dy\, dz\, du\, dv\, dw}{\int\int\int\int\int\int m^3 e^{-\mu\epsilon}\, dx\, dy\, dz\, du\, dv\, dw} \tag{352}$$

141. Whereas the sum in the denominator of (351) is a pure number, the integral in (352) is not dimensionless. If, however, we multiply both numerator and denominator in (352) by any quantity **b**, the equation is unchanged; we may then choose for **b** a quantity whose dimensions are the reciprocal of those of the integral. The denominator containing **b**, now dimensionless, will have the usual properties of the partition function, since it only differs from the usual sum-over-states in that the summation has been replaced by an integral. We shall obtain expressions corresponding to those of Chapter 2. For example, in a change of volume, the external work done, corresponding to (108), will be

$$\delta A = -\frac{n}{\mu}\, \delta[\, \ln\, (\mathbf{b}m^3\int\int\int\int\int\int e^{-\mu\epsilon}\, du\, dv\, dw\, dx\, dy\, dz)] \tag{353}$$

$$= -\frac{n}{\mu}\, \delta \ln P \tag{354}$$

The absolute scale of temperature will be introduced as in Chapter 2, and we shall write $\mu = 1/kT$. When the molecules of the gas are not subject to any external field (such as a gravitational field), the energy ϵ is not a function of x, y, z, and the integral $\int\int\int dx\, dy\, dz$ yields only the volume of the vessel v. Using (350), the partition function takes the form

$$m^3 v \mathbf{b} \int e^{-\frac{1}{2}mu^2/kT}\, du \int e^{-\frac{1}{2}mv^2/kT}\, dv \int e^{-\frac{1}{2}mw^2/kT}\, dw \tag{355}$$

Using for this integral the result obtained in Note 2 of the Appendix, we obtain

$$m^3 v \mathbf{b}\, \sqrt{\frac{2\pi kT}{m}}\, \sqrt{\frac{2\pi kT}{m}}\, \sqrt{\frac{2\pi kT}{m}} \tag{356}$$

which is equal to

$$\mathbf{b}(2\pi m kT)^{\frac{3}{2}} v \tag{357}$$

Like (142), this is proportional to the volume of the vessel. Classical mechanics did not assign to the partition function a definite numerical magnitude, since the expression contains the arbitrary quantity **b**. In spite of this, if we take (357) to be the partition function, we find from (78)

$$E = nkT^2\left(\frac{\partial \ln P}{\partial T}\right)_v = nkT^2\, \frac{d}{dT}\, (\ln\, T^{\frac{3}{2}}) = \frac{3}{2}\, nkT \tag{358}$$

in agreement with (145). If we look to see how the factor $\frac{3}{2}$ has arisen, we see that each of the integrals in (355) contributed $\sqrt{T}$ to (356), and hence each contributed $\frac{1}{2}nkT$ to (358). In the problem of Fig. 44, where there was only one degree of freedom, we should have had only $\frac{1}{2}nkT$; when we deal with a rotating and vibrating molecule with more degrees of freedom, we shall have a contribution $T^{\frac{1}{2}}$ from each and hence a contribution to the energy of $\frac{1}{2}nkT$ from each. This is the familiar classical law of the equipartition of energy, that for each particle $\frac{1}{2}kT$ is associated with each degree of freedom.[1] This arises because the classical partition function, unlike that of quantum theory, necessarily contains $T^{\frac{1}{2}}$ for each degree of freedom.

The dimensions that we chose for **b** are the same as the dimensions of h^{-3}, where h is the constant introduced by Planck; in fact, if we write $\mathbf{b} = 1/h^3$, we obtain from (357)

$$\left(\frac{2\pi mkT}{h^2}\right)^{\frac{3}{2}} v = Bv \tag{359}$$

which is the same as (141) in Sec. 70, the partition function for the translational motion of a quantized perfect gas. The method of procedure using phase space thus leads to results in agreement with quantum theory if for a system with three degrees of freedom the elementary volume of phase space, instead of being taken infinitely small, is taken to be of finite size equal to h^3. In the one-dimensional problem of Fig. 45, where there was one degree of freedom, the area of each elementary rectangle must be taken equal to h. Similarly when dealing with a molecule that has s degrees of freedom, the elementary volume of phase space must be taken equal to h^s.

For a monatomic gas subject to a gravitational or other external field, a term $V(x, y, z)$ for the potential energy of a particle must be added to (350). In this case the integration over x, y, and z, instead of giving simply the volume of the vessel v, as in (357), gives the integral $\int\int\int e^{-V/kT} dx\,dy\,dz$, which must be substituted for v in (357). If throughout any elementary volume dv the value of V is zero, this will clearly make the contribution dv, as before; on the other hand, where V differs from zero, the element of volume will be weighted according to the appropriate value of $e^{-V/kT}$; any volume where V has a positive value large compared with kT will make a negligible contribution. We shall find below that a similar weighting according to the value of $e^{-V/kT}$ must be introduced when, in dealing with an imperfect gas, V denotes the mutual potential energy of two particles.

[1] See L. Landau and E. Lifschitz, "Statistical Physics," Oxford, 1938, which deals exclusively with classical mechanics.

142. Interacting Particles. It was pointed out at the end of Sec. 132 that when a vessel contains n particles of an imperfect gas, their mutual potential energy cannot be split into separate parts; when an imperfect gas is in equilibrium at temperature T, it possesses a definite amount of potential energy, which belongs to the gas as a whole. We have then to consider how (352) and (355) may be replaced by a treatment that regards the group of n particles as a single unit. As an introduction to this problem, we may ask how to treat *two* particles as a single system, that is, how to deal only with the energy of the pair, instead of a separate amount of energy for each. We shall suppose that each particle has spherical symmetry and that the mutual potential energy of the two particles depends only on the distance between their centers. Let us first discuss two such particles constrained, as in Fig. 45, to move along a line of length l, denoting their positions at any moment by x_1 and x_2, respectively. If in Fig.46 we take x_1 as abscissa, x_2 as ordinate, and $OA = OB = l$, any point within the square corresponds to a possible position for the pair of particles. The point Q, for example, denotes the situa-

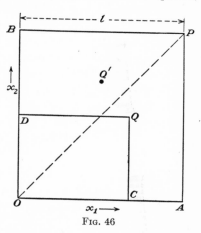

Fig. 46

tion where $x_1 = OC$ and $x_2 = OD$. If $V(x_1, x_2)$ denotes the mutual potential energy, this will have large values near the diagonal OP, since all points near the diagonal denote situations where the particles are near to each other. If the two particles have the same mass m, the energy will be $\epsilon = \frac{1}{2}mu_1^2 + \frac{1}{2}mu_2^2 + V(x_1, x_2)$. If we take a four-dimensional phase space for x_1, x_2, mu_1, and mu_2, the motion of the pair of interacting particles may be represented by the motion of a single point in this phase space. In obtaining the partition function, we shall require the integral

$$\iiiint m^2 e^{-\epsilon/kT}\, du_1\, du_2\, dx_1\, dx_2 \tag{360}$$

which will be equal to

$$m^2 \int e^{-\frac{1}{2}mu_1^2/kT}\, du_1 \int e^{-\frac{1}{2}mu_2^2/kT}\, du_2 \iint e^{-V/kT}\, dx_1\, dx_2 \tag{361}$$

The last integral in (361) is to be taken over the area of the square in Fig. 46.

In the problem of Fig. 46 we needed in (360) a phase space of four dimensions. For a pair of atoms moving in a three-dimensional vessel, we shall need a phase space of 12 dimensions; and for a group of n atoms we shall need a $6n$-dimensional phase space. The motion of the whole group of n particles may be represented by the motion of a single representative point in this phase space.[1]

At the beginning of this book, we studied in Chapter 1 a group of particles sharing a fixed total energy E. In the classical phase space for such a group of particles, if the total energy has a value lying between E and $(E + dE)$, the representative point for the group will move only through cells of phase space corresponding to energies between E and $(E + dE)$.

If we go on to consider an ensemble of independent systems of the same kind, the ensemble will be represented by a swarm of representative points. If each group in the ensemble possesses the same energy, all the representative points in the swarm will have a motion confined to that shell of phase space corresponding to energies between E and $(E + dE)$; traditionally such an ensemble is called a "microcanonical ensemble."

In order to derive the partition function for a group of particles, let us first raise a question with reference to the pair of particles of Fig. 46. Our interest in constructing any partition function lies in its relation to the value of ln W, which determines the physical behavior of the particles considered. In this connection consider the point Q' in Fig. 46, the point that is symmetrically placed with respect to the diagonal, corresponding to the point Q. The point Q' denotes the situation where $x_1 = OD$ and $x_2 = OC$. If the two particles are of different species this situation is of course distinguishable from the situation where $x_1 = OC$ and $x_2 = OD$. But if they are of the same species, we cannot, according to quantum theory, obtain a new situation by interchanging the particles. This viewpoint was an innovation of quantum mechanics; in the days of classical mechanics it had not been grasped that the particles must be treated as indistinguishable.[2] Consider then an element of area $dx_1 \, dx_2$ at the point Q and a similar element of area at the point Q'; the contribution from one of these must be discarded. Hence when we are dealing with two particles the last integral in (361) must be divided by 2.

When we go on to consider a pair of atoms moving in an ordinary three-dimensional vessel, the function $e^{-V/kT}$ will have to be integrated over the six coordinates x_1, y_1, z_1, x_2, y_2, and z_2. (In any problem, the space

---

[1] In their development of statistical mechanics, both Boltzmann and Maxwell hoped that something better might be done than merely to make the assumption of equal a priori probabilities for equal volumes of phase space. They hoped that it might be possible to prove the truth of a hypothesis, which was called by Boltzmann the "ergodic hypothesis." Consider the representative point for an isolated system having a certain energy; the suggestion was that this point, moving in phase space, would pass in succession through every point compatible with the energy of the system before finally returning to its original position in phase space. The hypothesis is not true in general and is mentioned here only for its historical interest. See Tolman, *op. cit.*, Chapter 3.

[2] See Herzfeld, *op. cit.*, pp. 149–150.

over which $e^{-V/kT}$ has to be integrated is called "configuration space," in contrast to the phase space that includes the momentum coordinates.) When one of these two atoms is at the point x_1, y_1, z_1, and the other is at x_2, y_2, z_2, the representative point Q will fall in a certain cell of configuration space. There will also be a point Q' representing the situation where the two particles have been interchanged. If the two particles are indistinguishable, this contribution and all similar contributions must be eliminated; the integral must be divided by 2. Likewise, when we treat three interacting particles, the corresponding integral must be divided by 3!, and when we deal with n interacting particles, it will have to be divided by $n!$. This necessity of dividing by 2 or by 3! or by $n!$ is quite similar to that which in Sec. 92 was introduced for the same purpose, namely, to ensure that all redundant configurations have been removed.

When the method of (361) is applied to a group of n interacting particles, we treat the whole group as a single system having $3n$ degrees of freedom. We are concerned only with the values of the total energy E of the whole group, and thus we aim at obtaining a partition function analogous to the P of Chapter 8. This energy E is partly kinetic and partly potential; the potential energy belongs to the group as a whole and is a function of the positions of all the particles. The integrals over u_1 and u_2 in (360) are now replaced by integrals over u, v, and w for each of the n particles. Since each integral is similar to (355), their product, if we introduce Planck's constant h, will be simply equal to B^n, where B is given by (359). The partition function is thus

$$\frac{B^n}{n!} \int \cdots \int e^{-V/kT}\, dx_1\, dy_1\, dz_1 \cdots dx_n\, dy_n\, dz_n \tag{362}$$

143. The expression (362) applies to matter in any state of aggregation, gaseous, solid, or liquid, and is the general expression for any group of n particles of the same kind. We began in connection with Fig. 46 to inquire how a pair of particles could be treated as a single unit; and we went on later to inquire how a group of n particles could be treated as a single unit. We did not impose any restrictions on the form of the potential energy V. Thus (362) is applicable to any aggregate of n particles, such as a solid or a liquid, as well as to an imperfect gas or vapor.

If we consider, for example, a vessel containing n atoms of the same species, between which the interaction is such that they tend to form diatomic molecules according to the reaction $2A \rightleftarrows A_2$, the integral in (362), being taken over all possible configurations of the particles, will include all possible degrees of dissociation consistent with the total energy E of the group of particles. The partition function (362) thus has the same character as the examples of P discussed in Sec. 138, which involve a sum over all possible states. In both cases the free energy will be $-kT \ln P$.

In Chapter 6 we saw that the tendency for atoms to form diatomic molecules is small or large according as the characteristic dissociation energy D has a small or a large value. In the configuration space of (362) there will be small regions where, according to Fig. 30, the quantity V/kT will have a large negative value. Although these portions of configuration space may comprise a small fraction of the total, nevertheless they may receive from the factor $e^{-V/kT}$ an enormous weighting, so that they become important or even predominant, according to the magnitude of the dissociation energy D.

We have already noticed in Sec. 137 that $-kT \ln \mathsf{P}$ differs somewhat from the quantity identified with the free energy in Chapter 5. For a vessel containing n_1 atoms and n_2 homonuclear molecules, the free energy F, according to (201), would be given by

$$- \frac{F}{kT} = n_1 \left(\ln \frac{P_1}{n_1} + 1 \right) + n_2 \left(\ln \frac{P_2}{n_2} + 1 \right) \tag{363}$$

In (362) the quantity B is the reciprocal of a volume, while the integral has the dimensions of a volume to the nth power. In treating a perfect monatomic gas, we should set the potential energy V equal to zero everywhere; in this case the whole integral is simply v^n. Since $B^n v^n$ is, according to (143), equal to $P_{tr}{}^n$, we see that (362) yields for F/kT a value in agreement with (185b). When we treat an imperfect gas or a partially dissociated diatomic gas, the integral will have the same dimensions but will differ numerically from v^n.

If (363) is to be equivalent to the logarithm of (362) in this problem, it should be a simple matter to show that (363) contains the quantity B^n multiplied by a quantity having the dimensions of (volume)^n. Since the B in (362) refers to the free atoms, we have $P_1 = Bv$; and the translational part of P_2, according to (142), will be $2^{\frac{3}{2}} Bv$, since the mass of the molecule is twice that of the free atom. These terms together will give $(n_1 + n_2) \ln B$, which will not yield B^n, since the total number of atoms is $n = (n_1 + 2n_2)$. We can, however, define a molecular volume v_{in} related to the internal partition function P_{in} of Sec. 75, by writing

$$v_{in} = \frac{2^{\frac{3}{2}} P_{in}}{B}$$

Then we obtain

$$n_2 \ln P_2 = n_2 \ln (2^{\frac{3}{2}} Bv P_{in})$$

$$= n_2 \ln \left(2^{\frac{3}{2}} Bv \frac{Bv_{in}}{2^{\frac{3}{2}}} \right)$$

$$= n_2 [\ln B^2 + \ln (vv_{in})]$$

Thus in (363) the atoms and molecules together yield the product

$$B^n [v^{(n_1 + n_2)} (v_{in})^{n_2}]$$

which has the required form; the quantity in the large bracket has the dimensions of (volume)^n and has a value smaller than v^n.

144. London Forces. In Sec. 86 and again in Sec. 91 we have discussed the attraction between two atoms that combine to give a chemically stable molecule. We may now recognize that some attraction is present between two atoms (or molecules) of any species. When the problem is treated according to quantum mechanics,[1] it is found that the interaction between the electron cloud of one atom and the electron cloud of the other atom gives rise to a small attraction, which passes over into the usual repulsion at smaller distances. Thus the mutual potential energy between any two atoms (or molecules) has the form represented in Fig. 30. Between a pair of argon atoms, for example, the depth of the potential minimum is about $\frac{1}{100}$ electron-volt.

In the familiar van der Waals equation

$$\left(p + \frac{an^2}{v^2}\right)(v - nb) = nkT \tag{364}$$

the term $- nb$ arises from the mutual repulsion and the term $+ an^2/v^2$ from the mutual attraction.[2] It is the forces of attraction that give rise to the condensation of the particles of any vapor to form a liquid or solid, as was recognized by van der Waals in 1873. Thus the problem of condensation is one aspect of the problem of imperfect gases.

The London forces between particles are additive; thus when three particles of the same kind are mutually in contact, the work required to remove any one from the other two will be twice as great as the work required to separate the remaining pair. Similarly, when four particles are mutually in contact, the work required to remove any one particle from the other three will be three times the work required to separate the members of an isolated pair. Consider next a solid, such as solid argon, whose atoms are held together by London forces. In Chapter 6 the work per particle required, at the absolute zero of temperature, to break up the crystal into its component atoms was denoted by *s*. If each atom in the solid has z other atoms in contact with it, the value of *s* would be $\frac{1}{2}z$ times the work required to separate the members of a pair of atoms, if only nearest neighbors contributed, the factor $\frac{1}{2}$ being introduced to ensure that each contact is not counted twice. In practice the ratio will be greater than $\frac{1}{2}z$, owing to the contributions from next-nearest neighbors, and so on. In a close-packed structure, for which $z = 12$, the ratio would be 6 if only nearest neighbors contributed; however, the ratio will actually be near 7.4 owing to contributions from more distant atoms.[3]

We have already seen that the van der Waals forces between two

[1] F. London, *Zeit. f. phys. Chem. B.*, **11**, 222 (1930).

[2] See, for example, E. H. Kennard, "The Kinetic Theory of Gases," Chapter 5, McGraw-Hill, 1938.

[3] See, for example, S. Brunauer, "The Adsorption of Gases and Vapours," Chapter 7, Princeton, 1943.

particles lead to a potential energy having the general form of Fig. 30, where the horizontal line corresponds to zero interaction between the particles. The integral in (362) will receive contributions from the part of the curve that lies above the horizontal line and from the part that lies below; when the two contributions are of the same order of magnitude they partially cancel each other, since $e^{-V/kT}$ is less than unity for the former and greater than unity for the latter. In discussing a diatomic gas at low pressure in Sec. 143, the problem was different in two respects: the forces between the separate atoms were not additive, and secondly, the contribution from the repulsion was negligible in comparison with that from the strong attraction. We shall consider next a hypothetical case that is the converse, namely, where the attraction between atoms is absent or makes a contribution negligible in comparison with that arising from the repulsion. If attraction is absent, we shall have, instead of Fig. 30, a curve that remains horizontal until it rises steeply at a certain small separation of the atoms. This steep curve can be approximately replaced by a vertical straight line; we thereby treat the particles as hard spheres having a definite radius. A gas at moderate pressure may now be discussed by the method used in Sec. 122 for a dilute solution; we shall suppose that it is a rare event for three particles to be in mutual contact.

145. Repulsion between Molecules of a Gas. In discussing the dilute solution of Sec. 122, we said that there were N choices for the position of the first particle, $(N - r)$ choices for the position of the second, $(N - 2r)$ for the third, and so on. Let ρ be the number of sites per unit volume; then if v is the volume of the solution, $v\rho = N$. Similarly, we may define a small volume v_a by writing $v_a\rho = r$. Then the above statement may be put into the following form: There are $v\rho$ choices for the first particle, $(v - v_a)\rho$ choices for the second particle, $(v - 2v_a)\rho$ choices for the third, and so on. The value of W for this dilute solution is found from the product of n terms

$$v\rho(v - v_a)\rho(v - 2v_a)\rho \cdots$$

the whole to be divided by $n!$.

In the case of an imperfect gas, when we take into account the finite size of the molecules, the volume v_r does not contain a number of definite sites; there is nevertheless a definite small volume to be excluded. The total volume to be excluded corresponds to the part of configuration space that in (362) will receive zero weight because $e^{-V/kT}$ is zero there. In (143) we had for a perfect gas

$$n \ln P_{tr} = \ln(B^n v^n)$$

In an imperfect gas we use an argument similar to that which led to (308) and find that the quantity v^n must be replaced by a slightly smaller quantity having the same dimensions, namely,

$$v(v - v_a)(v - 2v_a)(v - 3v_a) \cdots \qquad (365)$$

to n terms. Dividing (365) by v^n, we find that, since the factor B^n cancels, the ratio between the partition function P of an imperfect gas and P_{tr} for a perfect gas will be given by

$$n \ln \frac{P}{P_{tr}} = \ln \left(\frac{v}{v} \frac{v - v_a}{v} \frac{v - 2v_a}{v} \frac{v - 3v_a}{v} \cdots \right)$$

$$= \sum_j \ln \left(1 - j \frac{v_a}{v} \right) \qquad (366)$$

where j takes the integral values from unity to $(n - 1)$. If the density of the gas is not too high, the value of jv_a/v will be small compared with unity even when j has the value $(n - 1)$; in this case we may write $- jv_a/v$ instead of $\ln(1 - jv_a/v)$ and the sum on the right-hand side of (366) to n terms is equal to

$$- \frac{n(n - 1)}{2} \frac{v_a}{v} \qquad (367)$$

The magnitude of v_a depends on the size of the molecule considered. If we define, for any species, a volume b by writing $\frac{1}{2}(n - 1)v_a = b$, we see that (367) takes the value $- nb/v$, which may be put back into the form $\ln(1 - nb/v)$ since nb/v is taken to be small. For the translational partition function in this imperfect gas to replace (143), we have from (366)

$$Bv(1 - nb/v) = B(v - nb) \qquad (368)$$

The gas behaves as if it were a perfect gas contained in a volume $(v - nb)$ instead of v. Thus, to this approximation, the term $(v - nb)$ in the van der Waals equation (364) is justified.

146. Unsaturated and Saturated Vapor. In discussing vapor pressure in Chapter 6, we considered a vessel of fixed volume v and inquired how many particles would be required to fill it with saturated vapor at temperature T. In order to explore the relation between unsaturated and saturated vapors, it will be convenient to repeat the argument in a different form. We take a variable volume containing a fixed number of particles n, all of the same kind. Starting with a sufficiently large volume, we may begin with an unsaturated vapor at temperature T; if we reduce the volume at constant temperature, the pressure rises until a certain volume v_{sat} is reached. Up to this point, the greatest value of w is when all the n particles are in the form of vapor; beyond this point, the greatest value of w is when some of the n particles have condensed to form either solid or liquid, according as the temperature T is below or above the freezing point of the liquid. Let p_{sat} denote the pressure exerted by the vapor when the volume reaches the value v_{sat}.

If, in accordance with (143), we write in (222) $P_{tr} = Bv$, we see that (222) gives the condition that Bv is equal to Bv_{sat}. Similarly, for a liquid at low temperatures, where the vapor may be treated as a perfect gas, if P_l denotes the partition function for a particle in the liquid that will be formed by condensation, we have the expression analogous to (222)

$$v_{sat} = \frac{n\mathbf{P}_l}{Be^{-s/kT}} \tag{369}$$

When the volume of the vessel is reduced below the value v_{sat}, the pressure

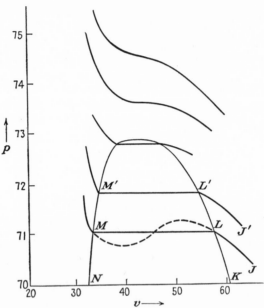

FIG. 47. Pressure-volume relations for carbon dioxide between 29 and 32°C.

does not continue to rise but remains constant at whatever value p_{sat} has already been reached.

At higher temperatures and pressures the phenomena are similar. Figure 47 gives some experimental curves in a small portion of the pressure-volume diagram of carbon dioxide.[1] The ordinates run only between 70 and 76 atmospheres; the isothermals are for temperatures between 29 and 33°C. A curve such as JL represents the relation between p and v for the unsaturated vapor, while the straight line LM corresponds to the constant vapor pressure during progressive formation of liquid at the same temperature.[2] For an unsaturated vapor at a higher temperature, the volume can be reduced to a smaller value before condensation takes

[1] A. Michels, B. Blaisse, and C. Michels, *Proc. Roy. Soc. A.*, **160**, 367 (1937).

[2] Curves of the same shape are obtained for monomolecular films that behave like two-dimensional vapors. N. K. Adam, "Physics and Chemistry of Surfaces," 3d ed., Oxford, 1941; W. Band, *J. Chem. Phys.*, **8**, 178 (1940).

place, as in the curve $J'L'$. The curve KLL' is a plot of p_{sat} against v_{sat}. In this diagram the curve NMM' refers to the liquid and shows the increase in volume that takes place with rise in temperature, in spite of the increase in pressure to which the liquid is subject. For any horizontal line such as LM or $L'M'$, the liquid of density corresponding to the point M can be in equilibrium with vapor in the state represented by the point L. In this range of temperature, the van der Waals equation (364), as is well known, gives continuous isothermals having the form shown by the dotted line in Fig. 47. For high temperatures (364) gives isothermals in which dp/dv is everywhere negative; at a certain temperature (364) gives an isothermal that has dp/dv equal to zero at one point, identified with the critical point.

147. In Fig. 36 the abscissas were the values of $n_A/(n_A + n_B)$. If we take a fixed value for the total number of particles $(n_A + n_B)$ and consider the case where the A-particles and the B-particles are of the same size, the total volume occupied by the particles is constant. The abscissas in Fig. 36 may be taken to be n_A/v, the number of A-particles per unit volume. Then, disregarding the B-particles, we may say that the point Y in Fig. 36 gives the value of n_A/v for a certain *small* number of A-particles that, at the temperature considered, can be in equilibrium with a certain *large* number of A-particles per unit volume represented by the point Z. From this point of view the scheme is analogous to that shown in Fig. 47, where the point L represents a certain small number of particles per unit volume (vapor), which, at the temperature considered, can be in equilibrium with a certain large number of particles per unit volume (liquid) represented by the point M. If we could make the necessary calculations, we could, in fact, construct for the vapor and liquid a diagram similar to Fig. 36, plotting the free energy against n/v, and we could find from the diagram the value of n/v for the saturated vapor and the value of n/v corresponding to the density of the liquid (or solid) at the temperature considered.

From (289) it can be shown that with rise of temperature the points Q and S in Fig. 36 approach one another and at a certain temperature coincide; above this critical temperature no separation occurs. Similarly, in the condensation problem, with rise of temperature the points L and M in Fig. 47 approach one another, as at $L'M'$. Above a certain temperature, no visible formation of liquid occurs if the volume of the vapor is reduced, however far the reduction in volume is carried.

Next let us consider Fig. 44. The discussion of Fig. 44 that was given in Sec. 130 applies to both solids and liquids. The most elementary fact about a solid or a liquid is that, when placed in a large vessel, the material does not fill the vessel like a gas, but at any temperature T retains a characteristic volume, namely, the volume for which the free energy is a minimum at this temperature. The purpose of the diagram was to show the factors that determine the value of the characteristic volume. From Fig. 44 the existence of a critical temperature above which the liquid cannot exist seems quite reasonable. In the upper curve of Fig. 44 the minimum had a certain depth below the horizontal line. At any higher temperature the middle curve, obtained by adding the ordinates, will clearly have a shallower minimum. With a further rise of temperature, the broken curve becomes progressively steeper and there must come a temperature at which the resultant curve has no minimum at all; that is, there is no characteristic volume for which the free energy of the n particles is a minimum, so the material will fill the whole vessel, as a gas.[1] Returning to Fig. 47, we have seen that with rise of temperature no separation occurs; instead, we obtain only an imperfect gas with a density comparable to that of a liquid.

148. Condensation of a Vapor. The mutual potential energy between two atoms or between two simple molecules, which we considered in Sec. 144, is independent of temperature. The very diverse phenomena to which the forces of attraction give rise, above and below the critical temperature, are the result of other factors. First consider any gas above its critical temperature; if we diminish the volume, the mean distance between particles is progressively diminished until the particles form a single aggregate or cluster. Before this final stage is reached, smaller clusters will be present; their presence is due to the fact that the vessel is so small that many particles are inevitably near together.

If we discuss the condensation of the same vapor at a much lower temperature, the situation is different. The volumes that we deal with are large enough even at saturation for the vapor to consist entirely of separate atoms. If clusters are present, this is because their presence yields a greater value of w than would be possible without them, when the particles share the same total energy E. Let us consider the nature of a supersaturated vapor in contact with a thermal reservoir at temperature T. Suppose we are given a volume v containing n particles of the same kind, no large clusters being present. In order to test whether the vapor is supersaturated, we have to compare the given situation with an alternative situation where some particles have combined to form one or more large clusters. We may take into account the possibility of clusters of all sizes, from those consisting of two, three, or four particles, up to clusters containing many particles.

It is clear that, if our aim is to explain the existence and the character of the critical phenomena, we must consider clustering that may or may

---

[1] Using the model of a dense gas mentioned in Sec. 97, theoretical values of the critical temperature were calculated for certain gases and gave rather good agreement with the experimental values. J. E. Lennard Jones and A. F. Devonshire, *Proc. Roy. Soc. A.*, **163**, 54 (1937).

not lead to the formation of liquid. The discovery of a mathematical device for handling the integral (362) in this problem was made by J. E. Mayer[1]; all possible configurations of clusters are considered. It is found that critical phenomena are to be expected over a certain range of temperature rather than at one critical temperature. The theory has been extended by Born and Fuchs.[2] An adequate account of this work unfortunately cannot be given in less than 30 or 40 pages. In this book we shall not add anything further to the discussion of the critical point given in Sec. 147; instead, we shall examine the simpler problem of condensation at lower temperatures.

149. It may well be that during condensation the structure of any cluster is initially far from regular, that is, it is more full of holes than a portion of normal liquid (or solid) at the same temperature. With transient structures, however, we are not concerned. In discussing w_{max} at fairly low temperatures, we are interested only in possible equilibrium states and we must suppose that in the interior of a large cluster the situation for a particle is not appreciably different from the situation of the same particle in the interior of a droplet of liquid, or else in a crystallite, according as the temperature is above or below the freezing point of the liquid. If for the vibration of such a particle in the interior we use the usual partition function $P = \mathbf{P}e^{-s/kT}$, the partition function of the whole aggregate, consisting of q particles, according to (342) will be P^q, provided that the number of surface particles is small compared with the number in the interior of the cluster.

In discussing (219), we noticed that since P_A, P_B, and P_{AB} each contains the volume of the vessel, this leaves the volume in the numerator of (219) to influence the equilibrium. If we steadily reduce the volume, a progressive combination of atoms to form additional molecules takes place. But the ratio of the number of molecules to free atoms is not very sensitive to changes in volume. If we write down the analogous expressions for the dissociation of a triatomic molecule into free atoms, we find that the equilibrium depends on v^2 instead of v; that is to say, this equilibrium is rather more sensitive to changes in volume. In general, let A_q denote an aggregate or cluster of q atoms, all of the same species, which may dissociate into q free atoms

$$A_q \rightleftarrows qA \tag{370}$$

Then, if P_q denotes the partition function of the polyatomic cluster, it follows from Sec. 86 that the expression for equilibrium will be

$$\frac{n_1{}^q}{n_q} = \frac{P_1{}^q}{P_q} \tag{371}$$

[1] J. E. Mayer and S. F. Harrison, *J. Chem. Phys.*, **6**, 87 (1938); J. E. Mayer and M. G. Mayer, "Statistical Mechanics," pp. 265–315, Wiley, 1940.

[2] M. Born and K. Fuchs, *Proc. Roy. Soc. A.*, **166**, 391 (1938).

If the vapor contains clusters of different sizes, the most probable state is that in which the ratios n_2/n_1, $n_3/n_1 \ldots n_q/n_1$ are in accordance with (371). We may, for example, write down the expression for a cluster containing more than q particles, say, for a cluster containing $(q + r)$ particles

$$\frac{n_1^{(q+r)}}{n_{q+r}} = \frac{P_1^{(q+r)}}{P_{q+r}} \tag{372}$$

Dividing (371) by (372), we obtain an expression for the number of clusters of size $(q + r)$ which, at the temperature considered, will be in equilibrium with clusters of size q

$$\frac{n_{q+r}}{n_q} = \frac{P_{q+r}}{P_q} \left(\frac{n_1}{P_1}\right)^r \tag{373}$$

In a monatomic vapor, the n_1 in (371) and (373) denotes the number of free atoms; in a substance consisting of diatomic or polyatomic molecules, n_1 denotes the number of single molecules.

150. It was shown by Band[1] that the expression (373) is extremely sensitive to changes in the volume of the vessel and, in fact, leads us to expect condensation at a particular volume that we shall identify with v_{sat}. At low temperatures and pressures, it leads to results that in this respect are similar to those obtained by Mayer's rigorous treatment.

We shall find that under appropriate conditions a small change of volume of the vessel may cause the value of (373) to change by a factor of 1 million or more; thus, we shall be only interested in orders of magnitude, and shall need only a cursory examination of the partition functions in (373). For brevity we shall write down expressions for clusters that are sufficiently large that the difference between surface atoms and internal atoms may be neglected. For such clusters we have already decided in Sec. 149 to use $(Pe^{s/kT})^q$ for the contribution from the vibration of each particle among its neighbors. The moments of inertia of a nearly spherical cluster about three principal axes will be nearly equal; in clusters of uniform density each will be proportional to $q^{\frac{5}{3}}$; the value of the rotational partition function of the cluster (regarded as a polyatomic molecule) will be approximately proportional to $q^{\frac{5}{2}}$. Extending what was said in Sec. 143, the translational partition function of the cluster will be $q^{\frac{3}{2}}Bv$. Hence it will be sufficient if we take for the ratio

$$\frac{P_{q+r}}{P_q} = \left(\frac{q + r}{q}\right)^4 (Pe^{s/kT})^r \tag{374}$$

Substituting in (373),

$$\frac{n_{q+r}}{n_q} = \left(\frac{q + r}{q}\right)^4 \left(\frac{n_1 Pe^{s/kT}}{Bv}\right)^r \tag{375}$$

---

[1] W. Band, *J. Chem. Phys.*, **7**, 324 and 927 (1939).

For clusters that are not too small, this is true for any positive value of r. Let us, as usual, start with our vapor in a large volume v and ask how (375) changes when we diminish the volume at constant temperature. We are discussing a vapor for which the pressure-volume relation scarcely differs from that of a perfect gas, even up to the saturation point; at this point n_1 in (375) differs only slightly from the constant value n, and all the other factors in the large bracket are constant except v. If the initial value of v is sufficiently large, the quantity in the large bracket will be less than unity and will increase as we *diminish* the volume. We shall show below that, at low temperatures, this quantity will reach and pass through the value unity when v reaches a certain value, which we may denote by v_0. Let us examine the variation of (375) in the neighborhood of this value v_0, say, when the volume of the vessel is reduced from a value that is greater than v_0 by one part in a million to a value that is less than v_0 by one part in a million. Taking logarithms, the value of $\ln(v_0/v)$, with the usual approximation, will go from

$$\ln(1 - 10^{-6}) = -10^{-6} \qquad \text{to} \qquad \ln(1 + 10^{-6}) = +10^{-6}$$

Hence, the value of $(v_0/v)^r$ will go from $\exp(-10^{-6}r)$ to $\exp(10^{-6}r)$. In (375) let us take, for example, both q and r equal to 10^7. In this case we find that when the volume of the vessel is reduced by two parts in a million, the value of the quantity in the large bracket in (375) increases from e^{-10} to e^{10}, that is to say, from 10^{-4} to 10^4.

It remains to be shown that at low temperatures there will necessarily be a volume that makes the quantity in the large bracket equal to unity, and secondly, that there is an additional reason for identifying this volume with v_{sat}. As soon as we equate the quantity from (375) to unity, writing

$$\frac{n_1 \mathbf{P} e^{s/kT}}{Bv} = 1$$

and recall that the factor $\mathbf{P}$ denotes the value of $\Sigma e^{-\epsilon_r/kT}$ for a particle in the interior of the aggregate, it is obvious that this expression is identical with either (222) or (369), according as the temperature is above or below the freezing point. We find then that under these conditions the volume that induces large clustering to take place is the same as that obtained in Sec. 92 for equilibrium between a solid (or liquid) and its vapor. The two methods of approach are thus shown to be consistent at temperatures where the saturated vapor behaves as a perfect gas.[1]

A process that somewhat resembles condensation is gel formation in the polymerization of molecules. This problem has been treated by similar statistical methods.[2]

[1] For conditions near the critical point, see Mayer and Mayer, *op. cit.*, Chapter 14.
[2] P. J. Flory, *J. Am. Chem. Soc.*, **63**, 3096 (1941); W. H. Stockmayer, *J. Chem. Phys.*, **12**, 125 (1944).

Problems

1. Two vessels of the same size contain equal quantities, A and B, of a certain perfect gas at 10°K. An amount of heat is allowed to flow into A, sufficient to raise the temperature to 11°K. The specimen B is put through the following cycle: it is compressed adiabatically, altering the set of energy levels, until the energy of the gas corresponds to a temperature of 20°; the same amount of heat is now added to B as was added to A; finally B is allowed to expand adiabatically until it regains its original volume. What is the final temperature of B? Describe how the population of the energy levels has changed during each of the three steps.

2. Given n particles of the same species, in how many different ways can one form n_2 pairs, leaving n_1 of the particles unpaired? Comparing (363) with (362), examine whether this question throws light on the occurrence of the quantity

$$n_1\left(\ln\frac{1}{n_1} + 1\right) + n_2\left(\ln\frac{1}{n_2} + 1\right)$$

in (363) instead of $\ln(1/n\,!)$ in the logarithm of (362).

CHAPTER 10

Vibration of Molecules and of Crystal Lattices—The Density of States—Evaluation of the Partition Function of a Solid

151. Vibrational Partition Function. It was mentioned in Sec. 90 that Fig. 30 depicts the form of the mutual potential energy of two atoms that form a molecule. Near the potential minimum this curve is a parabola; as a result the spacing of the lower energy levels is uniform. Between the upper energy levels the spacing becomes progressively narrower but in most molecules these upper levels are not appreciably populated at terrestrial temperatures and may be neglected.

In Chapter 2 we did not evaluate the partition function for a set of single levels with uniform spacing but we need this for three purposes: (1) for the vibrations of a diatomic molecule, (2) for the simple model of a solid, discussed in Chapter 1, and (3) for any one of the lattice vibrations of a crystal lattice, mentioned in Sec. 132 and discussed below in Sec. 154. For a set of energy states with uniform spacing u, we find from (72) for the sum of n terms, writing $u/kT = x$,

$$S = 1 + e^{-x} + e^{-2x} + \cdots + e^{-(n-1)x} \tag{376}$$

$$Se^{-x} = e^{-x} + e^{-2x} + \cdots + e^{-(n-1)x} + e^{-nx} \tag{377}$$

Subtracting (377) from (376),

$$S(1 - e^{-x}) = 1 - e^{-nx}$$

Thus as n tends to infinity, we obtain for the partition function

$$\mathbf{P} = \frac{1}{1 - e^{-u/kT}} \tag{378}$$

When comparing different substances for which the spacing u has different values, it is convenient to define for each substance a characteristic temperature Θ by writing $k\Theta = u$; thus for each substance Θ is the temperature at which kT becomes equal to the interval between two successive levels, then $P = (1 - e^{-\Theta/T})^{-1}$. For the energy associated with this vibration we have

$$E = nkT^2 \frac{\partial \ln \mathbf{P}}{\partial T} = \frac{nu}{e^{u/kT} - 1} \tag{379}$$

$$= \frac{nk\Theta}{e^{\Theta/T} - 1} \tag{380}$$

According to (380), if values of E for different substances are plotted, not against T but against T/Θ, the values should lie on a single curve when the appropriate value of Θ has been assigned to each substance.

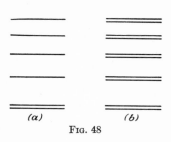

For comparison with (380), it is useful to consider a slightly different set of levels, namely, where all the levels have a normal wide spacing, except for the two lowest levels ϵ_0 and ϵ_1, which are separated by a very small amount, as in Fig. 48a. If we take, as usual, the level ϵ_0 as the zero of energy, the term $e^{-\epsilon_1/kT}$ in (72) will be very nearly unity at ordinary temperatures, so that (72) is approximately

(a)   *(b)*

FIG. 48

$$\mathbf{P} = 2 - e^{-\epsilon_2/kT} - e^{-\epsilon_3/kT} - \cdots$$

Here the value of $\mathbf{P}$ varies with temperature in the normal way but, as the temperature falls, tends toward the value 2 instead of toward unity. At the absolute zero, however, all the particles will fall into the level ϵ_0 and $\mathbf{P}$ must reach the value unity. This takes place as depicted in Fig. 49; as the temperature falls, as soon as kT becomes comparable with $(\epsilon_1 - \epsilon_0)$, the curve, which has been tending toward the value 2, falls rapidly to unity. If $(\epsilon_1 - \epsilon_0)$ is very small, this fall may take place below 1°K and so may not be revealed by measurements made above 1°K. The same behavior will be found if other levels occur in very narrow pairs, as illustrated in Fig. 48b.

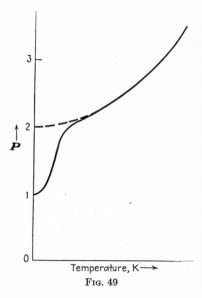

FIG. 49

152. Vibrational Heat Capacity. In the year 1819 two French physicists, Dulong and Petit, published the results of measurements of the specific heats of 13 elements in the solid state near room temperature. They had found that the values of the specific heats were nearly inversely proportional to the atomic weights, indicating that the heat capacity per atom was approximately the same for each of these elements. Later, other elements were added to the list and the law of Dulong and Petit was put into the following form: At room temperature the heat capacity of 1 gram-atom of any element in the solid state has a value between 6.2 and 6.6 calories, or thereabouts.

It was mentioned in Sec. 141 that the classical law of equipartition ascribes to each degree of freedom an amount of kinetic energy equal to $\frac{1}{2}kT$ per particle. In any harmonic motion the total energy is half kinetic and half potential energy. We have two cases to consider. In a diatomic molecule we are concerned only with the changes in the distance between the nuclei, that is, the vibration is one-dimensional. Classical theory thus leads to the expected value kT per particle, namely, $\frac{1}{2}kT$ kinetic energy and an equal amount of potential energy.

In a solid a vibrating atom has three degrees of freedom, and the classical value for the energy is $3kT$ per particle. For the specific heat the classical value is thus $3k$ per particle or $3R$ per gram-atom.

Let us now discuss the expression (378) for a quantized oscillator. For large values of T the value of $e^{-u/kT}$ in the denominator tends to $(1 - u/kT)$. Thus at high temperatures the partition function tends to the value kT/u, while the energy E will not differ appreciably from nkT. The vibrational energy per molecule, kT, is thus equal to the classical value at these temperatures. For a three-dimensional oscillator the partition function must be obtained by the method used in (158) and (345); the oscillator will have a uniform set of levels associated with motion in the x-, y-, and z-directions, and the partition function will be the product of three factors. For an isotropic oscillator the partition function will be (378) raised to the third power, while the partition function for a group of n such oscillators will be given by

$$\ln \mathsf{P} = -3n \ln \left(1 - e^{-u/kT}\right) \tag{381}$$

In any case, at high temperatures the value of P will tend to $3kT/u$, while the energy will not differ appreciably from $3kT$, the classical value. At these high temperatures the specific heat is independent of temperature and equal to $3k$ per particle or $3R$ per mole.

By differentiating (380) with respect to T, we obtain an expression for the variation of the heat capacity with temperature for a linear oscillator. Writing $nk = R$, we find for one mole

$$R\left(\frac{\Theta}{T}\right)^2 \frac{e^{\Theta/T}}{(e^{\Theta/T} - 1)^2} \tag{382}$$

In Fig. 50 the curve is a plot of (382), the scale on the left being for a linear oscillator and the scale on the right for a three-dimensional oscillator. For several of the common diatomic gases the spacing of the vibrational levels is known from an analysis of their emission and absorption spectra; the values are given in Table 8 in Sec. 161, together with the corresponding value of Θ. When the heat capacity of these gases is measured it is found that in each case the contribution from the molecular vibrations agrees well with the curve of Fig. 50, when this is drawn with the value of Θ derived from the molecular spectrum.

For solids, on the other hand, although the heat capacity shows a variation similar to that of Fig. 50, quantitative agreement cannot be obtained with any value of Θ. Treating the particles of a solid as independent oscillators is not a good approximation. The vibrations of the crystal lattice, mentioned in Sec. 132, must be quantized; when this is done, better agreement with experiment is found (see Sec. 154).

The steep part of the curve in Fig. 50 or Fig. 53 will give a rather rapid variation of heat capacity with temperature. Nevertheless, for most solids and diatomic gases at room temperature, the heat capacity is almost

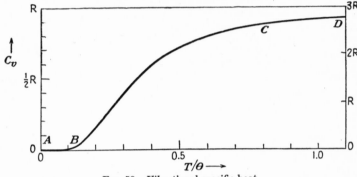

Fig. 50. Vibrational specific heat.

independent of temperature. Recalling that, at room temperature, the value of kT is only $\frac{1}{40}$ electron-volt, we see from Table 8 in Sec. 161 that for nitrogen, oxygen, and so on, the spacing of the levels is relatively wide. In gaseous nitrogen, for example, the value of kT will not become equal to the spacing u until the temperature is raised above 3000°C; at room temperature the value of kT is less than one-tenth of the spacing between the lowest vibrational level and the next, and as a result nearly all the molecules remain in the lowest vibrational level. At room temperature, the contribution to the heat capacity will be represented by a point on the portion AB of the curve in Fig. 50, and similarly for hydrogen, oxygen, and other gases.

From Table 8 in Sec. 161 it will be seen that for the lithium, sodium, and potassium molecules the spacing of the vibrational energy levels is much closer; the force between the atoms is weaker than in nitrogen and oxygen. The same is true for the atomic vibrations in most solids; the value of Θ that gives best agreement with (382) is small, with the result that at room temperature the value of the heat capacity of the solid is given by a point on the nearly horizontal portion CD of the curve in Fig. 50, or of the corresponding portion of the curve in Fig. 53. Thus it comes about that for most solids and for the common diatomic gases near room temperature the heat capacity is almost independent of temperature, but for different reasons—in gaseous nitrogen, oxygen, and so on the vibrations are scarcely excited at all, while in most solids they are almost fully excited.

153. In treating solids, we usually discuss a solid either under the pressure of its own vapor or under atmospheric pressure. When the pressure is as small as this, it makes no appreciable difference what its value is, since the changes of volume that a solid undergoes are so small. The difference between the specific heats C_p and C_v is important for both gases and solids, but for entirely different reasons. In the case of a gas at constant pressure, the external work done is comparable with the specific heat itself. In the case of a solid the external work is negligibly small, but the cohesive forces are so strong that in thermal expansion a considerable amount of energy is transformed into potential energy, that is, when the temperature of a solid is raised, an appreciable fraction of the heat supplied goes into work done against the interatomic forces of attraction (see Sec. 130).

We have seen that, at temperatures where kT is large compared with the spacing between the energy levels, the value of C_v for a solid should reach the classical value $3R$ per mole. Since $R = 1.987$ cal/mole, the value of C_v should be 5.96 cal/mole. According to the law of Dulong and Petit mentioned above, the specific heat of many solids at room temperature, as ordinarily measured, is in the neighborhood of 6.4 cal/mole. This is because, when the temperature is raised at constant pressure, an additional amount of energy, in the neighborhood of 7 per cent, is absorbed and goes into work done against the cohesive forces; if the specific heat were measured at constant volume, the value obtained would be smaller by something in the neighborhood of 7 per cent; but no two substances show precisely the same behavior.

These remarks apply to room temperature. The difference between the specific heats at any temperature T is given by

$$C_p - C_v = T \left(\frac{\partial v}{\partial T}\right)_p \left(\frac{\partial p}{\partial T}\right)_v$$

$$= - \frac{T(\partial v/\partial T)^2}{(\partial v/\partial p)_T} = \frac{\alpha^2 v T}{n\beta} \tag{383}$$

where α is the coefficient of thermal expansion and β is the compressibility of the substance. At low temperatures the difference between the specific heats is quite small. The way in which the difference increases at high temperatures is indicated in Fig. 53.

154. Lattice Vibrations. We shall now make the departure suggested in Sec. 132; we abandon the idea that each particle in a solid has a set of energy levels, and we begin to discuss the vibrations of the solid as a whole. Our problem is to describe how the total energy E will be distributed among the various modes of vibration of the lattice. The problem is similar to that of Sec. 75, where we discussed how the total energy of a diatomic gas would be divided between the translational and internal forms; we considered the conversion of an amount of energy dE from one form to the other. So here we may fix attention on any two modes of vibration of the lattice; consider a state of the crystal, in which energy is associated with these modes of vibration, and suppose that we transfer a certain amount of energy from one mode to the other. If such a transfer is accompanied by an increase in w for the crystal, the transfer will occur spontaneously. The same remark applies to any two modes of vibration of the lattice. The state that is adopted by the crystal may thus be described as one in which the transference of a small amount of energy from any mode of lattice vibration to any other is not accompanied by any change in w.

It was pointed out in Sec. 75 that, when the internal energy of the molecule is subdivided into rotational and vibrational energies, the two summations in the denominator of (158) would be replaced by three. In the problem of the crystal containing n atoms of the same kind, there are not three sets of allowed energies but $3n$, corresponding to the $3n$ modes of vibration of the lattice. Thus, the denominator corresponding to (158) will be the product of $3n$ terms, each term being summed over the allowed energies of one mode of vibration. Since each mode of lattice vibration is harmonic, its allowed energies are "equally spaced"; the amount of thermal energy associated with the rth mode can take the values 0, u_r, $2u_r$, $3u_r$ .... Consequently each of the $3n$ terms has the simple form discussed in Sec. 151. From (378) we find at once that the partition function P for the whole crystal will be given by

$$P = \frac{1}{1 - e^{-u_1/kT}} \frac{1}{1 - e^{-u_2/kT}} \cdots \tag{384}$$

$$\ln P = \sum \ln\left(\frac{1}{1 - e^{-u_r/kT}}\right) = -\sum \ln\left(1 - e^{-u_r/kT}\right) \tag{385}$$

The problem would now be solved if we knew the set of values of u_r to be inserted in (385). Debye, who first gave this treatment for a crystal, made the approximation of supposing that the frequencies of vibration of the lattice could be obtained from those of a continuous elastic solid having the same elastic properties as the crystalline solid under consideration. In a solid with rectangular faces, the sides of which have lengths equal to a, b, and c, the normal modes are standing waves that have a nodal plane coinciding with each of the six faces of the solid; that is, where a is equal to an integral number of half-wavelengths in the x-direction, and so on; the expression for these material waves is in fact similar to that of the ψ-waves of Sec. 70. The single standing wave belonging to the lowest energy E_0 will have the character described toward the end of Sec. 74.

Adopting the $3n$ modes of smallest energy from this elastic solid and introducing the values of $u_r = h\nu_r$ into (385), Debye obtained an expression for the heat capacity that gives much better agreement with experiment than (382). A comparison of (385) with (381) shows at once wherein the two treatments differ. If the $3n$ modes of vibration, instead of having different values of u_r, had the same value u, the expression (385) would be identical with (381). Thus, the model that regards the crystal as consisting of n independent particles, each having the same set of equally spaced levels, is equivalent to replacing the set of u_r in (385) by some average value of u_r, to be used for every mode of vibration of the lattice. This difference is especially important at very low temperatures. The nearly horizontal portion of the curve AB in Fig. 50 is due to the fact that according to (381) the body cannot receive any increment in energy smaller than u. But in the Debye model of a solid the body can receive increments of energy much smaller than the *average* value of u_r, since some of the modes of vibration have values of u_r much smaller than the average; in fact, the values of u_r extend from near zero up to a certain maximum u_{max}. Consequently, the solid can pick up increments of energy, even very near the absolute zero of temperature; in this region, according to the Debye theory, the heat capacity of any solid will vary as T^3; for most substances for which data exist this is in rather good agreement with experiment.

As mentioned above, the possible amounts of energy that can be associated with any mode of vibration are connected with the frequency of ν_r of this vibration by the quantum relation $u_r = h\nu_r$, $2u_r = 2h\nu_r \cdots$. For any solid the whole set of allowed values for all possible modes of vibration is usually referred to as the "frequency spectrum" of the solid. Since for each value of r the levels are equally spaced, the expression (378) applies to each mode of vibration and C_v is to be obtained by summing over all values of r, that is, over the $3n$ modes of vibration. When this summation is replaced by an integral, the expression takes the following form[1]

$$C_v = nk\frac{9}{x_0^3}\int_0^{x_0} \frac{x^4 e^x}{(e^x - 1)^2}\, dx \tag{386}$$

where $x = u/kT$ and $x_0 = u_{max}/kT$. In so far as the experimental values agree with this expression, it should be possible to deal with all elements in the solid state in a manner analogous to that of Sec. 151, that is, by ascribing to each element a characteristic temperature. For each solid

[1] See, for example, F. Seitz, "The Modern Theory of Solids," Chapter 2, McGraw-Hill, 1940.

this so-called "Debye temperature" Θ_D is related to the highest frequency assigned to the crystal, thus

$$k\Theta_D = u_{max} = h\nu_{max} \tag{387}$$

If values of C_v are plotted against T/Θ_D, the experimental points for all elements should lie on the same curve. Further, the best value of Θ_D should agree with the theoretical value calculated from the elastic constants of the solid; for several metals this agreement is within 1 per cent.

TABLE 4. CONSTANTS ASSIGNED TO SOLIDS

Solid	Electron-volts, $u_{max} \times 10^3$	Θ_D, °K
Ne^{20}........	5.43	63
Ne^{22}........	5.17	60*
A............	7.3	85
Pb..........	7.6	88
Tl...........	8.3	96
Hg..........	8.4	97
I............	9.1	106
Cd..........	14.5	168
Na..........	14.8	172
Ag..........	18.5	215
Zn...........	20.3	235
Cu...........	27.1	315
Al...........	34.3	398
Be..........	86.3	1000
C (diamond)..	160.3	1860
KBr........	15.3	177
KCl........	19.8	230
NaCl.......	24.2	281

*W. H. Keesom and J. Haantjes, *Physica*, **2**, 986 (1935).

The curve for the heat capacity of metallic zinc, for which Θ_D is 235°K, is shown in Fig. 53 in Sec. 158. In recent years attempts have been made to obtain from theory the correct frequency spectrum for some elements and simple compounds, but there is still some doubt as to the finality of these calculations. For the low frequencies it is found that the simple spectrum assumed by Debye agrees well with the more correct spectrum; it is for this reason that the simple theory shows such surprisingly good agreement with experiment, including the T^3 law at low temperatures.

155. In Chapter 8, by considering a group of N identical samples in thermal contact, we were able to make an approach to the problems of statistical mechanics different from that of Chapters 1 to 5. We were able to introduce the ideas of temperature and entropy without referring to the states of individual particles but only to the states of n interacting particles. We found that the value of w would be a maximum when the total energy was distributed among the N samples according to the expression

$$N_r = \frac{NZ_r e^{-E_r/kT}}{P} \tag{388}$$

where

$$P = \Sigma Z_r e^{-E_r/kT} \tag{389}$$

At the beginning of Sec. 135 attention was drawn to the degree of similarity between the derivation of (334) and that of (95) in Sec. 44. The expression (95) gave the average number of particles in a particular state to which the label r had been allotted and so gave for a perfect monatomic gas what in Chapter 1 we called the shape or form of the population. This, as we have seen, is not the same as giving the number of particles with energies lying in the interval between ϵ and $(\epsilon + \delta\epsilon)$; it was only in Sec. 74 that we asked what the number of states is with energies lying in the interval between ϵ and $(\epsilon + \delta\epsilon)$. The situation with regard to (338) is very similar; the expression (338) gives the degree to which any state having energy E_r is populated on the average; in (338) this is expressed by the quantity N_r/Z_r, which may be denoted by q_r. Neither (334) nor (338) says anything about the number of multiple levels that lie within the interval between E and $(E + dE)$. Let this number be denoted by $\nu(E)\ dE$. Then, if (338) is multiplied by $\nu(E)\ dE$, the product will give the number of samples in the group that have energies in the range between E and $(E + dE)$. In this interval each level has multiplicity Z, which may be taken as a continuous function of E; in the interval dE the total number of states is thus $Z(E)\nu(E)\ dE$. The total number of states per unit energy interval is often called the "density of states"; if this is denoted by $\rho(E)$, we have

$$\rho(E) = Z(E)\nu(E) \tag{390}$$

The number of samples having energies lying in a range dE is conveniently obtained in the form $q(E)\rho(E)\ dE$, where q denotes N/Z from (338):

$$q\rho = \frac{N\rho e^{-E/kT}}{P} \tag{391}$$

The brief discussion in Sec. 131 of the sharing of energy between two samples made use only of the relation between Z and C_v; it seemed to show that large fluctuations were extremely improbable, although one could set no definite limits to the interval within which the energy would fluctuate.

In deriving (338), likewise, the treatment has assigned no bounds to the possible fluctuations of E; in fact, when a uniform temperature prevails through the group, the expression (338) assigns values of N_r to all allowed energies E_r, even down to the lowest, as was pointed out in Sec. 135. Results obtained from (391) will be in agreement with experience only if the values of N are negligibly small except in a narrow range of energy. When a particular value has been chosen for the prevailing temperature, the denominator in (391) is a constant and the quantity kT in the numerator is a constant; thus the value of $N(E)$ in (391) is proportional to the product of ρ and $e^{-E/kT}$. If the values are to be negligibly small except in a narrow interval, this must be because the product $\rho e^{-E/kT}$ passes through a very sharp maximum at a certain value of E. In order that a maximum shall exist at some value of E, it is necessary that, for low values of E, the rate of *increase* of ρ with E shall be greater than the rate of *decrease* of $e^{-E/kT}$.

As for the position of the maximum, this has to fulfil certain obvious requirements. Consider, for example, samples of the same composition but of different sizes. Clearly, at a given temperature T a large sample should have more energy than a small sample of the same kind. If, for example, the first sample is *twice* as large as the second, the product $\rho e^{-E/kT}$ should pass through its maximum at a value of E that is *twice* as great as in the case of the smaller sample; and similarly for samples of all sizes. In the second place, the product $\rho e^{-E/kT}$ should pass through its maximum at a value of E that is correlated for each chemical substance with the prevailing temperature in accordance with the heat capacity of this substance. The position of the maximum of (391) at different temperatures is sufficient to determine the specific heat.

From the discussion of the quantity Z, which began in Sec. 21, we know that Z is intimately connected with the concept of the temperature and with the specific heat. If the expressions (388) and (391) are to fulfil all the requirements that we have enumerated, this must be by virtue of the connections between Z and the quantities E, C_v, and C_p of the substance concerned.

156. We shall discuss a group of samples where each sample consists of n interacting particles of the same species. The expressions (338) and (340) derived in Chapter 8 are correct irrespective of the zero of energy chosen for E, the energy of a sample. As our zero of energy it is natural to choose E_0, the energy of the sample at the absolute zero of temperature; then E will denote the thermal energy of the sample. In this chapter we have discussed the variation of E with temperature for solids, and for monatomic and diatomic gases and vapors, and have found that over large ranges of temperature it is of the form

$$E = \alpha n k T \qquad (392)$$

where α is a small numerical factor, almost independent of temperature over the ranges mentioned. For a monatomic perfect gas $\alpha = \frac{3}{2}$, for a solid above a certain temperature α is a little more than 3, and for many diatomic gases over a wide range of temperature $\alpha = \frac{5}{2}$.

Let us consider a sample consisting of n interacting particles of any substance whose heat capacity remains constant and equal to $\alpha n k$ down to a certain very low temperature T_1, at which temperature its entropy has a value to be denoted by S_1. Then we can show that (388) fits into a consistent scheme, if we take $\rho(E)$ to be given by

$$\frac{\rho}{\rho_1} = \left(\frac{E}{E_1}\right)^{\alpha n} \tag{393}$$

In this case we have from (291)

$$\ln(\rho q) = \ln \rho_1 + \alpha n \ln \frac{E}{E_1} - \frac{E}{kT} + \ln \frac{N}{P} \tag{394}$$

To find at what value of E this has its maximum value, when a constant temperature T prevails through the group, we differentiate with respect to E and set the result equal to zero. We find

$$\frac{\alpha n}{E} = \frac{1}{kT} \tag{395}$$

Hence (394) passes through its maximum at a value of E given by

$$E^0 = \alpha n k T$$

In this way we verify that, when we use (393) for ρ, we have the total energy of a sample proportional to n, that is, proportional to the size of the sample; and, moreover, that this total energy is appropriate to the heat capacity $\alpha n k$ of the sample.

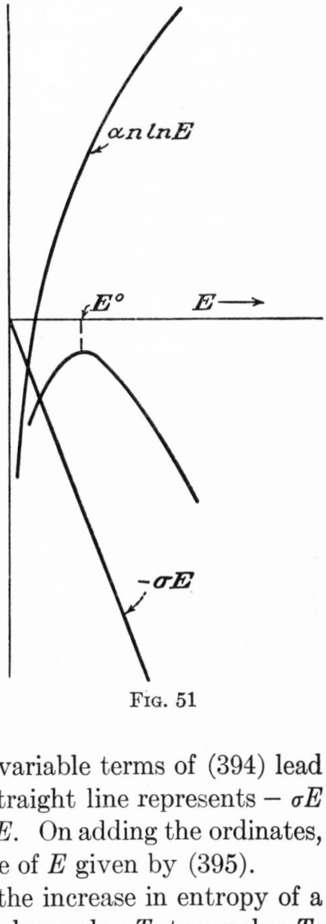

The maximum at E^0 is so sharp that it is impossible to draw a quantitative diagram; Fig. 51, however, shows qualitatively how the variable terms of (394) lead to a resultant curve with a maximum. The straight line represents $-\sigma E$ or $-\mu E$, while the upper curve represents $\alpha n \ln E$. On adding the ordinates, we obtain a curve with a maximum at the value of E given by (395).

FIG. 51

We can now write down an expression for the increase in entropy of a sample when its temperature is raised from the low value T_1 to a value T:

$$\frac{1}{k}\int_{T_1}^{T} \frac{1}{T} \frac{dE}{dT}\, dT = \int_{T_1}^{T} \frac{\alpha n}{T}\, dT$$

$$= \alpha n \ln \frac{T}{T_1}$$

$$= \alpha n \ln \frac{E^0}{E_1}$$

Hence the entropy increases from S_1 at temperature T_1 to the value S given by

$$\frac{S}{k} = \frac{S_1}{k} + \alpha n \ln \frac{E^0}{E_1} \tag{396}$$

Comparing (396) with (393), we see that the expressions are self-consistent if the entropy is given by

$$S = k \ln \rho \tag{397}$$

To find how sharp is the peak in Fig. 51, as given by (391), let us denote by $\ln(\rho^0 q^0)$ the value of (394) belonging to the energy E^0 at the top of the peak, and let us investigate the value of $q\rho$ belonging to a slightly different value of the energy, say, $(E^0 + \eta)$. From (394) we obtain

$$\ln \frac{\rho q}{\rho^0 q^0} = \alpha n \ln\left(1 + \frac{\eta}{E^0}\right) - \left(\frac{E^0 + \eta}{kT} - \frac{E^0}{kT}\right)$$

Expanding the logarithm,

$$\ln \frac{\rho q}{\rho^0 q^0} = \frac{\alpha n \eta}{E^0} - \frac{\alpha n}{2}\left(\frac{\eta}{E^0}\right)^2 + \cdots - \frac{\eta}{kT}$$

The first and last terms cancel each other in accordance with (395), and to this approximation we obtain

$$\frac{\rho q}{\rho^0 q^0} = e^{-\gamma \eta^2} \tag{398}$$

where $\gamma = \alpha n / 2E^{0^2}$. Comparing (398) with (332), we see that the width of the peak in Fig. 51 will be of the same order of magnitude as that given by (332), the expression that was found in Sec. 131 for a pair of samples in contact. Thus, when we are dealing with a sample containing, say, 10^{20} particles, the range of energy in which ρq is appreciable will be equivalent to about 10^{-10} of the thermal energy of the sample. We give to (398) the following interpretation: when a sample is in contact with a heat reservoir, which may or may not consist of $(N - 1)$ other samples, its energy will fluctuate about a value E^0, and the probability of the energy differing from E^0 by an amount η may be found from (398).

157. The Partition Function and the Density of States. We have found that, although according to (389) the partition function P at any temperature T purports to be a summation over all allowed energies from the lowest level E_0 upward, in practice it is only a summation over the allowed energies in the immediate neighborhood of the energy E^0 appropriate to the temperature T. Suppose that we take E as abscissa and mark off along the axis the allowed values of E_r for a sample of a certain size. Suppose then that for each allowed value of E_r a vertical line is erected of length equal to $Z_r e^{-E_r/kT}$. The diagram will have the same character as Fig. 9, since the vertical lines will be large only in the neighborhood of $E = E^0$. The sum of the lengths of all the vertical lines will be equal to P, just as the sum of the horizontal lines in Fig. 14 was equal to P. The examples given below in Fig. 52 are merely schematic since in practice there will be many millions of vertical lines within the narrow range of energy.

In Secs. 158 and 159 we shall discuss in detail the partition function for pure solids. Let us here consider briefly some less simple cases. In the group of crystals discussed in Sec. 133 each crystal could, for example, be a piece of an alloy of the type examined in Sec. 66, and the temperature prevailing through the group could be a temperature where some degree of order is to be expected. In such a crystal, if we count all states having an energy E_r, there is W_{cf} to be taken into account, as well as W_{th}. This will be included in the Z_r of (388) and (389) but will not greatly affect the result. The very rapid decrease in the value of $e^{-E/kT}$ with increasing E ensures that the crystal will not be found to have an energy appreciably greater than E^0. It makes no difference whether the excess energy is thermal energy or potential energy due to an excess of displaced atoms, as discussed in Sec. 68. In both cases an excess of energy is improbable, and an energy appreciably less than E^0 is likewise improbable.

Let us fix attention on the batch of levels embracing the whole narrow peak of Fig. 51; adapting the notation of Sec. 133, we may say that the batch contains p^0 levels each having a multiplicity Z^0. Among the states that comprise this batch will be states of higher and of lower degree of order. But, presumably, if we were to examine Z^0, we should find that states of a particular degree of order are predominant, and further, if we were to examine the batch of states appropriate to a higher temperature, we should find that states with a lower degree of order were predominant.

A similar point of view can be adopted in the problem of vapor pressure. It was suggested in Sec. 138 that the N samples could be N vessels each containing more than enough particles to form a saturated vapor. In this case the set of levels E_r in (389) is the set of allowed values for the whole of the n particles, irrespective of what fraction of them are in the form of solid or liquid, and $-kT \ln \mathsf{P}$ is the free energy of the whole sample. At any temperature T we are interested in a batch of levels embracing the whole of the peak of Fig. 51. If we ask what states are predominant, we shall presumably find that the predominant states are those in which the number of particles in the form of vapor is close to a certain value n_v.

In practice, in discussing the vapor pressure of different elements and compounds, one usually deals with (389) in a simpler way, namely, one replaces (189) by

$$\left[n_s \ln \wp_s + n_v \left(\ln \frac{P_v}{n_v} + 1 \right) \right] kT \tag{399}$$

where $\mathcal{P}_s$ is derived from P_s in accordance with (344). The permissible use of (399) as a substitute for a summation over all possible states is analogous to the permissible use of $k \ln W$ instead of $k \ln Z$. We have already come across a similar substitution when comparing (363) with (362) in Sec. 143.

The value of P given by (389) depends on the zero of energy from which the energies E_r are measured. In Sec. 155 we chose the zero of energy by writing $E_0 = 0$. If the expressions of Sec. 156 were written out in full, E, E_1, and E^0 would be replaced by $(E - E_0)$, $(E_1 - E_0)$, and $(E^0 - E_0)$, respectively. When we wish to compare the partition functions

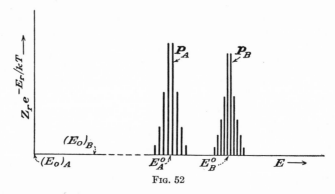

Fig. 52

for equal groups of particles of the same species but in a different state of aggregation, the same zero of energy must be used for both. Let A and B denote two modifications of a solid. At the absolute zero of temperature neither will have any thermal energy but one will have more potential energy than the other. If, for example, we could take a piece of rhombic sulfur at the absolute zero and rearrange the atoms on a monoclinic lattice, a certain amount of work would be required; in the notation of Chapter 6, for n atoms this amount of energy is nu. In the two sets of levels let the ground levels be denoted by $(E_0)_A$ and $(E_0)_B$, respectively. If P^* denotes the partition function of B referred to $(E_0)_B = 0$, the same referred to $(E_0)_A = 0$ will be given by

$$\mathsf{P}_B = \mathsf{P}_B^* e^{-nu/kT}$$

The two sets of vertical lines in Fig. 52 are intended to represent schematically the values of P_A and P_B for equal quantities of A and B at a certain temperature T. In the representation of P_B more vertical lines have been crowded into the interval, corresponding to a greater density of states. In this way it is possible that the greater density of states will compensate for the presence of the factor $e^{-nu/kT}$ and so lead at a certain temperature to the condition

$$\mathsf{P}_A = \mathsf{P}_B = \mathsf{P}_B^* e^{-nu/kT}$$

We have seen that, when multiplied by k, the logarithm of the density of states $\rho(E)$ may be identified with the entropy of the group of particles. In earlier chapters, where we used the simpler and less satisfactory method of quantizing the energies of individual particles, we intentionally avoided stressing the part played by the density of states, that is, the number of states lying in an interval between ϵ and $(\epsilon + d\epsilon)$. This was avoided in order to give precedence here to the more satisfactory use of the density of states associated with the energy E of the whole group. We may now, however, notice that several aspects of earlier equilibrium problems may be thought of in terms of the relative density of the states in the sets of levels through which the particles are distributed. In the vapor pressure problem, for example, the ground level ϵ_0 for a particle in the vapor is considerably higher than that of the same particle in the solid. But the enormously greater density of states for a particle of the vapor compensates for this difference in ground level. Further, it was pointed out in Sec. 92 that, according to (226), a transition will take place only if u and $\ln(\mathbf{P}_B/\mathbf{P}_A)$ are of the same sign. That is, it is essential that the set of levels that has the higher ground level shall contain a greater density of states; otherwise the necessary compensation will not occur and a transition from one modification to the other will not take place at any temperature.

The solubility of a sparingly soluble substance may be regarded from the same point of view. In a solid solution there is no guarantee that the spacing of the energy levels for a solute particle in the interior of the solvent will be narrower than in the pure solute. But we must consider the density of states in the whole solution. If there are N sites for a solute particle in the very dilute solution, there are N places where it can have an energy ϵ_0, or ϵ_1, or ϵ_r. Thus when we include all the states in the solution, the level ϵ_0 has a multiplicity N; and each of the states $\epsilon_2 \ldots \epsilon_r$ has a multiplicity N. If N is greater than 10^{22}, the density of states is comparable with that of a particle in a gas or vapor. Thus, a substance will be appreciably soluble even if the work required to take a particle into solution is several times kT.

We shall return now to samples that are simple and homogeneous and shall study the details of the partition functions of solids.

158. The Heat Capacity. In previous chapters when we have discussed a set of allowed energies $\epsilon_0 \ldots \epsilon_j \ldots \epsilon_r \ldots$, the values in any set all belonged to the same value of the volume v. In (388) and (389), on the other hand, there is no need for us to take the values $E_0 \ldots E_j \ldots E_r \ldots$ as belonging to the same volume. Suppose that we take a solid at the absolute zero of temperature and supply energy to it, allowing it to expand under a negligible applied pressure; the value of E in the process will pass through a series of allowed energies $E_j \ldots E_k \ldots E_r \ldots$ as the temperature rises. In this series an " allowed energy E_r" means a value that is allowed when the volume of the solid is the volume appropriate to the possession of an amount of energy E equal to E_r or approximately equal to E_r. For a crystal of any substance we obtain in this way a set of quantized energies covering the whole range of temperature and appropriate to the crystal undergoing its usual thermal expansion under a negligible applied pressure.

We have seen that, when E is taken as abscissa, a graphical representation of P is very similar to Fig. 9. Now the curves of Fig. 18 in Sec. 52 have the same contour as Fig. 9; hence, if the abscissas in Fig. 18 are taken to be E, this diagram may be used to illustrate the way in which the value of P increases with temperature. A higher temperature implies a larger value of E^0; that is to say, the position of the contour is shifted to the right and so embraces a somewhat different set of vertical lines. In (78), where we differentiated P with respect to T, the values of ϵ_r were taken as constants. So here the values of E_r are constants, though for a different reason, and we shall obtain an expression corresponding to (78):

$$\frac{\mathsf{E}}{\mathsf{N}} = E^0 = kT^2 \frac{\partial \ln \mathsf{P}}{\partial T}$$

Hence, integrating

$$\ln \mathsf{P} = \int_0^T \frac{E^0}{kT^2} \, dT \tag{400}$$

In this integral the values of E^0 do not refer to a particular volume but are the energies of the solid, expanding as the temperature rises from zero to T. If measurements of the heat capacity C_p, made at low temperatures, are extrapolated to the absolute zero and if this extrapolation can be trusted, we have empirical values for E^0 and hence an empirical value for the partition function P:

$$\ln \mathsf{P} = \int_0^T \frac{1}{kT^2} \, dT \int_0^T C_p \, dT \tag{401}$$

If we consider 1 mole of the substance so that $nk = R$, then if C_p denotes the heat capacity of 1 mole, we have from (344)

$$\ln \wp = \frac{1}{n} \ln \mathsf{P} = \int_0^T \frac{1}{RT^2} \, dT \int_0^T C_p \, dT \tag{402}$$

159. Evaluation of the Partition Function. Since the specific heat cannot be measured at the absolute zero, in order to obtain a reliable value of the partition function from (402), it is necessary to extrapolate correctly to the absolute zero the values of the specific heat obtained at low temperatures. When metals are discussed in Chapter 12, it will be shown that there are good theoretical reasons for believing that complicating factors will be absent. We shall therefore illustrate the use of (402) by calculating the partition functions of zinc and magnesium from the measured values of the specific heat. The specific heat of magnesium has been measured down to 11°K, and that for zinc down to 2°K; the values for zinc plotted in Fig. 53 have already been referred to in Sec. 152. If now a vertical line is erected at any temperature in Fig. 53, the area enclosed under the curve is equal to the value of E at this temperature. Let this value of E be divided by RT^2, and, again taking the absolute temperature as abscissa, let this value of E/RT^2 be plotted. When this procedure is carried out for various values of T, the upper curve in Fig. 54 is obtained for zinc and the lower curve for magnesium.[1] If now in Fig. 54 a vertical line is erected at any temperature, it is clear that the area enclosed under the curve is precisely the integral (402); the area is thus numerically equal to ln $\mathcal{P}$ at this temperature.

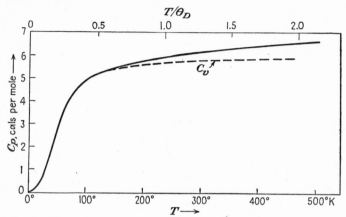

FIG. 53.   The observed specific heat C_p for metallic zinc, and values of C_v calculated from (386).

We know that the heat capacity of 1 mole at room temperature has a value near $3RT$.   Hence E/RT^2 is of the order of magnitude $3/T$, or 0.01 at room temperature.   It will be seen that the values plotted in Fig. 54 are of this magnitude.   The numerical value of the area under the curve will therefore be somewhat less than $T/100$.   An inspection of Fig. 54 shows that for magnesium the area under the curve will reach the value 2

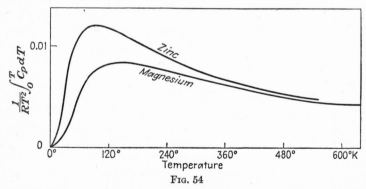

FIG. 54

at a temperature rather above room temperature.   That is to say, near room temperature the value of **P** is rather less than e^2, that is, less than 7.4. It is clear from Fig. 54 that for zinc the value of **P** will be considerably larger.

[1] F. F. Coleman and A. Egerton, *Phil. Trans. Roy. Soc.*, **234**, 177 (1935).

For various solids, the values of **P** obtained in this way are given in Table 5. It will be seen that for zinc at 300° the value of ln **P** is 2.74, that is, the value of **P** is 15.6.

Table 5. Partition Functions of Solids

Values of $\log_e \wp$ derived from (402)*

Temp., °K	Carbon diamond	Carbon graphite	Sodium	Aluminum	Copper	Zinc	Cadmium	Mercury	Lead
20	....	....	0.038	0.003	0.005	0.018	0.065	0.319	0.190
30	....	0.001	0.120	0.010	0.017	0.059	0.175	0.609	0.459
50	....	0.006	0.392	0.045	0.074	0.216	0.496	1.20	1.06
100	0.003	0.035	1.22	0.263	0.393	0.795	1.39	2.43	2.34
200	0.025	0.132	2.58	0.921	1.22	1.89	2.74	4.06	4.00
300	0.081	0.265	3.57	1.56	1.94	2.74	3.71	....	5.08
400	0.172	0.418	....	2.11	2.56	3.42	4.44	....	5.90
500	0.289	0.584	....	2.60	3.09	4.00	5.06	....	6.57
600	0.424	0.750	....	....	3.54	....	....	....	7.13
700	0.569	0.921	....	....	4.30				
800	0.715	1.09	....	....	4.63				
900	0.861	1.24	....	....	4.93				
1000	1.00	1.40	....	....	5.20				

*Using data from Landolt and Bornstein's tables.

When in Sec. 31 we first attached the name "partition function" to the expression (68), we proposed that this choice for localized particles should be regarded as provisional. In Sec. 31 we proposed to look for quantities that could be used to prescribe conditions of equilibrium in the simplest terms. We include in the partition functions only those factors which are relevant to our purpose. We have introduced in (142) a factor g for the multiplicity arising from electronic spin but we have omitted the similar factor arising from the presence of nuclear spin. In the study of the gases H_2, D_2, and HD in Sec. 166 we shall have to pay attention to the spin of the nuclei, but in all other equilibrium problems the *ratio* of the partition functions will be unaffected. The absolute value of each partition function would be increased by a factor similar to g, but in every problem of equilibrium between phases these additional factors would cancel each other out, since each phase contains the same nuclei.

Let us discuss next the question of isotopic mixtures. The expression (342) gives the relation between P and $\wp$ for a group of n particles of the same kind, that is, for a pure isotope. When a solid consists of a mixture of two isotopes A and B, it will in addition have a W_{cf} given by (243), since isotopes necessarily form a substitutional solution. The $\wp$ for n similar particles will have to be multiplied by W_{cf}. Consider next a monatomic vapor having the same isotopic composition. The additional entropy will be given by (197) in Sec. 85. We have already noticed in Sec. 113 that in a substitutional solution the additional entropy is the same as in a mixture of perfect gases. Hence, in discussing the vapor pressure of this mixture of isotopes, using the expression P_v/P_s, we see that the factor W_{cf} will occur both in the numerator and denominator and will not affect the equilibrium. This is true also for diatomic or polyatomic vapors. It is thus a simple matter to handle substances having any isotopic composition. The question of heteronuclear molecules formed from different isotopes will be dealt with in Chapter 11.

In evaluating the ratio P_v/P_s, if we know accurately the value of P_v relative to the energy of an atom at rest, we need to know the absolute value of P_s referred to the same zero of energy. When measurements of the heat capacity C_p have been taken down to a certain low temperature, the integral (402) can tell us only the difference between the value of $\mathcal{P}$ at this temperature and $\mathcal{P}$ at any higher temperature. In Sec. 151, in discussing Figs. 48 and 49, we foresaw the possibility that a large change in the partition function could occur below the accessible range of temperature. In Sec. 154 we saw that, as far as the lattice vibrations of the crystal are concerned, the lowest state E_0 of a pure crystal would be single, if there is no special factor that introduces a multiplicity. In Chapter 11 we shall introduce for the solid a factor g_s similar to that in (142); and in solids consisting of molecules there is an additional factor to be taken into account. In the crystal there may be two or more distinguishable orientations of the molecule with almost the same energy. Following Fowler and Guggenheim, we shall introduce an orientation factor o, which in most substances is unity but which may be greater than unity. In using (402), it will be assumed that in the experimental range of temperature the factors o and g_s have made no contribution to the specific heat.

Problems

1. Construct a diagram similar to Fig. 54 for a solid that at a certain temperature changes from a low-temperature modification A_l to a high-temperature modification A_h. Discuss the significance of the area under the curve and its relation to the quantity $(E_h - E_l)$ at the transition point and to the difference between the energy of A_l and of metastable A_h at the absolute zero.

2. Calculate the value of the partition function of liquid mercury at 250°K, taking the value of the heat capacity of the liquid below this temperature to be 6.95 cal/mole/degree and using the following data for solid mercury: at the melting point, $234.3°K$, the thermal energy E is 1260 cal/mole, the value of $\log_e P$ is 4.49 and the heat of fusion 555 cal/mole.

3. The accompanying table gives the values of C_p in calories per mole for one of the elements listed in Table 5. Plotting the values, construct diagrams similar to Figs. 53 and 54. Evaluate the partition function at 300°K with sufficient accuracy to identify the element by comparison with the values given in Table 5.

T, °K	C_p
10	0.65
20	2.55
30	4.07
50	5.20
100	5.84
200	6.16
300	6.41

The Rotation of Diatomic Molecules—Vapor Pressure Constants and Chemical Constants—Orthohydrogen and Parahydrogen

160. Rotation of Diatomic Molecules. In the study of liquid nitrogen, liquid oxygen, and liquid hydrogen, the vapor pressure of these substances is measured. For comparison with experiment, a knowledge of the partition function for such diatomic gases is desired at very low temperatures as well as at room temperature and above. We saw in (158) that for a diatomic gas at low pressure the translational part of the partition function for a molecular weight M is the same as for a monatomic gas. In (159) we had

$$P = P_{tr}\Sigma e^{-\mathcal{E}_i/kT}$$

where the summation is to be taken over all the allowed values of the internal energy. We have already discussed the vibrational levels in Sec. 152. We must now obtain the partition function for the rotational levels.

The spacing of the rotational levels depends on the moment of inertia $\mathcal{J}$ of the molecule, the spacing being narrow when $\mathcal{J}$ is large. At low and at medium temperatures a diatomic molecule may be treated as a rigid rotator, and a simple expression gives the value of the partition function accurately. At high temperatures one must take into account the fact that the molecule is not a rigid rotator and must add terms to allow for the "stretching" of the molecule; we shall consider the latter below.

For a rigid rotator the allowed energies are given by

$$\epsilon_j = \mathbf{B}j(j+1) \qquad (403)$$

where j is the rotational quantum number and where the energy $\mathbf{B}$, which determines the characteristic spacing of the rotational levels, is connected with the moment of inertia of the molecule by the relation

$$\mathbf{B} = \frac{h^2}{8\pi^2\mathcal{J}} \qquad (404)$$

The spacing of the levels given by (403) is evidently not uniform but becomes progressively wider as j takes successive integral values 0, 1, 2 .... Since the spacing of the rotational levels derived from an analysis of the molecular spectra is found to be in accordance with the theoretical expression (403), one can obtain for each molecular species the characteristic value of **B** and hence of the moment of inertia of the molecule. At each of the energies given by (403) there are $(2j + 1)$ different states, coinciding in energy. Introducing this multiplicity, we therefore require for the rotational partition function the sum

$$\mathbf{P}_{rot} = \Sigma(2j + 1)e^{-Bj(j+1)/kT} \tag{405}$$

The interval between the lowest rotational level ϵ_0 and the next higher level ϵ_1, obtained by writing $j = 1$ in (403), has the value $2\mathbf{B}$. Each of the values for various molecules given in Table 6 is 1000 times the interval $(\epsilon_1 - \epsilon_0)$.

TABLE 6. INTERVAL BETWEEN THE TWO LOWEST ROTATIONAL LEVELS

Molecule	Electron-volts, $(\epsilon_1 - \epsilon_0) \times 10^3$	Θ_{rot}, °K
H_2	14.7	171
D_2	7.34	85
HD	11.0	127
HCl	2.63	30.5
NO	0.425	4.93
O_2	0.359	4.17
N_2	0.498	5.78
CO	0.477	5.53
Cl_2	0.0597	0.693
Br_2	0.0201	0.233
I_2	0.0093	0.108
Li_2	0.169	1.96
Na_2	0.0385	0.447
K_2	0.0140	0.162

Recalling that the value of kT at room temperature is $\frac{1}{40}$ electron-volt, we see from Table 5 that the spacing of the rotational levels is relatively narrow. Even at temperatures lower than room temperature the sum (405) may be replaced by an integral. Writing $\mathbf{B}j(j + 1)/kT = x$, we have

$$(2j + 1)\ dj = \frac{kT}{\mathbf{B}}\ dx$$

Hence (405) may be taken as equivalent to

$$\mathbf{P}_{rot} = \frac{kT}{\mathbf{B}}\int_0^\infty e^{-x}\ dx = \frac{kT}{\mathbf{B}}\left(1 + \frac{\mathbf{B}}{3kT} + \cdots\right) \tag{406}$$

For each species of molecule it is convenient to define for the rotations, as was done for the vibrations, a characteristic temperature, Θ_{rot}, such that $k\Theta$ is equal to the interval between the lowest levels. We obtain then

$$\mathbf{P}_{rot} = \frac{2T}{\Theta}\left(1 + \frac{\Theta}{6T} + \cdots\right)$$

Values of Θ have been included in Table 6.[1] Corresponding to the narrow spacing of the levels, for most molecules the characteristic temperature is near the absolute zero. This expression for P_{rot} gives the correct value for any heteronuclear molecule, that is, for any diatomic molecule in which the two nuclei are not identical. In such a molecule, if we could at any moment interchange the two nuclei (for example, the two nuclei in the molecule $O^{16}O^{18}$), the resulting state would be distinguishable from the initial state. In a homonuclear molecule, on the other hand, it is meaningless to speak of interchanging the nuclei. In consequence of this, a homonuclear molecule will not have so many rotational states as a heteronuclear molecule.[2] A symmetry factor σ may therefore be introduced, as in (316), into the above expression

$$P_{rot} = \frac{2T}{\sigma\Theta}\left(1 + \frac{\Theta}{6T} + \cdots\right) \tag{407}$$

where $\sigma = 2$ for homonuclear, and $\sigma = 1$ for heteronuclear molecules. For example, the value given in Table 7 of $\ln P_{in}$ for the molecule $Cl^{35}Cl^{35}$ at 1000°K is 7.8876, whereas it would have been 8.5808 if the amount $\ln 2 = 0.6932$ had not been subtracted.

At high temperatures, say above 600°C, since molecules are not rigid rotators, (403) does not give the energy levels with sufficient accuracy and other terms have to be added to allow for the stretching of the molecule. Although (405) will often give values of P_{rot} correct to 1 per cent, more accurate values can be obtained using the following expression for the allowed energies

$$\epsilon = Bm^2 + Dm^4 + Fm^6 \tag{408}$$

where $m = (j + \frac{1}{2})$ and the coefficients B, D, and F have slightly different values for each vibrational state of the molecule. Some results for various molecules at different temperatures between 1000 and 3000°K are given in Table 7.

TABLE 7*

Molecule	°K	$\log_e P_{in}$
HCl^{35}	1000	4.214
	2000	4.291
	3000	5.631
$Cl^{35}Cl^{35}$ . . .	1000	7.8876
CO	3000	7.4989
$O^{16}O^{16}$	3000	8.3699
$Br^{79}Br^{81}$ . . .	1500	10.8358

* A. R. Gordon and C. Barnes, J. Chem. Phys., 1, 297 (1933).

[1] In some books the values of Θ_{rot} tabulated are half the values given here. This is because Θ_{rot} has there been defined by setting $k\Theta_{rot}$ equal to half the interval between the lowest rotational levels, that is to say, equal to B.

[2] See Fowler and Guggenheim, op. cit.

Corresponding to the values of $\ln \mathbf{P}_{in}$ given in the table, the values of $\mathbf{P}_{in}$ itself at 1500°K range from 68 for HCl to more than 30,000 for Br_2, illustrating well how the density of states depends upon the moment of inertia of the molecule.

161. It was mentioned in Sec. 152 that the uniform spacing of the vibrational levels of diatomic molecules is derived from an analysis of their spectra. The values for several molecules are given in Table 8, together with the values of Θ calculated from the relation $k\Theta = u$.

TABLE 8. SPACING OF THE VIBRATIONAL LEVELS OF DIATOMIC MOLECULES

Molecule	Electron- volts	Θ_{vib}, °K
H_2	0.529	6140
HCl	0.371	4300
O_2	0.195	2260
N_2	0.291	3380
NO	0.236	2740
CO	0.269	3120
Cl_2	0.070	810
Br_2	0.041	470
I_2	0.027	310
Li_2	0.043	500
Na_2	0.020	230
K_2	0.012	140

In discussing the vibrational energy of nitrogen and oxygen in Sec. 152, it was pointed out that at room temperature nearly all the molecules will be in their lowest vibrational level. If the rotational levels of molecules were more widely spaced than they are, a similar effect would be observed for rotation at some accessible temperature; nearly all the molecules in the gas would fall into the lowest rotational level and we should have a diatomic gas without any appreciable internal energy. This gas would behave like a monatomic gas, with $C_v = \frac{3}{2}R$. This condition is, in fact, observed for H_2 below 40°K, and for D_2 and HD (see Sec. 166 below), but for no other diatomic gases.

Consider the terms in (407); it is clear that at temperatures for which the value of T/Θ is greater than 17, the second term in the bracket will make a contribution of less than 1 per cent. In the case of nitrogen, for example, this condition is already satisfied at 100°K; for most gases the second term in the bracket makes a negligible contribution to the heat capacity of the gas, even below room temperature. When this second term is omitted, we obtain

$$\ln \mathbf{P}_{rot} = \ln T + \ln \frac{8\pi^2 \mathcal{I}k}{\sigma h^2} \tag{409}$$

In accordance with (78) the rotational energy may be expressed in terms of $\mathbf{P}_{rot}$

$$E_{rot} = nkT^2 \frac{\partial}{\partial T} (\ln \mathbf{P}_{rot}) \tag{410}$$

Since the second term on the right-hand side of (406) is independent of temperature, we find from (410) that when the temperature is not too low the value of E_{rot} for 1 mole of the gas is equal to RT. This is the classical value, demanded by equipartition for two degrees of freedom, as in Sec. 141. For H_2 this condition is found only at temperatures above 300°K and for D_2 at temperatures above 150°K. For all other diatomic gases the condition is already satisfied at very low temperatures; the rotational specific heat is independent of temperature and is equal to R the classical value.

162. In contrasting the portions AB and CD of the curve in Fig. 46, attention was drawn to the difference between a set of levels that is highly populated and one that is not. From what has been said, it is clear that for several diatomic gases there is a wide range of temperature over which the rotations are fully excited while the vibrations are scarcely excited at all. As a result, the contribution to the heat capacity is R from the rotations, zero from the vibrations, and $\frac{3}{2}R$ from the translational motion, as for a monatomic gas. The total value of C_v should thus be constant and equal to $\frac{5}{2}R$ over a wide range of temperature. As in (151), the value of C_p is equal to $(C_v + R)$, that is to say, $\frac{7}{2}R$. Thus the expected ratio of the specific heats is $\frac{7}{5}$, or 1.40. From the experimental results given in Table 9 it will be seen that, with the exception of hydrogen, there is good agreement with the theoretical value. The degree to which the value is independent of temperature is shown for O_2 and N_2.

It has been mentioned above that for H_2 at temperatures below 40°K the behavior should be similar to that of a monatomic gas. From (151) one expects for any monatomic gas the value

$$\frac{C_p}{C_v} = \frac{5}{3} = 1.6667$$

The experimental values for helium and neon, given in Table 9, are in good agreement with this figure. Further, the result for H_2 at 17°K, given in Table 9, is in good agreement with the same theoretical value.

In view of the fact that the value of C_p for many gases is constant over wide ranges of temperature, it is of interest to notice the form that (402) will take at temperature T, if it is a sufficiently good approximation to assume that C_p is constant over the whole range from absolute zero to T. From (402) we obtain

$$\ln P = \int_0^T \frac{C_p}{RT} \, dT = \frac{C_p}{R} \ln T$$

For monatomic and diatomic gases we have to substitute $\frac{5}{2}R$ and $\frac{7}{2}R$, respectively. If this is not a sufficiently good approximation, the integral must be carried out with a variable C_p. In the remainder of this chapter, for the sake of simplicity, the terms $\frac{5}{2} \ln T$ and $\frac{7}{2} \ln T$ will be used; an additional term can readily be added to take into account a C_p that varies with temperature.

TABLE 9*

Gas	Temperature, °C	C_p/C_v
Values of C_p/C_v for Monatomic Gases		
He............	− 258	1.661
	− 183	1.662
Ne............	− 245.3	1.667
	0.0	1.666
Values of C_p/C_v for Diatomic Gases		
O_2............	− 195.7	1.408
	0.0	1.402
N_2............	− 190.2	1.400
	− 107.2	1.400
H_2............	− 256.0	1.661
NO............	7.6	1.400
CO............	10.3	1.404
HCl..........	15.0	1.40

* W. H. Keesom, A. van Itterbeek, and J. A. van Lammeren, *Proc. Amsterdam*, **34–37** (1931–1934).

163. The value of the vapor pressure at any temperature may be obtained from the expression (222)

$$n_v = \frac{\mathbf{P}_v}{\mathbf{P}_s} e^{-s/kT} \tag{411}$$

It is necessary only to insert the values of $\mathbf{P}_v$, $\mathbf{P}_s$, and $\mathbf{s}$. For the partition function of a monatomic gas we had already obtained an expression in Sec. 71. Now that we have in Secs. 160 and 161 obtained the necessary expressions for diatomic molecules also, we are in a position to make a comparison between experimental and theoretical values.

In the days before quantum statistics the following expression, based on (217), had been derived for the vapor pressure of a solid from purely thermodynamic considerations

$$\ln p = -\frac{\mathbf{s}_0}{kT} + \frac{C_p}{k} \ln T - \int \frac{dT}{T^2} \int \frac{C_{ps}}{k} \, dT + i \tag{412}$$

where $\mathbf{s}_0$ is the latent heat of evaporation extrapolated to the absolute zero, C_p is the specific heat of the vapor at constant pressure, C_{ps} is the specific heat of the solid, and i is a constant of integration, which was called the "chemical constant." For various substances empirical values of i were derived from the experimental data on vapor pressure.

Inserting in (224) the expressions (142) for $\mathbf{P}_{tr}$ and (402) for $\mathbf{P}_s$, we obtain

$$\ln p = \ln \frac{nkT}{v}$$

$$= -\frac{\mathbf{s}}{kT} + \frac{5}{2} \ln T - \int \frac{dT}{T^2} \int \frac{C_{ps}}{k} \, dT + \ln \left(\frac{(2\pi m)^{\frac{3}{2}} k^{\frac{5}{2}} g_v}{h^3 g_s} \right) \qquad (413)$$

On comparing this expression with (412), it will be seen that each of the four terms corresponds to a term of (412). Thus quantum theory provides a theoretical expression for the empirical constant i, and the best way of making a systematic comparison between experimental and theoretical values of vapor pressures is to fix attention on the values of i.

The name "chemical constant" was originally given to i because it was thought to be necessarily the same as an integration constant that occurs in the analogous expression for equilibrium in any chemical reaction in which the same substance takes part. As it is now known that the two constants do not necessarily have the same value (see Sec. 165 below), the constant i that occurs in (412) is now often called the "vapor pressure constant." Comparing the last term of (413) with (412) and expressing the mass m as the product of the atomic weight M and the mass of the hydrogen atom m_H, we obtain the theoretical expression

$$i = \ln \left(\frac{(2\pi m_H)^{\frac{3}{2}} k^{\frac{5}{2}}}{h^3} \right) + \ln \left(M^{\frac{3}{2}} \frac{g_v}{g_s} \right) \qquad (414)$$

The expression (413) gives the vapor pressure in dynes per square centimeter. In dealing with the experimental values, it is customary to give the pressures in atmospheres and to use logarithms to the base 10. If i when expressed in these practical units is denoted by i', we have the relation

$$i' = \frac{i - \log_e b}{\log_e 10} \qquad (415)$$

where b is the value of 1 atmosphere in dynes per square centimeter, which is approximately 10^6 dynes per square centimeter. The first term in (414) contains only the universal constants h, k, and m_H. Hence i' may be written in the form

$$i' = C + \frac{3}{2} \log_{10} M + \log_{10} \frac{g_v}{g_s} \qquad (416)$$

where C is a universal constant whose value is in the neighborhood of -1.589.

We are now in a position to examine the comparisons that have been made between theory and experiment. Two procedures, which are equivalent, have been used. One procedure is to calculate from the observed vapor pressures an empirical value of the constant C and to compare the value with the theoretical -1.589. The other procedure is to calculate a theoretical value for i' by setting C equal to -1.589, and to compare the result with the value of i' consistent with the vapor pressure measurements.

TABLE 10. MONATOMIC VAPOR PRESSURE CONSTANTS

Molecule	Electronic state	g_v	i' calculated	i' observed
He.....	^1S	1	-0.684	-0.68
Ne²⁰....	^1S	1	0.364 ⎫	0.39*
Ne²²....			0.427 ⎭	
A.....	^1S	1	0.814	0.81
Kr.....	^1S	1	1.297	1.29
Xe.....	^1S	1	1.590	1.60
Na.....	^2S	2	0.757	⎧0.63 / 0.97 / 0.78⎫
K......	^2S	2	1.102	⎧0.92 / 1.13⎫
Mg.....	^1S	1	0.492	0.47
Zn......	^1S	1	1.136	1.21
Cd.....	^1S	1	1.488	⎧1.45 / 1.57⎫
Tl......	$^2P_{\frac{1}{2}}$	2	2.180	2.37
Hg.....	^1S	1	1.866	1.95

*The vapor pressures of neon with different isotopic compositions were measured by W. H. Keesom and J. Haantjes, *Physica*, **2**, 986 (1935). Other references for Tables 10 and 12 are R. H. Fowler, "Statistical Mechanics," 2d ed. Cambridge, 1936; A. Eucken, "Grundriss der physikalischen Chemie," 3d ed., Leipzig, 1930; and revised values from R. H. Fowler and E. A. Guggenheim, "Statistical Thermodynamics," Cambridge, 1939, where a discussion of the halogen atoms Cl, Br, and I is also given.

TABLE 11. EMPIRICAL VALUES OF THE CONSTANT $-C$
(Theoretical value: $-C = 1.589$)

He........	1.59	Mg.......	1.61
Ne........	1.56	Zn.......	1.51
	1.59	Cd.......	1.63
A.........	1.61		1.51
Kr........	1.59	Hg.......	1.62
Na........	1.57	Tl........	1.40
	1.41	Pb.......	1.7
K.........	1.47		1.21

R. W. Ditchburn and J. C. Gilmour, *Rev. Modern Physics*, **13**, 310 (1941).

Results are shown in Tables 10 and 11; the values are from independent surveys, those of Table 11 being the more recent. In both tables it has been assumed that the value of g_s is unity for every element. It will be seen that this assumption leads to good agreement between theory and experiment in every case.

In the vapor all the atoms except Na, K, and Tl are in singlet S states, with $g_v = 1$. In the vapor of Na and K the atoms are in a doublet S state, while in Tl vapor the atoms are in a $^2P_{\frac{1}{2}}$ state with $g_v = 2$, the energy of the upper state $^2P_{\frac{3}{2}}$ of the electronic doublet lying so far above the ground level that it makes no contribution at these temperatures. Although for such metals as Na, K, and Tl we have g_v greater than unity, in the solid state $g_s = 1$. From each atom in the metal the valence electron has become free, leaving behind a positive core with a rare gas structure. The state of the free electrons themselves is discussed in Sec. 176.

164. Vapor Pressure, Diatomic Molecules. The discussion of Sec. 161 led to the conclusion that for the common gases at ordinary temperatures the vibrational partition function does not differ appreciably from unity and that for diatomic molecules except H_2, D_2, and HD the rotational specific heat has the value k, the classical value; the value of C_p for the vapor is thus $(\frac{5}{2} + 1)k = 7k/2$. For all common molecules except H_2, D_2, and HD the procedure is the same as that followed for monatomic gases. From (402) and (404) we obtain

$$\ln p = \ln \frac{n_v kT}{v} = \ln \frac{kT}{v} + \ln \left(\frac{\mathbf{P}_{tr}\mathbf{P}_{rot}e^{-s/kT}}{\mathbf{P}_s} \right) \tag{417}$$

$$= -\frac{s}{kT} + \frac{7}{2} \ln T - \int \frac{dT}{T^2} \int \frac{C_{ps}}{k} \, dT + \ln \left(\frac{(2\pi m)^{\frac{3}{2}} k^{\frac{7}{2}} 8\pi^2 \mathfrak{g} g_v}{h^5 \sigma o g_s} \right) \tag{418}$$

If this is compared with the thermodynamic expression (412), it is again seen that each term corresponds to one term of (412) and that quantum theory gives a theoretical expression for the vapor pressure constant i. After converting to practical units by means of (415), the values given in column 6 of Table 12 are values calculated from the expression

$$i' = 36.815 + \frac{3}{2} \log M + \log \mathfrak{g} + \log \frac{g_v}{\sigma o g_s} \tag{419}$$

Table 12. Vapor Pressure Constants of Diatomic Molecules

Molecule	$\mathfrak{g} \times 10^{40}$	Electronic state	g_v	o	i' calculated	i' observed	og_s
N_2......	13.8	$^1\Sigma$	1	2	-0.175	-0.16	1
O_2......	19.1	$^3\Sigma$	3	2	0.53	0.55	1
CO......	14.3	$^1\Sigma$	1	1	-0.16	-0.07	2
HCl.....	2.61	$^1\Sigma$	1	1	-0.42	-0.40	1
HBr.....	3.27	$^1\Sigma$	1	1	0.19	0.24	1
HI......	4.40	$^1\Sigma$	1	1	0.62	0.65	1
Cl_2......	113*	$^1\Sigma$	1	2	1.35	1.66	1
Br_2......	342	$^1\Sigma$	1	2	2.35	2.59	1
I_2.......	742	$^1\Sigma$	1	2	2.99	3.08	1

*The moment of inertia of the molecule $Cl^{37}Cl^{37}$ is a few per cent larger than that of the molecule $Cl^{35}Cl^{35}$.

For a discussion of the molecule NO, see Fowler and Guggenheim, *op. cit.*

assuming for the product og_s the values given in the last column. The values of g and g_v are known from spectroscopic data.

A normal mixture of isotopes will contain both homonuclear and heteronuclear molecules. For these molecules the values of o and σ will be different but the value of i is the same, since this depends on the product $o\sigma$. Thus, the homonuclear molecule $Cl^{35}Cl^{35}$, for example, has $\sigma = 2$ in the vapor and $o = 1$ in the solid, whereas the heteronuclear species $Cl^{35}Cl^{37}$ has alternative positions in the solid with $o = 2$, while in the vapor $\sigma = 1$. The values of σ listed in Table 10 refer to the homonuclear species.

It will be seen from Table 12 that for HCl, HBr, and HI agreement is obtained by assuming $o = 1$. This is to be expected. Each of these molecules has a large electric moment and they can therefore have only one unique direction of equilibrium in the crystal at low temperatures; hence $o = 1$, and presumably $g_s = 1$, as in the vapor. If we were to assume $o = 1$ for CO likewise, we would obtain $i'_{calc} = +0.14$, which is not in agreement with the observed value. It has been suggested[1] that the CO molecules have such a small electric moment and are so nearly symmetrical that at the low temperatures at which measurements have been made the molecules have not adopted a unique direction in the crystal and consequently agreement with observation is obtained with $o = 2$. For solid oxygen we would have expected $g_s = 3$ since in the gas $g_v = 3$. Agreement with experiment,[2] however, is obtained with $og_s = 1$; the correct explanation of this is at present uncertain.

For simplicity, both in expressions (413) and (418) we have been considering the vapor pressure at temperatures where the molecular vibrations make no contribution. At higher temperatures, (418) will contain a vibrational partition function P_{vib} whose value is no longer unity and the thermodynamic expression (412) will contain a corresponding term, so that the constant i is unaffected and has the same value as before.

If (413) is examined, it will be seen that for a monatomic vapor, we have the following relation between P'_{tr} and i:

$$\ln P_{tr} = i + \frac{3}{2} \ln T - \ln \frac{k}{vg_s} \qquad (420)$$

Similarly, for a diatomic vapor we obtain from (418) the following relation:

$$\ln P = i + \frac{5}{2} \ln T - \ln \frac{k}{vog_s} \qquad (421)$$

We shall make use of these expressions in the next section.

165. Equilibrium in a Gaseous Reaction. The expression (418) was derived by substituting in (224) for P_v and P_s. In a gaseous reaction the

[1] J. O. Clayton and W. F. Giauque, *J. Am. Chem. Soc.*, **54**, 2610 (1932).
[2] W. F. Giauque and H. L. Johnston, *J. Am. Chem. Soc.*, **51**, 2300 (1929).

partition function for the solid will not occur, and we have only to substitute for the partition functions of the gaseous molecules taking part. In Sec. 96 for a reaction of the type

$$A_2 + B_2 \rightleftarrows 2AB \tag{422}$$

we obtained an expression of the form

$$\frac{\mathbf{P}_{AB}{}^2}{\mathbf{P}_{A_2}\mathbf{P}_{B_2}} e^{-s/kT} \tag{423}$$

By substituting for the partition functions, we could obtain an expression analogous to (417) in terms of the moments of inertia of the reacting molecules, and so on. On the other hand, by use of (420) and (421), we can obtain an expression containing the constants i_{A_2}, i_{B_2}, and i_{AB}. At temperatures where the molecular vibrations are unexcited we find

$$\ln K = \ln \frac{c_{AB}{}^2}{c_{A_2}c_{B_2}}$$

$$= -\frac{s}{kT} + 2i_{AB} - i_{A_2} - i_{B_2} + 2\ln(og_s)_{AB}$$
$$- \ln(og_s)_{A_2} - \ln(og_s)_{B_2} \tag{424}$$

In general we may consider a gaseous reaction in which a moles of a species A react with b moles of a species B, and so on, to give as products l moles of a species L and m moles of a species M, and so on. Thus

$$aA + bB + \cdots \rightleftarrows lL + mM + \cdots \tag{425}$$

For such an equilibrium an expression analogous to (412) had been derived from classical thermodynamics; at temperatures where the molecular vibrations are not excited, this takes the form

$$\ln K = -\frac{s_0}{kT} + \frac{\Sigma C_p}{k} \ln T + J \tag{426}$$

where s_0 is the limiting value of the heat of reaction extrapolated to the absolute zero; ΣC_p is the algebraic sum of terms, one for each molecular species in equilibrium, namely, $\frac{7}{2}k$ for each diatomic and $\frac{5}{2}k$ for each monatomic molecule occurring in (425), the values being positive for those on the right-hand side and negative for those on the left; and J is a constant of integration.

Let us first consider (426) as applied to the particular reaction (422). In this case the sum ΣC_p contributes nothing since there are two diatomic molecules on the right and two on the left. Comparing (426) with (424), we see that we obtain an expression for the integration constant J in terms of i, o, and g_s. If we define three quantities j_{A_2}, j_{B_2}, and j_{AB} by writing for each

$$j = i + \ln(og_s) \tag{427}$$

we see that J is given by

$$J = 2j_{AB} - j_{A_2} - j_{B_2} \tag{428}$$

In general, in any gaseous equilibrium, J is equal to the algebraic sum of the j's for the various reacting species.

In the nineteenth century it was recognized by Nernst that J was the algebraic sum of constants contributed by each of the reacting molecules. He believed that these constants were for each species the same as the constant i that occurs in the expression for the vapor pressure; that is why the vapor pressure constant i was originally called the "chemical constant" of the substance.

TABLE 13. THEORETICAL AND OBSERVED VALUES OF $\Sigma j'$

Reaction	j' calculated		$\Sigma j'$ calculated	$\Sigma j'$ observed
$2HCl \rightleftarrows H_2 + Cl_2$	H_2	-3.37	-1.18	-1.12
$2HBr \rightleftarrows H_2 + Br_2$	Br_2	2.35	-1.40	-1.25
$2HI \ \ \rightleftarrows H_2 + I_2$	I_2	2.99	-1.62	-1.50
$2HD \ \ \rightleftarrows H_2 + D_2$	$\begin{cases} HD & -2.68 \\ D_2 & -2.61 \end{cases}$		-0.62	-0.63
$Cl_2 \ \ \rightleftarrows 2Cl$	Cl	1.44	1.53	1.40
$Br_2 \ \ \rightleftarrows 2Br$	Br	1.87	1.39	1.41
$I_2 \ \ \rightleftarrows 2I$	I	2.17	1.35	1.35

For those species not included in Column 2 the calculated values of j' are the same as the calculated values of i' in Table 12. For the sources of the data see Table 10.

A purely gaseous equilibrium of course cannot depend on any properties of the solid state; now that we know that the vapor pressure constant i depends on g_s and o, characteristic of the solid form of the substance, it is clear that J cannot be the sum of the i's. When the product og_s is unity the values of j and i are the same, as is clear from (427).

A comparison between calculated and observed values for various gaseous reactions is given in Table 13. In the third column each value is the algebraic sum of the appropriate calculated values given in the second column; the last column gives the corresponding experimental value.

166. Orthohydrogen, Parahydrogen, Orthodeuterium, and Paradeuterium. Discussion of hydrogen and deuterium has been omitted from the foregoing sections in order to give here a separate account of the special behavior of H_2, D_2, and HD. In Sec. 161 it was pointed out these are the only molecules in which we can hope to observe the disappearance of the rotational specific heat at low temperatures. Below room temperature the specific heat of H_2 begins to fall below the value $\frac{5}{2}k$, and below 40°K has the value $\frac{3}{2}k$ characteristic of a monatomic gas; at these temperatures the energy is entirely translational. The specific heat of HD varies with temperature in the manner to be expected from the expressions obtained for diatomic molecules in Sec. 160. The behavior of H_2, however, (and likewise D_2) was found to show an unexpected deviation from theory. The explanation of this discrepancy was given in 1927, when it was recognized that H_2 behaves like a mixture of two gases, to which the names orthohydrogen and parahydrogen were given. This special behavior is due to the fact that the molecule is homonuclear and the nuclei (the protons) possess spin. Anomalous behavior must be present in all gases consisting of homonuclear molecules with nuclear spin, but only in H_2 and D_2 does the effect on the specific heat become large at temperatures where it can be observed; for other substances the required temperatures are too low.

In any homonuclear molecule the wave functions for molecular rotation must be either symmetrical or antisymmetrical in the coordinates of the nuclei. The lowest rotational state is that for which the quantum number j in (403) is zero. For this state and likewise for $j = 2, 4, 6 \ldots$ the rotational wave function is symmetrical, while for $j = 1, 3, 5 \ldots$ it is antisymmetrical. When we cool a gas down toward the absolute zero, we expect that all the molecules will begin to fall into the lowest rotational state, namely, the state with $j = 0$. But transitions between antisymmetrical states and symmetrical states are forbidden transitions and in the absence of perturbations will not occur. Hence, although all the molecules in the even states, with $j = 2, 4, 6 \ldots$, fall into the lowest level in the usual way, molecules in the odd states, with $j = 3, 5 \ldots$, fall into the state with $j = 1$ and may remain there for days before falling into the level with $j = 0$. Thus the gas behaves like a mixture.[1] In one component, known as "parahydrogen," each molecule has an antisymmetrical nuclear spin wave function (nuclear singlets); these molecules have the even rotational states and the partition function is obtained by summing over the values $j = 0, 2, 4 \ldots$. For the other component the partition function is obtained by summing over the odd values $j = 1, 3, 5 \ldots$; in these molecules, known as "orthohydrogen," the spin wave function is symmetrical (nuclear triplets). Since these odd rotational states are three times as plentiful, it is found that in H_2 at room temperature one-quarter of the gas is in even rotational states (para), and three-quarters in odd rotational states (ortho). When the gas is cooled to a low temperature, this 3:1 ratio does not change but remains "frozen in," owing to the forbidden transitions. In this metastable mixture the rotational heat capacity at any temperature T is thus the sum of two contributions

$$C^{\text{rot}} = \tfrac{1}{4}C^{\text{rot}}_{\text{para}} + \tfrac{3}{4}C^{\text{rot}}_{\text{ortho}} \tag{429}$$

[1] D. M. Dennison, *Proc. Roy. Soc. A.*, **115**, 483 (1927); A. Farkas, "Orthohydrogen, Parahydrogen and Heavy Hydrogen," Cambridge, 1935.

To the specific heat of deuterium similar considerations apply; the gas behaves as if it consisted of two components but the details are different. The spin of the nucleus is the resultant of the spins of the proton and neutron that make up the deuteron. The name "paradeuterium" is given, as in the case of hydrogen, to the molecules which have an antisymmetric nuclear spin wave function, and the name "orthodeuterium" to those which have the symmetric spin wave function. But in deuterium the odd rotational states are associated with the para component and the even rotational states with the ortho component. At room temperature one-third of the gas is in the form of paradeuterium and two-thirds in the form of orthodeuterium. On cooling to a low temperature, this ratio remains frozen in and the heat capacity of the metastable mixture is given by

$$C^{\text{rot}} = \tfrac{1}{3}C^{\text{rot}}_{\text{para}} + \tfrac{2}{3}C^{\text{rot}}_{\text{ortho}} \tag{430}$$

The experimental values for both H_2 and D_2 are in very good agreement with the values predicted from (429) and (430).

Problem

In a stellar atmosphere the temperature is so high and the density so low that many atoms lose a valence electron. This ionization may be treated as a dissociation: atom $\rightleftarrows$ ion $+$ electron. In the chromosphere of the sun many calcium ions lose a second electron to form Ca^{++}. Extending the method of Sec. 86, consider calcium vapor at $5000°$ with a density of only 10^{-16} gram per cubic centimeter, and make a rough estimate of the relative numbers of Ca, Ca^+, and Ca^{++} particles in the vapor. The first ionization potential of Ca is 6.09 electron-volts, and the work to remove a second electron is 11.82.

CHAPTER 12

Particles in Electric and Magnetic Fields—Order and Disorder in Crystals—Fermi-Dirac Statistics—Free Electrons in a Metal—Bose-Einstein Statistics—Atomic Nuclei

167. Electric and Magnetic Fields. When a substance is placed in an external electric field it acquires an electric polarization, which in many respects is similar to the magnetic polarization that a paramagnetic substance acquires when placed in an external magnetic field. It is well known that, as regards their dielectric properties, substances may be divided into two classes, namely, those whose molecules have no permanent electric moment, and those in which each molecule has a permanent electric moment and may be treated as an electrical dipole. The behavior of such electrical dipoles in an external field is, in some respects, similar to the behavior of paramagnetic particles in an external magnetic field; we may therefore approach the two problems together.

It is clear from Secs. 29 and 134 that our definition of an absolute scale of temperature is closely connected with our ability to alter, at will, the quantized values of the energy of a system. This shifting of the energy levels is usually obtained by altering the volume in which the particles are confined, and the usual Carnot cycle is a pressure-volume cycle. By the use of a helium or hydrogen gas thermometer, very low temperatures may be measured on the absolute scale. In the neighborhood of the absolute zero, however, the necessary experiments with a gas cannot be performed. Instead, we may make use of the fact that the quantized levels of a paramagnetic substance may be shifted at will by means of changes in the intensity of an applied magnetic field, which is under our control. This method of shifting the allowed values of the energy is as satisfactory as that discussed in Chapter 2 and enables us to extend the absolute scale of temperature below 1°K.[1] At the same time, by the method of magnetic cooling, it has been possible to reach temperatures as low as 0.005°K—lower than those which have been reached by any other method.

---

[1] N. Kürti and F. Simon, *Phil. Mag.*, **26**, 840 (1938); E. F. Burton, H. Grayson Smith, and J. Wilhelm, "Phenomena at the Temperature of Liquid Helium," Reinhold, 1940; M. Ruhemann, "Low Temperature Physics," Cambridge, 1937.

(The electrical analogue of the magnetocaloric effect plays an important role in ionic solutions; see Sec. 172).

The dielectric and paramagnetic properties of solids and liquids provide a complex problem, because there is strong interaction between each particle and its neighbors. In a gas at low pressure the interaction between the particles will be small, but in a detailed treatment the most important aspect is the dynamical problem of the motion of the particle in the external field—a problem in quantum dynamics.[1] There is another system in which the interaction between particles is small; we may dissolve a substance whose particles have a permanent electric moment in a solvent whose particles have no permanent electric moment; or (and) we may dissolve a paramagnetic substance in one that is not paramagnetic. When the solution is sufficiently dilute, the interaction between the solute particles will be negligible; the

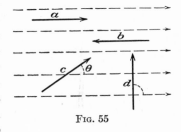

Fig. 55

solution may be either solid or liquid; each solute particle will be vibrating in a small volume, like the particles discussed in Chapter 1.

168. Energies in an External Field. In this chapter we shall give a brief and somewhat schematic discussion, treating only a few aspects of this wide problem; we may begin by inquiring how the methods of Chapters 1 and 2 would have to be modified. We consider, as before, a group of particles vibrating at various points $A, B, C \ldots$. In the absence of an external field each particle has a set of quantized energies. We have to introduce the fact that in an external field, whose intensity will be denoted by H, the allowed values of the energy are no longer the same but will depend on the intensity of the field. Let us first recall what are the possible values of the energy according to classical mechanics. Figure 55 depicts four possible positions for the axis of a dipole: (a) parallel to the field, (b) antiparallel, (c) making an angle θ with the field, and (d) at right angles to the field. When a dipole having a moment M lies parallel to the field, it requires an amount of work $2MH$ to turn the dipole through 180°. When a dipole is lying at right angles to the field, its energy is the same as in the absence of the field; if in zero field its energy is ϵ, then its energy is still ϵ. In the other cases depicted in Fig. 55 the values will be (a) $(\epsilon - MH)$; (b) $(\epsilon + MH)$; and (c) $(\epsilon - MH \cos \theta)$. All directions of the dipole are possible; this means that all values of the energy are possible between $(\epsilon - MH)$ and $(\epsilon + MH)$. In quantum mechanics, as usual, from among these energies only a discrete set is allowed. The simplest case is where there are only two allowed values, namely, $(\epsilon_r - MH)$ and $(\epsilon_r + MH)$, where ϵ_r denotes any one of the values that are allowed

[1] J. Van Vleck, "Electric and Magnetic Susceptibilities," Oxford, 1932.

in zero field; in a field H the levels occur in pairs, as shown in Fig. 56 where the set of levels labeled c is intended to represent the levels in a strong external field, while those labeled b represent the same set of states in a weaker field. The separation in each pair, namely $2MH$, decreases as the field is reduced; and if the field were completely eliminated, each pair of states would coincide in energy. The broken lines in Fig. 56 represent the energies at which the states become coincident in zero field.

If we fix attention on the set of levels for a particular value of H and consider the population of these levels, the discussion will be in no way different from that of Chapters 1 and 2. The population will adopt the

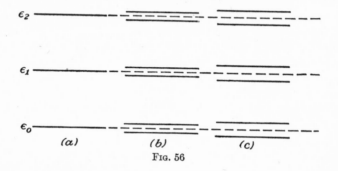

Fig. 56

usual exponential form. The reason that we give this problem a separate discussion is that we are interested in what happens when the intensity of the field is changed. As our zero of energy, we must choose an energy that is independent of H. In Fig. 56b or 56c we cannot take the lowest energy state as the zero of energy, since this has a value depending on the field; we will take instead the value of the lowest energy level in zero field. Denoting this by ϵ_0, the values of the corresponding pair of energy states in any field H will be $(\epsilon_0 - MH)$ and $(\epsilon_0 + MH)$.

The methods of dealing with states coinciding in energy were mentioned in the footnote to Sec. 14. It was pointed out that in some cases it would be more convenient to use the concept of multiple levels and, instead of numbering the individual states, to assign a number or a letter to each multiple level. This is such a case; in zero field let the allowed energies be denoted by $\epsilon_0, \epsilon_1, \epsilon_2 \ldots \epsilon_r \ldots$, each level having a multiplicity greater than unity; in the simple case that we are discussing the multiplicity of each level is 2.

169. The Partition Function in an External Field. Let P_0 denote the partition function in zero field. It is obvious that for the set of double levels the value of P_0 will be twice as great as it would be if the levels were single, since each term will occur twice. We may now raise the question whether the application of an external field at constant temperature will cause the value of the partition function to rise above or to fall below the initial value P_0. In a field H the value will be

$$P = e^{-(\epsilon_0 - MH)/kT} + e^{-(\epsilon_0 + MH)/kT} + \cdots + e^{-(\epsilon_r - MH)/kT} + e^{-(\epsilon_r + MH)/kT} + \cdots$$

$$= \tfrac{1}{2} P_0 (e^{-MH/kT} + e^{MH/kT}) \tag{431}$$

In this chapter we shall discuss ordinary weak fields, for which MH/kT is small compared with unity. Writing $MH/kT = x$, we shall have approximately

$$P = \tfrac{1}{2} P_0 (1 - x + \tfrac{1}{2}x^2 + \cdots + 1 + x + \tfrac{1}{2}x^2 + \cdots)$$

$$= P_0 \left[1 + \frac{1}{2} \left(\frac{MH}{kT} \right)^2 \right] \tag{432}$$

$$\ln P = \ln P_0 + \frac{1}{2} \left(\frac{MH}{kT} \right)^2 \tag{433}$$

We see that at any temperature T the splitting of the energy levels depicted in Fig. 56 due to the external field has the effect of increasing the value of $\ln P$. This will be true for levels of any multiplicity greater than unity. We have found in (433) that in the familiar expression (70)

$$\ln W = n \ln P + \frac{E}{kT}$$

the value of the first term on the right-hand side is increased by the presence of an external field, the increment being $\tfrac{1}{2}n(MH/kT)^2$.

In the absence of a field the directions of the dipoles are random, being uncontrolled, and we are accustomed to thinking of the external field as introducing a certain amount of order, owing to the control that it exercises on the dipoles; that is to say, we expect a decrease in $\ln W$. Now, when a weak field is applied at any constant temperature T, the change in $\ln W$ will be given by

$$\Delta \ln W = n(\ln P - \ln P_0) + \frac{E - E_0}{kT}$$

We have just seen that the first term on the right-hand side is positive. If, then, the whole is negative, the last term must not only be negative in sign but greater in magnitude. By using (78) we can express this last term in a convenient form, and obtain

$$\Delta \ln W = \frac{n}{2} \left(\frac{MH}{kT} \right)^2 + \frac{1}{kT} \left[nkT^2 \frac{\partial}{\partial T} (\ln P - \ln P_0) \right]$$

$$= \frac{n}{2} \left(\frac{MH}{kT} \right)^2 - n \left(\frac{MH}{kT} \right)^2 \tag{434}$$

We see that, when the weak field is applied, the last term decreases by an amount that is double the increment in the preceding term. We thus verify that the field introduces a certain amount of order.

170. The Polarization. If we have a group of n particles, each with a permanent moment M, the greatest total moment that we could obtain, if they are rigid dipoles, is nM. This is only obtainable at the absolute zero of temperature, when all are aligned by the field. At room temperature we may expect to find that the total moment is given by nM multiplied by a number that is small compared with unity.

Consider now the free energy F. Since the quantities F and MH both have the dimensions of an energy, it follows that, if we differentiate F with respect to H at constant temperature, the result will have the dimensions of a moment. If we consider the number of particles in unit volume in the simple problem under discussion the result will, in fact, be the "moment per unit volume" of the substance. From (433) we obtain

$$\left(\frac{\partial F}{\partial H}\right)_T = -nkT\left(\frac{\partial \ln P}{\partial H}\right)_T = -\frac{nkT}{2}\left(\frac{M}{kT}\right)^2 2H = -nM\left(\frac{MH}{kT}\right) \quad (435)$$

Now MH/kT is a small dimensionless quantity. We have therefore obtained nM multiplied by a number that is small compared with unity.

We obtain the same expression if we suppose that each particle makes to the total moment a contribution equal either to M or to $-M$ according as its energy in the field is either $-MH$ or $+MH$, the former being the energy of each of the n_- dipoles that have their component along the field, and the latter being the energy of each of the n_+ dipoles that have their component against the field. The contributions of the latter must be added together and subtracted from the contributions of the former. The total resultant moment will be

$$n_-M - n_+M = M(n_- - n_+)$$

$$= \frac{Mn}{P}\sum\left[e^{-(\epsilon_r - MH)/kT} - e^{-(\epsilon_r + MH)/kT}\right]$$

$$= \frac{Mn}{P}\sum e^{-\epsilon_r/kT}(e^{MH/kT} - e^{-MH/kT})$$

$$= \frac{Mn}{P}\sum e^{-\epsilon_r/kT}(1 + x + \cdots - 1 + x + \cdots) \quad (436)$$

Since the numerator contains terms in x, the x^2 by which P differs from P_0 may be neglected. The numerator contains a sum equal to $\frac{1}{2}P_0$. We obtain then

$$\frac{nM}{P_0}\frac{P_0}{2}\left(1 + \frac{MH}{kT} - 1 + \frac{MH}{kT}\right) = nM\frac{MH}{kT} \quad (437)$$

The sum of all the contributions is thus found to be equal to the value of the total moment that was found in (435).

Since the thermal agitation of the particles tends to spoil the alignment in the external field, we should expect that the total moment would decrease with rise of temperature. We see from (437) that so long as MH

is small compared with kT, the resultant moment is inversely proportional to the absolute temperature.

We have throughout been studying cases where each dipole reacts with the field independently of the others, the mutual interaction between dipoles being negligible. The expression (435) applies to this case. When there is a small or large interaction between the dipoles, the polarization will show the usual decrease with rise of temperature (due to the increasing disorder), but at a rate that differs from (437) to a smaller or larger extent.

If we consider, on the other hand, a solid whose structure already contains a high degree of order in the absence of a field, we can imagine cases in which over a certain range of temperature the application of an external field will produce (instead of order) disorder by altering the initial relations between the particles. In fact, crystals exist whose behavior in electrostatic fields at low temperatures can be accounted for in this way.[1] As a necessary consequence, the dielectric constant increases with rise of temperature, instead of decreasing.[2]

171. We shall turn now to the other aspect of these external fields that was mentioned in Sec. 167; we shall consider the fact that a change in field strength enables us to produce changes in the energy levels similar to those which accompany a change in volume. We may construct a diagram analogous to Fig. 17. Figure 57a is intended to represent populated levels in an external field of moderate strength. The six horizontal lines represent the numbers of particles in the various energy states (three double levels split by the field). An exponential curve passes through the ends of the six horizontal lines. Figures 57b and 57c show the effect of suddenly decreasing or increasing the strength of the field. The lengths of the lines are the same as before, indicating that there has not been time for a rearrangement to take place, but the separation of the levels in each pair is narrower in the weaker field and wider in the stronger field. Neither in Fig. 57b nor in Fig. 57c is it possible to draw an exponential curve through the six points; the population of the levels is out of equilibrium. The total energy E has a different value in each of the three situations; in each case the value of w is less than the w_{max} appropriate to the amount of energy shared by the particles. A rearrangement of the particles will at once take place, of a kind that allows w to take higher values.

It is not important whether we say that the group of particles is thermally isolated or not. If the group is in contact with a thermal reservoir, it takes a certain amount of time for heat to be transferred; in the meantime the particles behave as if the total energy had to remain constant.

[1] J. Kirkwood, *J. Chem. Phys.*, **8**, 211 (1940).

[2] For example, hydrogen bromide, C. P. Smyth and C. S. Hitchcock, *J. Am. Chem. Soc.*, **55**, 1835 (1933).

We may therefore discuss the case of thermal isolation. Consider each pair of levels in Fig. 57b. In the relative population of each pair there is too great a disparity; in Fig. 57c the disparity is not great enough. Let us discuss Fig. 57b first. In each pair of levels in Fig. 57b, if the population is to regain an exponential form, some particles must be transferred from the member that contains more particles to the member that contains fewer, that is, from the lower member of each pair to the upper member. To raise particles in this way requires energy. If E is to remain constant, this energy must be borrowed from that shared by the population. For example, if a *few* particles fall down from the double level $(\epsilon_1 \pm MH)$

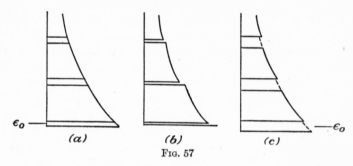

ϵ_0

(a)   (b)   (c)

ϵ_0

Fig. 57

to the double level $(\epsilon_0 \pm MH)$, or from the double level $(\epsilon_2 \pm MH)$, and so on, this will liberate sufficient energy to raise *many* particles from the lower to the upper member of each double level. In this way the population can regain an exponential form. Since this enables w to take larger values, the process will take place spontaneously.

In Sec. 22 we adopted the point of view that in any exponential population the temperature is higher when the value of μ is smaller. Perhaps no physical phenomenon illustrates this so strikingly as the magnetic (or electric) heating and cooling that is under discussion. When the value of the external field is suddenly changed from H to $(H + \delta H)$ or to $(H - \delta H)$, the level system is slightly altered and the total energy E likewise. As for the temperature, the only question to be asked is whether the population, when it has regained an exponential form, will be exponential with the same value of μ or with a larger or a smaller value. We have examined the situation of Fig. 57b, which is for a reduction in the intensity of the field H. We have found that, in the population as a whole, a falling of particles from higher to lower levels is a necessary part of the spontaneous rearrangement that will take place. This means that the population will be exponential with a slightly greater value of μ; in other words, the temperature is lower. It has been mentioned previously that by making use of this process matter has been reduced to temperatures lower than can be attained by any other means.

Throughout this chapter we have been paying attention only to those particles which react with the external field H. In the common paramagnetic salts the metallic ions are paramagnetic, while the anions and the water of crystallization are not. As mentioned above, mixed crystals are often used, in which the paramagnetic ions are present to only a small percentage. When such a crystal is in thermal equilibrium, the value of μ for one component cannot differ from that of the others. Thus, when the crystal is demagnetized and the value of μ for the paramagnetic ions is made to increase, the whole crystal is, of course, cooled by an amount depending on the heat capacity of the crystal.

Turning now to Fig. 57c, we see that here the process is the converse of the preceding. In each multiple level, particles need to be transferred from the upper member to the lower; this would liberate energy. If E is to remain constant, in the population as a whole there must be a tendency for particles to be thrown up from lower to higher levels. This means the adoption of a smaller value of μ, and consequently a rise in temperature.

172. The ratio between the number of particles that have energy $(\epsilon + MH)$ to the number that have energy $(\epsilon - MH)$ has the same value, $e^{-2MH/kT}$, whether we use classical or quantum mechanics. When the multiplicity is greater than 2, there will be one or more states within this interval. In classical mechanics all energies within the interval $(\epsilon \pm MH)$ are possible, and the population of these energies will be exponential; the number of particles which have energy $(\epsilon - \eta)$ in this interval will be slightly more numerous than those which have the corresponding energy $(\epsilon + \eta)$, the ratio being $e^{2\eta/kT}$; this is equivalent to saying that at any moment the number of particles whose moment has a component parallel to the field is slightly greater than the number whose moment has an equal component antiparallel to the field; the exponential population thus implies a polarization of the substance in the external field. The behavior will be quite similar to that described in Secs. 170 and 171 and the expressions will differ only by a numerical factor.

A basic problem involving strong interaction between dipoles was treated by Froelich, who considered in detail a crystal in which each molecular dipole has only two positions of equilibrium, differing in direction by 180°.[1] In a polar liquid such as water, the problem is more complex, even near the freezing point.[2] In both cases, if we apply a strong external field of some kilovolts per centimeter, we disturb the initial state only slightly. The number of dipoles with a component parallel to the field is slightly greater than the number with a component antiparallel to the field.

When small positive and negative ions are introduced into such a

[1] H. Froelich, *Proc. Roy. Soc. A.*, **185**, 399 (1946).
[2] J. Kirkwood, *J. Chem. Phys.*, **7**, 911 (1939).

liquid, those polar molecules which happen to be near to one of these ions at any time are subject to a very strong field. In this case the electrical analogues of the magnetic cooling and heating give rise to large effects. In general, when the polar dielectric, as a result of any process, is subjected to additional ionic fields, that is, when ions are introduced into the liquid or when a neutral molecule in the liquid dissociates into a pair of ions, there is a heating effect. Conversely, when ions are removed, this is equivalent to shutting off the external field. When, for example, positive and negative ions recombine to form neutral molecules, there is a pronounced cooling.

The dissociation of a molecule into ions or into atoms, treated in Sec. 89, requires a certain amount of work, the potential energy being of the form depicted in Fig. 30. If the atoms or ions recombine to form the molecule, the potential energy is reconverted into kinetic energy and usually appears as heat. When ions in a polar solvent recombine, there is the cooling effect to be taken into account as well. Three cases are found: the cooling (absorption of heat) may be either greater than, equal to, or less than the amount of potential energy released (evolution of heat).[1]

In discussing the order-disorder problems of Secs. 65 to 69, it was natural to start from the state of perfect order and to discuss the introduction of a certain amount of disorder. On the other hand, in studying the paramagnetic and dielectric problems, we have started from the state of complete disorder and have evaluated the degree of order introduced by the field. This difference in treatment somewhat obscures the fact that all three problems are analogous. The amount of work $2MH$ corresponds to (1) the work required in Sec. 65 to remove a particle and place it on the surface of the crystal, and (2) the work required in Sec. 66 to interchange a pair of particles. In all these problems there belongs to each temperature T an appropriate amount of disorder. In discussing the vacant lattice points of Sec. 65 it is clearly impossible to take as our starting point a state of complete disorder. In a discussion of the paramagnetic and dielectric problems, on the other hand, we can start from the state of perfect order (not attained in practice), discuss the equilibrium in terms of W_{cf} and W_{th}, and reach the same conclusions as those reached in Sec. 170. In Secs. 173 and 174 we shall return to the problems of Chapter 3 and give a more quantitative treatment.

173. Lattice Defects in Crystals. In deriving (243) for a substitutional solution, we began by placing the solute particles in position and pointed out that this left n_A sites vacant, to accommodate the n_A solvent particles. Since the allocation of the solvent particles to these available sites could be made in only one way, this last step added nothing to the value of

---

[1] R. W. Gurney, "Ions in Solution," Chapter 13, Cambridge, 1936; *J. Chem. Phys.*, **6**, 499, 1938.

W_{cf}. We may notice now that we could equally well have begun by placing the solvent particles in position, leaving n_B sites vacant for the n_B solute particles; since the latter can be allocated to these sites in only one way, the allocation adds nothing to the value of W_{cf}. In a dilute substitutional solution, from this point of view the function of the solute is to increase the number of sites available to the solvent particles—to increase the number of sites from n_A to the slightly larger value $(n_A + n_B)$.

We can readily take the same point of view with regard to the formation of vacant lattice points by the process depicted in Fig. 22. If n_B denotes the number of vacant lattice sites formed, this has the effect of increasing the number of sites available to the n_A particles of the crystal; the number of sites is increased from the value n_A for the perfect crystal to the slightly larger value $(n_A + n_B)$ for the imperfect crystal containing n_B holes in the interior. With this notation, (243) gives the value of W_{cf} for the crystal.

The formation of additional holes does not continue indefinitely because it takes a certain amount of work V to remove a particle from the interior and place it on the surface. A discussion of this amount of work will take the same form as in Secs. 126 to 128. In a crystal at temperature T, we are interested in the amount of work needed to form the hole and leave the crystal at the original temperature T, that is to say, the work required for an isothermal process. It is not true to say that this work is equal to the change in the free energy when holes are formed, since the change in the free energy includes the change in the quantity $kT \ln W_{cf}$. As in (321), the total change in the free energy is equal to the sum of V and the change in $kT \ln W_{cf}$. It can easily be shown that the number of lattice defects will increase exponentially with temperature. Most diffusion in solids is ascribed to the presence of mobile lattice defects, which are also responsible for the ionic conductivity of polar crystals.[1]

174. Order and Disorder in Alloys. We described briefly in Sec. 66 the special kind of order that appears in certain alloys, which are said to possess a superlattice. We shall give here the theory of their behavior in the form in which it was put forward by Bragg and Williams[2]; we shall confine our attention to a crystal that contains equal numbers of A and B atoms. Starting with a state of perfect order, we showed in Sec. 66 how the exchange of A- and B-particles leads to a progressively increasing degree of disorder. At least, it does so up to a point. If all the A-particles were transferred to β-sites and all the B-particles to α-sites, we should clearly have obtained again a state of perfect order. The state of complete disorder lies halfway, that is, when as many A-particles are in α-

[1] N. F. Mott and R. W. Gurney, "Electronic Processes in Ionic Crystals," Oxford, 1940.
[2] W. L. Bragg and E. J. Williams, *Proc. Roy. Soc. A.*, **145**, 699 (1934).

sites as in β-sites. To handle this problem, let S denote the "degree of order" and let us define S in such a way that its value goes from unity, for perfect order, to zero, for complete disorder. If we divide the number of particles that occupy "right" sites by the total number of particles, the ratio gives the probability r of finding a particular particle on a right site. If now we write $(1 - r) = w$, this gives the probability of finding this particle on a wrong site. Further, if we write

$$\frac{r - w}{r + w} = S \tag{438}$$

this S will be a suitable measure of the long-distance order in the crystal.

The value of W_{cf} may be found from (243). If the number of A-particles on α-sites is A_α and the number of B-particles on α-sites is B_α, we have

$$\frac{(A_\alpha + B_\alpha)!}{A_\alpha! B_\alpha!} = \frac{N_\alpha!}{A_\alpha!(N_\alpha - A_\alpha)!} \tag{439}$$

This must be multiplied by the corresponding expression for the number of ways in which the particles on β-sites can be arranged. We now have to proceed as we did in Sec. 128. In a crystal at temperature T in a state of perfect order it takes a certain amount of work to interchange an A-particle with a B-particle isothermally. This amount of work is equal to the change in the free energy of the crystal when two particles occupying particular sites are exchanged at this temperature. It may be regarded as being due to the modification of the partition functions of all the particles concerned, namely, the two particles exchanged and the other particles occupying sites adjacent to their sites; when dm particles are transferred, the work done per particle may thus be written in the form

$$V = kT \frac{\partial}{\partial m} \sum n_i \ln \frac{P_i'}{P_i} \tag{440}$$

where the summation is over the various particles concerned. Using (439), we shall have then, as in (321),

$$\frac{\partial F}{\partial m} = V - kT \frac{\partial}{\partial m} \ln W_{cf} \tag{441}$$

Equating this to zero, for equilibrium, we obtain the result

$$\frac{w}{r} = e^{-V/2kT} \tag{442}$$

From (438) we find

$$S = \tanh\left(\frac{V}{4kT}\right) \tag{443}$$

A crystal with nearly perfect order is like a very dilute solution; we are unlikely to find two wrong particles occupying adjacent sites. But as the disorder increases this will no longer be true, and the average amount of work to interchange additional pairs of particles will be different, in fact smaller.   In the state of complete disorder the distinction between right and wrong sites has been lost and consequently the work to interchange a pair of particles must be zero.   Thus the value of V will fall from an initial value V_0, for perfect order, to the value zero for complete disorder.   Bragg and Williams made the simple assumption that V is proportional to S as defined by (438); thus

$$V = V_0 S \qquad (444)$$

It follows from (443) and (444) that for any crystal of this kind there will be a characteristic temperature above which S is zero, that is to say, above which there is complete disorder.   This behavior is analogous to the disappearance of ferromagnetism at the

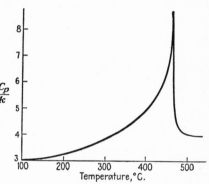

FIG. 58.   Specific heat of a copper-zinc alloy possessing a superlattice.

Curie temperature.   The critical temperature for the disappearance of order, according to (443), will be

$$T_c = \frac{V_0}{4k} \qquad (445)$$

Over the range of temperature, where atoms are being displaced, there is a large increase in the heat capacity, an example of which is given in Fig. 58. This is followed by a sudden drop in the heat capacity at the critical temperature.[1]   The theory predicts a considerable rise followed by a sudden drop, but the agreement is not quantitative.

175. Fermi-Dirac Statistics.   The difference between the Fermi-Dirac and the Bose-Einstein statistics was mentioned in the footnote to Sec. 39. The most familiar problem in which the Fermi-Dirac statistics must be used is that of the free electrons in a metal; we shall therefore discuss the statistics in connection with this problem.

In a metal we fix our attention on the valence electrons that provide the free conducting electrons.   The negative charge of these electrons is neutralized by the positive charge of the cores of the metal atoms.   Furthermore, in electrical theory it is usually stated that no electrical field can exist in a conductor in which no current is flowing.   If this were strictly true, the potential energy of an electron would be constant throughout the interior of the metal; actually there is a periodic field due to the

---

[1] C. Sykes and H. Wilkinson, *J. Inst. Metals*, **61**, 223 (1933).

positive cores of the atoms that form the lattice. To a first approximation this periodic field can be neglected, in which case the possible wave functions for a free electron in the metal will be the same as those given by (135) in Sec. 70 for a particle of a gas; the allowed energies will be given by (136) if the mass of the electron is inserted into this expression.

The treatment of the n electrons must be different from the monatomic gas of Sec. 37. It is well known that in an isolated atom there cannot be more than two electrons in the K-ring. There are two states (with opposite electron spin) associated with the K-ring, and there cannot be more than one electron in each state. This is one example of the Pauli exclusion principle. According to this principle, when a set of energy states is populated by electrons, there cannot be more than one electron in each state.

In Sec. 39 we supposed that the number of particles in each state was unrestricted and that (79) was the correct expression to use for each of the arbitrary batches of levels. Here, taking the energy levels given by (136), we shall again divide them into arbitrary batches; but instead of (79), the expression that gives the number of different ways in which n particles can be distributed among p states without putting more than one particle into each state is

$$\frac{p!}{n!(p-n)!} \tag{446}$$

Instead of (81) we shall thus have the expression

$$w = \frac{p_0!}{n_0!(p_0-n_0)!} \times \frac{p_1!}{n_1!(p_1-n_1)!} \times \cdots \times \frac{p_r!}{n_r!(p_r-n_r)!} \times \cdots \tag{447}$$

In each batch of levels the quantity $(p_r - n_r)$ is the number of vacant states. If the batches of levels are chosen such that in each case both n_r and $(p_r - n_r)$ are large compared with unity, we may use Stirling's approximation. For any rearrangement of the electrons

$$\delta \ln w = - \sum \ln\left(\frac{p_r}{n_r} - 1\right) \delta n_r \tag{448}$$

Introducing undetermined multipliers λ and $-\mu$, we may obtain

$$\ln\left(\frac{p_r}{n_r} - 1\right) = \mu\epsilon_r - \lambda \tag{449}$$

The usual identification is made between μ and $1/kT$, and the population of the levels at temperature T is given by

$$\frac{n_r}{p_r} = \frac{1}{e^{\epsilon_r/kT}e^{-\lambda} + 1} \tag{450}$$

It will be noticed that (450) differs from (93) only in that there is a plus sign instead of a minus sign in the denominator.

As in (93), the density of states depends on the volume v in which the particles move, while n_r depends on the total number of particles present in this volume. In a problem where few particles are present, p_r/n_r will be large compared with unity, even for the lowest batch of levels, and may be substituted for $(p_r/n_r - 1)$ in (449). In this case (450) reduces to (94). Thus when the number of particles per unit volume is not large, both forms of quantum statistics, the Bose-Einstein and the Fermi-Dirac, do not differ appreciably from the classical Maxwellian. In the case of a metal the number of free electrons per unit volume is very large, and we have to discuss (450).

The number of energy states for an electron in a narrow range of energy $d\epsilon$ will be denoted by $N(\epsilon) d\epsilon$, as in (154). In order to make use of this expression, it is convenient to replace n_r/p_r by a continuous function $q(\epsilon)$, similar to the $q(E)$ of Sec. 155

$$q(\epsilon) = \frac{1}{e^{(\epsilon/kT-\lambda)} + 1} \tag{451}$$

$q(\epsilon)$ taking the value unity for levels completely filled and the value zero for levels completely empty; the number of electrons having energy lying between ϵ and $(\epsilon + d\epsilon)$ will be given by the product $N(\epsilon)q(\epsilon) d\epsilon$.

It was pointed out in Sec. 34 that the value of n_r given for any energy level by (73) is independent of the zero from which the allowed energies are measured and that this necessary condition is satisfied because the energies occur in both the numerator and denominator. In (450), however, the ϵ_r occurs explicitly only once, so that if any arbitrary quantity is added to ϵ_r, the value of n_r/p_r appears to change and so to depend on the zero of energy from which ϵ_r is measured. Since this is impossible, we may conclude that the parameter λ contains an energy that is measured from the same zero of energy as ϵ_r; as λ is a pure number, it may be the ratio between two energies. If, for example, we write ϵ^*/kT for λ, (451) would take the form

$$q(\epsilon) = \frac{1}{e^{(\epsilon-\epsilon^*)/kT} + 1} \tag{452}$$

In this form, discussed below, the value of the right-hand side is independent of the zero of energy provided that ϵ^* is measured from the same zero as ϵ.

176. The expression (450) was based on the Pauli exclusion principle; let us now examine the condition of the metal at the absolute zero of temperature, according to the same principle. The electrons will have fallen into the lowest states of which they are capable; that is to say, the n electrons will occupy the n lowest states. The expression (153) gives the number of states of translational motion having energy less than ϵ. Here $n/2$ such states will accommodate the n electrons, since each of these states can accommodate a pair of electrons with opposite spin. To find the energy of the highest level that will be occupied by an electron at the absolute zero, we have to equate (153) to $n/2$; thus we find

$$\epsilon' = \frac{h^2}{8m}\left(\frac{3n}{\pi v}\right)^{\frac{2}{3}} \tag{453}$$

$$= 5.8 \times 10^{-27}\left(\frac{n}{v}\right)^{\frac{2}{3}} \text{ erg} \tag{454}$$

Thus at the absolute zero of temperature, for ϵ less than ϵ' we have $q(\epsilon)$ equal to unity, and for ϵ greater than ϵ' we have $q(\epsilon)$ equal to zero.

If we supply some thermal energy to the metal, a number of electrons will be thrown into levels above the critical level ϵ'. Thus for some levels

TABLE 14. VALUES OF $q(\epsilon)$ FROM (445)

ϵ	$e^{(\epsilon-\epsilon^*)/kT}$	$q(\epsilon)$
$\epsilon \gg \epsilon^*$		$\sim e^{-(\epsilon-\epsilon^*)/kT}$
$\epsilon = \epsilon^* + 2kT$	e^2	0.12
$\epsilon = \epsilon^*$	1	0.50
$\epsilon = \epsilon^* - 2kT$	$1/e^2$	0.86
$\epsilon \ll \epsilon^*$	~ 0	~ 1.0

below the critical level ϵ' at least, $q(\epsilon)$ will no longer be as great as unity, while for levels above ϵ' the value of $q(\epsilon)$ will be greater than zero. Let us now discuss the expression (452), which contains a critical energy denoted by ϵ^*. Near the absolute zero of temperature we can have the value of kT as small as we like; the situation will then be as follows. For energy levels lying below ϵ^* the value of $(\epsilon - \epsilon^*)$ is negative and the exponential term is small compared with unity; thus the value of $q(\epsilon)$ is somewhat less than unity. For energy levels lying above ϵ^* the value of $(\epsilon - \epsilon^*)$ is positive and the exponential term, being large compared with unity, may be brought up into the numerator with opposite sign

$$q(\epsilon) = e^{-(\epsilon-\epsilon^*)/kT} \tag{455}$$

Thus in the levels above ϵ^* we have an exponential population fed with electrons from the occupied levels below ϵ^*. At any temperature near the absolute zero, according to (452), there is a rapid change from nearly filled levels below the critical level ϵ^* to nearly empty levels above ϵ^*; thus at these temperatures the level ϵ^* is to be identified with ϵ', given by (453). For $\epsilon = \epsilon^*$ the value of $q(\epsilon)$ is $\frac{1}{2}$. This value, together with some others, is given in Table 14, which shows that the population of the levels falls from 86 per cent filled to only 12 per cent filled, within a range of energy $4kT$. The values from Table 14 are plotted in Fig. 59, where the energy

ϵ is, as usual, on a vertical scale and abscissas are $q(\epsilon)$. Only energies in the neighborhood of ϵ^* are included in the diagram. It has been mentioned that at room temperature kT is equal to $\frac{1}{40}$ electron-volt. Thus at $30°K$ the quantity $4kT$ would be equal to only $\frac{1}{100}$ electron-volt; this range of energy is thus very narrow compared with the kinetic energy of the majority of the electrons. As the temperature rises the transition from the filled levels to the empty levels becomes less sharp, but it is still fairly sharp at room temperature.

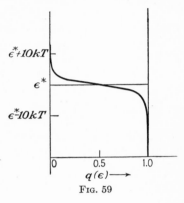

FIG. 59

Although we have pointed out that ϵ^* is to be identified with ϵ' near the absolute zero, we have not said that ϵ^* in (452) denotes a value independent of the temperature. Nevertheless it is true that at room temperature the value of ϵ^* differs very little from ϵ'. According to (154) and (451), the total number of electrons in the metal is given by

$$n = \int_{\epsilon_0}^{\infty} N(\epsilon)q(\epsilon)\, d\epsilon = 4\pi v \left(\frac{2m}{h^2}\right)^{\frac{3}{2}} \int_{\epsilon_0}^{\infty} \frac{\epsilon^{\frac{1}{2}}\, d\epsilon}{e^{(\epsilon/kT-\lambda)} + 1} \tag{456}$$

The form of $q(\epsilon)$ that results from the evaluation of this integral is (452), to a first approximation with $\epsilon^* = \epsilon'$ and to a second approximation with

$$\epsilon^* = \epsilon'\left[1 - \frac{\pi^2}{12}\left(\frac{kT}{\epsilon' - \epsilon_0}\right)^2\right] \tag{457}$$

It has already been pointed out with reference to Table 14 that at room temperature the value of kT is very small compared with $(\epsilon' - \epsilon_0)$, but the extra term in (457) may become important in connection with thermionic emission at high temperatures.

177. Bose-Einstein Statistics. When discussing a perfect gas in Chapter 2, we treated each molecule as a particle of mass m and disregarded the fact that the molecule is a composite particle, built up from certain elementary particles. It appears that each species of elementary particle, electrons, protons, neutrons, and neutrinos, obeys the Fermi-Dirac statistics, and that, as a result, a composite particle consisting of an even number of elementary particles will obey the Bose-Einstein statistics. (A unified rule concerning the antisymmetry of the wave functions expresses both these requirements.)

In Chapter 2 we discussed only the expression (94), which is the simple form of (93) when n_r/p_r is small compared with unity. We asserted that, in the treatment of nearly perfect gases, (94) covered all cases of practical interest; we may now seek to justify this statement.

Introducing a continuous function $q(\epsilon)$, we may put (93) into the form corresponding to (451)

$$q(\epsilon)\, d\epsilon = \frac{d\epsilon}{e^{(\epsilon/kT+\lambda)} - 1} \tag{458}$$

Since (154) gives the number of energy levels for the gas molecules, the expression for n, the total number of molecules, only differs from (456) in that the minus sign again occurs in the denominator and the factor 2, which was introduced into (453) for the alternative electron spins, will be absent. If we take the level ϵ_0 as the zero of energy, we have thus to evaluate the integral

$$\int_0^\infty \frac{\epsilon^{\frac{1}{2}}\, d\epsilon}{e^{(\epsilon/kT+\lambda)} - 1} \tag{459}$$

We now make the substitution $z = \epsilon/kT$ and thus put (459) into the form

$$(kT)^{\frac{3}{2}} \int_0^\infty \frac{z^{\frac{1}{2}}\, dz}{e^{(z+\lambda)} - 1} \tag{460}$$

The value of this definite integral is known to be

$$\int_0^\infty \frac{z^{\frac{1}{2}}\, dz}{e^{(z+\lambda)} - 1} = \frac{1}{2}\sqrt{\pi}\left(e^{-\lambda} + \frac{e^{-2\lambda}}{2^{\frac{3}{2}}} + \cdots\right) \tag{461}$$

If the value of $e^{-\lambda}$ is very small compared with unity, it will make no appreciable difference whether the second and succeeding terms are included. To test this, we retain only the term $e^{-\lambda}$ and obtain

$$n = \int_0^\infty \mathrm{N}(\epsilon)q(\epsilon)\, d\epsilon = \frac{(8mkT)^{\frac{3}{2}}v}{4h^3}\frac{\sqrt{\pi}}{2}e^{-\lambda} \tag{462}$$

Hence

$$e^{-\lambda} = \frac{nh^3}{v(2\pi mkT)^{\frac{3}{2}}} \tag{463}$$

This quantity is least likely to be small in the case of small m and small T. We may therefore evaluate it for the hydrogen atom at low temperatures. The value of n/v at standard temperature and pressure is 2.7×10^{19}. Taking the same value for n/v at, for example, 9°K, we find for (463) the value 0.005, which is sufficiently small compared with unity. Thus at this temperature (94) may be used instead of (93) for all gases and vapors at low densities. At temperatures still nearer to the absolute zero, however, the difference may become appreciable, though the effect will be difficult to disentangle from effects arising from the intermolecular van der Waals forces.

178. Atomic Nuclei. We have seen in Chapter 1 that for a group of 20 particles, the number of possible states may easily be greater than 10^{10}. Now in the nuclei of the heavier elements the number of particles is much greater than 20; thus in the plutonium nucleus Pu^{239} there are 145 neutrons and 94 protons. When the nuclear particles are sharing a total energy E, the group, will tend to adopt the states that can arise in the greatest number of ways. Hence, in writing down expressions that attempt to describe the properties of heavy nuclei, the usual exponential factor $e^{-\mu E}$ often occurs.[1] Bohr has given a discussion of nuclear fission in terms of a microcanonical ensemble.[2] The amounts of energy shared by nuclear particles are very large—usually to be measured in millions of electron-volts; as a result, when the exponential factor is written in the form $e^{-E/kT}$, the effective temperature T ascribed to the interior of the nucleus is very high.

Problems

1. Two similar specimens, A and B, of iron ammonium alum have been cooled to $2°K$ and are held in a magnetic field of 2000 gauss. An amount of heat is allowed to enter A sufficient to raise its temperature to $3°K$. The specimen B is put through the following cycle: the intensity of the magnetic field is rapidly increased to 20,000 gauss; then the same amount of heat is admitted to B as was admitted to A; the field is then reduced to 2000 gauss. Describe briefly how the population of the energy levels will have changed during each of these steps, both for the paramagnetic ions and for the other particles in the crystal, and state how the final temperature of B will compare with that of A.

2. The expression (213) in Sec. 88 gives the change in $\ln W$ when the energy levels are modified as a result of a change in pressure. What are the expressions corresponding to (213), (214), and (215) when the energy levels are altered by a change in the value of an external field H?

---

[1] V. Weisskopf, *Phys. Rev.*, **52**, 295 (1937); H. Bethe, *Rev. Modern Physics*, **9**, 80 (1937).

[2] N. Bohr, *Phys. Rev.*, **56**, 426 (1941).

APPENDIX

Note 1. Stirling's Approximation. The logarithm of factorial n is by definition

$$\ln n! = \ln n + \ln (n-1) + \ln (n-2) + \cdots \text{ to } n \text{ terms} \qquad (A1)$$

For comparison consider the logarithm of n^n; we have

$$\ln (n^n) = \ln n + \ln n + \ln n + \cdots \text{ to } n \text{ terms} \qquad (A2)$$

It is clear that the value of $(A1)$ is smaller than that of $(A2)$, and the question arises as to how great the difference is. Stirling was able to show that when n is very large compared with unity, the difference does not differ appreciably from n itself. That is to say, for large n we may write

$$\ln n! = n \ln n - n$$

Note 2. The Integral $\int_0^\infty e^{-b^2 z^2}\, dz$.

This is equal to

$$\frac{1}{b} \int_0^\infty e^{-b^2 z^2}\, d(bz)$$

The integral is a pure number, and we may either write

$$\mathcal{I} = \frac{1}{b} \int_0^\infty e^{-x^2}\, dx \qquad \text{or} \qquad \mathcal{I} = \frac{1}{b} \int_0^\infty e^{-y^2}\, dy$$

Multiplying these together we obtain

$$\mathcal{I}^2 = \frac{1}{b^2} \int_0^\infty \int_0^\infty e^{-(x^2+y^2)}\, dx\, dy$$

The quantity $dx\, dy$ may be taken to be the area of a small rectangle in the x,y plane, like that at the point R in Fig. 45. The quantity $\sqrt{x^2 + y^2}$ is the distance r between R and the origin. The line joining R to the origin makes an angle θ with the x-axis given by

$$x = r \cos \theta \qquad \text{and} \qquad y = r \sin \theta$$

at the same time

$$dx\, dy = r\, dr\, d\theta$$

Hence we obtain

$$\mathcal{I}^2 = \frac{1}{b^2} \int_0^{\frac{\pi}{2}} \int_0^\infty r e^{-r^2}\, dr\, d\theta$$

$$= \frac{1}{b^2} \frac{\pi}{4}$$

$$\mathcal{I} = \frac{1}{2} \sqrt{\frac{\pi}{b^2}} \qquad (A3)$$

By symmetry the value of the integral $\int_{-\infty}^{+\infty} e^{-b^2 z^2}\, dz$ is twice as great.

Note 3. The Method of Undetermined Multipliers. In Fig. 11 we considered a rearrangement of the particles in a set of energy levels; only three levels were involved. Let us consider a similar arrangement involving q levels (this q having no connection with the q of Sec. 15). If the levels involved are, for example, the ith, jth, kth, lth, and mth levels, we should have $q = 5$. We may use the word *increments* for the quantities dn_i, dn_j, dn_k, dn_l, and dn_m, recognizing that some of these quantities will be negative. If the rearrangement is one in which E and n remain unchanged, any two of these q increments may be regarded as a function of the remaining $(q - 2)$ increments; that is to say, if we are told the values of $(q - 2)$ of these increments, the values of the remaining two are known. Suppose, for example, that we are told the values of dn_i, dn_l, and dn_m; let us denote by dE' the change in energy due to these three increments. Then the remaining two increments dn_j and dn_k must involve a change in energy equal to $- dE'$ if the total energy is to remain unchanged; that is to say, we must have

$$\epsilon_j \, dn_j + \epsilon_k \, dn_k = - dE' \tag{A4}$$

Similarly, if dn' denotes the algebraic sum of dn_i, dn_l, and dn_m, we must have

$$dn_j + dn_k = - dn' \tag{A5}$$

Multiplying (A5) by ϵ_j or ϵ_k and subtracting from (A4), the values of n_j and n_k are at once found. Thus, in general, any two increments may be regarded as a function of the remaining $q - 2$ increments.

Equation (48) may be written in the form

$$\frac{\partial E}{\partial n_0} \, dn_0 + \frac{\partial E}{\partial n_1} \, dn_1 + \cdots = 0 \tag{A6}$$

Likewise (49) may be written

$$\frac{\partial n}{\partial n_0} \, dn_0 + \frac{\partial n}{\partial n_1} \, dn_1 + \cdots = 0 \tag{A7}$$

In Sec. 25 we wished to know the values of n_1, n_2, and so on for which $\ln W$ has its maximum value subject to the conditions (A6) and (A7). In a problem of this kind there may be one, two, or more such conditions to be satisfied. We shall here consider the case where there are two such requirements. In order to set out the method in a general form, instead of the three quantities $\ln W$, E, and n, let us write three quantities f, g, and h, respectively. Then, if there are altogether s levels and if x_1 stands for ϵ_0, and so on, (A6) takes the form

$$\frac{\partial g}{\partial x_1} \, dx_1 + \frac{\partial g}{\partial x_2} \, dx_2 + \cdots + \frac{\partial g}{\partial x_s} \, dx_s = 0 \tag{A8}$$

and (A7) takes the form

$$\frac{\partial h}{\partial x_1}\,dx_1 + \frac{\partial h}{\partial x_2}\,dx_2 + \cdots + \frac{\partial h}{\partial x_s}\,dx_s = 0 \tag{A9}$$

We wish to find the values of x_1, x_2 ... for which the following quantity is equal to zero:

$$\frac{\partial f}{\partial x_1}\,dx_1 + \frac{\partial f}{\partial x_2}\,dx_2 + \cdots + \frac{\partial f}{\partial x_s}\,dx_s \tag{A10}$$

A redistribution may involve all these s variables. But we have seen that the effect of two conditions, such as (A8) and (A9), is to reduce the number of independent increments from s to $(s-2)$. The undetermined multipliers of Sec. 25 may be used to eliminate two of the increments from (A10). Multiplying (A8) by μ and (A9) by λ, we add them to (A10) and obtain

$$\left(\frac{\partial f}{\partial x_1} + \mu\frac{\partial g}{\partial x_1} + \lambda\frac{\partial h}{\partial x_1}\right)dx_1 + \left(\frac{\partial f}{\partial x_2} + \mu\frac{\partial g}{\partial x_2} + \lambda\frac{\partial h}{\partial x_2}\right)dx_2 + \cdots$$
$$+ \left(\frac{\partial f}{\partial x_s} + \mu\frac{\partial g}{\partial x_s} + \lambda\frac{\partial h}{\partial x_s}\right)dx_s = 0 \tag{A11}$$

Let us now take dx_3, dx_4 ... dx_s as the independent increments, regarding dx_1 and dx_2 as the increments that are functions of the former; and let us fix our attention on the values that x_1 and x_2 will have when the quantity f has its maximum value, (corresponding to the population of the levels ϵ_0 and ϵ_1 when $\ln W$ has its maximum value). If the values of μ and λ are chosen so as to make the first two bracketed expressions in (A11) equal to zero, that is, to satisfy

$$\frac{\partial f}{\partial x_1} + \mu\frac{\partial g}{\partial x_1} + \lambda\frac{\partial h}{\partial x_1} = 0 \quad \text{and} \quad \frac{\partial f}{\partial x_2} + \mu\frac{\partial g}{\partial x_2} + \lambda\frac{\partial h}{\partial x_2} = 0$$

then the equation (A11) reduces to

$$\left(\frac{\partial f}{\partial x_3} + \mu\frac{\partial g}{\partial x_3} + \lambda\frac{\partial h}{\partial x_3}\right)dx_3 + \cdots + \left(\frac{\partial f}{\partial x_s} + \mu\frac{\partial g}{\partial x_s} + \lambda\frac{\partial h}{\partial x_s}\right)dx_s = 0 \tag{A12}$$

for any rearrangement involving x_1 and x_2.

For example, we may consider, as we did in Chapter 1, a rearrangement involving only three of the x's (that is to say, only three of the levels), for example, x_1, x_2, and x_r; all the increments in (A12) except dx_r are zero. It follows at once that

$$\frac{\partial f}{\partial x_r} + \mu\frac{\partial g}{\partial x_r} + \lambda\frac{\partial h}{\partial x_r} = 0$$

and likewise for any other of the x's. Thus, the quantity f has its maximum value when each of the bracketed expressions in (A11) is separately equal to zero. This is equivalent to the condition that was used in (52) to derive the exponential form of a population, which had already been derived in (22).

TABLE 15. THE ELEMENTS OF ATOMIC NUMBERS FROM 1 TO 30

Z	Element	A	Abundance, per cent	Z	Element	A	Abundance, per cent
1	H	1	99.98	19	K	39	93.38
		2	0.02			40	0.012
2	He	3	10^{-5}			41	6.61
		4	100	20	Ca	40	96.96
3	Li	6	7.5			42	0.64
		7	92.5			43	0.15
4	Be	9	100			44	2.06
5	B	10	18.4			46	0.0033
		11	81.6			48	0.19
6	C	12	98.9	21	Sc	45	100
		13	1.1	22	To	46	7.95
7	N	14	99.62			47	7.75
		15	0.38			48	73.45
8	O	16	99.757			49	5.51
		17	0.039			50	5.34
		18	0.204	23	V	51	100
9	F	19	100	24	Cr	50	4.49
10	Ne	20	90.00			52	83.78
		21	0.27			53	9.43
		22	9.73			54	2.30
11	Na	23	100	25	Mn	55	100
12	Mg	24	77.4	26	Fe	54	6.04
		25	11.5			56	91.57
		26	11.1			57	2.11
13	Al	27	100			58	0.28
14	Si	28	89.6	27	Co	59	100
		29	6.2	28	Ni	58	67.4
		30	4.2			60	26.7
15	P	31	100			61	1.2
16	S	32	95.1			62	3.8
		33	0.74			64	0.88
		34	4.2	29	Cu	63	70.13
		36	0.016			65	29.87
17	Cl	35	75.4	30	Zn	64	50.9
		37	24.6			66	27.3
18	A	36	0.307			67	3.9
		38	0.061			68	17.4
		40	99.632			70	0.5

TABLE 16.

Electronic charge......... $e = 4.802 \times 10^{-10}$ e.s.u.
Planck's constant......... $h = 6.624 \times 10^{-27}$ erg sec
Boltzmann's constant..... $k = 1.3805 \times 10^{-16}$ erg/degree
Avogadro's constant...... $L = 6.023 \times 10^{23}$
Mass of the electron...... $m = 9.107 \times 10^{-28}$ g.
Mass of the proton....... 1.6725×10^{-24} g.
Number of molecules in 1
  cubic centimeter of gas at
  N.T.P................. 2.687×10^{19}
1 calorie................ 4.185×10^7 ergs
1 electron-volt.......... $\begin{cases} 1.602 \times 10^{-12} \text{ erg} \\ 23{,}052 \text{ cal/mole} \end{cases}$

TABLE 17. THE EXPONENTIAL FUNCTION

x	e^{-x}	x	e^{-x}
1.0	0.3679	4.0	0.01832
1.5	0.2231	4.5	0.01111
2.0	0.1353	5.0	0.00674
2.5	0.0821	5.5	0.00409
3.0	0.0498	6.0	0.00248
3.5	0.0302	6.5	0.00150

NAME INDEX

A

Adam, N. K., 198

B

Band, W., 170, 198, 202
Barnes, C., 226
Bethe, H., 255
Blaisse, B., 198
Bohr, N., 255
Born, M., 6, 201
Bose, S. N., 49, 250, 253
Bragg, W. L., 247, 249
Brunauer, S., 195
Burton, E. F., 238

C

Carpenter, H., 148
Coleman, F. F., 221

D

Debye, P., 210, 212
Dennison, D. M., 236
Devonshire, A. F., 128, 129, 170, 200
Dirac, P. A. M., 49, 249, 251
Ditchburn, R. W., 231

E

Egerton, A., 221
Einstein, A., 49, 250, 253
Eucken, A., 231

F

Farkas, A., 236
Fermi, E., 49, 249, 251
Flory, P. J., 203
Fowler, R. H., 6, 109, 144, 164, 223, 226, 231, 232

Froelich, H., 245
Fuchs, K., 201

G

Giauque, W. F., 233
Gilmour, J. C., 231
Gordon, A. R., 226
Green, H. S., 6
Guggenheim, E. A., 108, 109, 144, 223, 226, 231, 232
Gurney, R. W., 38, 109, 246, 247

H

Haantjes, J., 119, 231
Harrison, S. F., 201
Herzfeld, K. T., 186, 192
Hildebrand, J. H., 149
Hill, T. L., 170
Hitchcock, C. S., 243

I

Itterbeck, J. A. van, 229

J

Johnston, H. L., 233

K

Keesom, W. H., 119, 229, 237
Kennard, E. H., 195
Kirkwood, J., 243, 245
Kurti, N., 238

L

Lammeren, A. van, 229
Landau, A., 190
Langmuir, I., 170
Lennard Jones, J. E., 128, 200

263

Lifschitz, E., 190
London, F., 195

M

McGuire, F., 157
Mayer, J. E., 201–203
Mayer, M. G., 201, 203
Michels, A., 198
Michels, C., 198
Miller, A. R., 145
Mott, N. F., 109, 247

P

Pauli, W., 48, 250

R

Rice, O. K., 174
Robertson, J. M., 148
Ruhemann, B., 238
Ruhemann, M., 238
Rushbrooke, G. S., 164

S

Schroedinger, E., 177
Seitz, F., 81, 129, 211

Simon, F., 238
Slater, J. C., 174
Smith, H. Grayson, 238
Smyth, C. P., 243
Snoek, J. L., 161
Steiner, L. E., 113, 150
Stockmayer, W. H., 203
Sykes, C., 249

T

Tolman, R. C., 9, 53, 186, 192
Troiano, A., 157

V

Van Vleck, J., 239

W

Weisskopf, V., 255
Wilhelm, J., 238
Wilkinson, H., 249
Williams, E. J., 247, 249

Z

Zener, C., 157, 159

SUBJECT INDEX

A

Absolute scale of temperature, 39, 63, 189, 238
Activity coefficient, 117, 150, 152, 163
Adiabatic process, 56, 58, 60, 62, 244
Adsorption, 169, 198n.
Alkali atoms, 89, 231
Allotropic modifications, 73, 103, 121, 123, 218
   as solvents, 154, 158
Alloys, 81, 130, 148, 217, 247
   of iron 157, 159
Alpha iron, 156, 161
Antisymmetric wave functions, 236, 237
Argon, 119, 174

B

Boltzmann's constant, 40, 182
Bose-Einstein statistics, 48, 52, 250, 253
Boyle's law, 91, 92, 120

C

Carbon, 130, 159, 161
Carbon dioxide, 198
Carbon monoxide molecule, 226, 233
Cementite, 160
Chemical constant, 230, 235
Chemical equilibrium, 126, 233, 235
Chemical potential, 108, 109, 150, 163
Chlorine, 95, 226, 233
Classical mechanics, 186
Clustering, 200, 203
CO molecule, 226, 233
Communal entropy, 109
Compressibility, 173, 209
Condensation, 73, 77, 101, 200, 203
Configuration space, 193, 194, 196
Cooling, magnetic, 238, 244
Coulomb forces, 166
Critical phenomena, 198, 200, 203

Crystals, 79, 118
   density of, 81, 103, **173**
   (*See also* Lattice)

D

Debye temperature, 212, 221
Degree of order, 81, 83, 145, 217, 249
Degrees of freedom, 190, 193, 207, 228
Density, of crystals, 81, 103, 173
   of states, 93, 213, 216, 219, 251
Diamond, 81, 212, 222
Diatomic molecules, 93, 164
   dissociation of, 111, 115, 123, 165, 185, 193, 246
   internal energy of, 94, 96, 226
   rotation, 93, 96, 224, 228, 236
   vibration, 93, 96, 227, 228
Deuterium, 222, 227, 232, 235
Deuteron, 237
Dielectric constant, 166, 243
Dielectric polarization, 245
Dipoles, 233, 238, 245
Disorder, 81, 83, 145, 217, 241, 243, 246, 249
Dissociation, molecular, 111, 115, 123, 165, 185, 193, 246
Dissociation energy, 115, 117, 126, 165, 194
Dulong and Petit's law, 206, 209

E

Einstein-Bose statistics, 48, 52, 250, 253
Elastic aftereffect, 161
Electron gas, degenerate, 250, 253
Electronic states, 89, 252
Electrostatic forces, 166
Ensemble, 181, 182, 192
Entropy, 105, 109, 168, 182, 212, 241
   of mixing, 110, 149, 223
Environments, method of, 134, 136, 145, 169

265

Equipartition, 190, 228
Evaporation, 73, 77, 101, 133
Exclusion principle, 48n., 250, 251
Expansion, thermal, 120, 172, 199, 209, 219
External work, 56, 61, 63, 90, 106, 189

F

Fermi-Dirac statistics, 49n., 249, 251
Field, external, 190, 238
Fluctuations, in density, 186
  in energy, 174, 213, 216
Free energy, 105, 108, 111, 129, 135, 149, 183, 190, 193, 207, 228, 242
Freedom, degrees of, 190, 193, 207, 228
Freezing point, 129
  depression of, 138, 142, 143, 153

G

Gamma iron, 156, 159, 161
Gas, diatomic, 93, 96, 164, 193
  monatomic, 45, 88, 90, 120, 187
  perfect, 90, 183, 186, 190

H

Halogens, 226, 231, 235
Harmonic oscillator, heat capacity of, 207
  partition function, 205
HBr, HCl, and HI molecules, 233, 235
HD molecule, 222, 227, 232, 235
Heat capacity, 91, 92, 208, 211, 215, 219, 227, 229, 236, 249
Heteronuclear and homonuclear molecules, 95, 164, 226, 233
Hydrogen, 222, 227, 229, 232, 235

I

Ice, 129, 141, 154, 162
Ideal solution, 149, 150
Imperfect gas, 177, 190, 193, 195, 197
Inertia, moment of, 202, 224, 232
Interstitial solution, 130, 132, 140, 157
Iron, body-centered, 156, 159
  face-centered, 156, 159
Iron carbon system, 161
Isothermal process, 56, 60, 101, 103, 166, 168, 247, 248

Isotopes, 90, 95, 226, 231
  mixture of, 111, 130, 222

K

Kelvin scale of temperature, 63, 64

L

Latent heat, 101, 229
Lattice, crystal, 81, 118
  imperfect, 79, 246
  vibrations of, 176, 205, 209, 211
Lead, metallic, 54, 212, 222
Liquid, 128, 130, 142, 146, 149, 180, 193, 198, 201
  freezing point, 129
  solutions, 129, 142, 153
Localized particles, 55, 70, 97, 99, 183
London forces, 195

M

Magnesium, 54, 119, 220, 221
Magnetic field, 238
  susceptibility, 239
Manganese, 157, 159
Melting point, 129, 138, 143, 153
Metallic alloys, 81, 148, 217, 247
Metals, 148, 232, 249, 251, 253
Miscibility, partial, 146, 148
Mixture, of gases, 109, 110, 149, 184
  of isotopes, 130, 222
Modification, allotropic, 73, 103, 121, 123, 218
  as solvent, 154, 158
Mole fraction, 110, 132, 142, 149
Molecular dissociation, 111, 115, 123, 165, 185, 193, 246
Molecular repulsion, 195, 197
Molecular rotation, 93, 96, 224, 228, 236
Molecular vibration, 93, 96, 227, 228
Moment of inertia, 202, 224, 232
Momentum, 187, 191, 193
Monatomic gas, 45, 88, 90, 120, 187
Multiple levels, 21, 39, 240
Multiplicity, 90, 120, 177, 180, 184, 213, 219, 222, 225, 232, 236
Multipliers, undetermined, 35, 37, 258

N

Neon, 119, 212, 228, 231
Nitrogen, 209, 228, 229, 232
Nuclear spin, 236, 237
Nucleus, atomic, 254, 255

O

One-for-one substitution, 130, 136, 150, 161
Order and disorder, 81, 83, 217, 241, 243, 246, 249
Orientation factor, 223, 232, 234
Orthodeuterium, 237
Orthohydrogen, 235
Oxygen, 228, 229, 233

P

Paradeuterium, 237
Parahydrogen, 235
Paramagnetism, 238, 245
Partially miscible substances, 146, 148
Partition function, 41, 53, 98, 135, 181, 183, 189, 193, 213, 216, 218, 220, 240
  diatomic gas, 93, 95
  monatomic gas, 88
  rotational, 225
  values, 54, 120, 222, 226
  vibrational, 205, 207, 210
Perfect gas, 90, 183, 186, 190
Phase space, 187, 189, 191, 192
Planck's constant, 88, 190, 224
Plutonium, 255
Polar molecules, 233, 245, 246
Polarization, 242
Polymerization, 203
Potassium chloride, 81, 212
Potential energy, 115, 119, 167, 190, 193, 195, 246
Pressure, 57, 62, 91, 103, 112, 230

Q

Quantization, 38, 57, 172, 176, 219
Quantum states, density of, 93, 213, 216, 219, 251

R

Raoult's law, 149
Repulsion, molecular, 196
Reversible process, 56, 60, 101
Rotation of molecule, 93, 96, 224, 228, 236

S

Samples, group of, 177, 181, 212, 217
Saturated solution, 129, 133
Saturated vapor, 76, 79, 87, 107, 117, 119, 122, 133, 184, 217, 219, 229, 232
  of solvent, 141, 149
Sodium, 54, 119, 174n., 222
Sodium chloride, 81, 212
Solid solutions, 128, 148, 219
Solubility, 129, 139, 148, 158, 169, 219
Solubility product, 152
Solutions, ideal, 149, 150
  interstitial, 130, 140, 157
  substitutional, 130, 136, 139, 162
Specific heat, 91, 92, 208, 211, 215, 219, 227, 229, 236, 249
Spin, 222, 236, 237, 252, 254
Steel, 157
Stirling's approximation, 257
Sublimation energy, 119, 120, 133, 195
Substitutional solutions, 130, 136, 139, 162
Sulfur, 73, 103, 218
Superlattice, 81, 247
Supersaturated vapor, 77
Surface, 55n., 118, 169
Susceptibility, 239, 242
Symmetric wave functions, 236, 237
Symmetry factor, 164, 226, 233

T

Temperature, 32, 37, 180, 181
  absolute, 39, 54, 63, 238
  transition (*see* Transition temperature)
  uniform, 177, 217
Thermal energy, 66, 69, 71, 83
Thermal expansion, 120, 172, 199, 209, 219
Transition temperature, 121, 123, 218
  depression of, 154, 156, 159
  raising of, 154, 158

Translational energy, 88, 90, 94, 96
    partition function, 120

U

Undetermined multipliers, 35, 37, 258
Unlocalized particles, 55, 70, 97, 99, 183
Unsaturated vapor, 77, 122, 197

V

Vacant lattice points, 79, 80, 246
Van der Waals equation, 195, 197, 199
Vapor, diatomic, 45, 88, 90, 94
    monatomic, 44, 64, 88, 117

Vapor, saturated, 76, 79, 87, 107, 117, 122, 133, 184, 197, 217, 219, 229, 232
    of solvent, 141, 149
Vapor pressure constants, 230, 231, 232
Vibration, lattice, 176, 205, 209, 211
    molecular, 93, 96, 227, 228

W

Wave functions, 38, 39, 57, 88, 186, 236
    antisymmetric, 236, 237
Work, external, 56, 61, 63, 90, 106, 189

Z

Zinc, 119, 159, 212, 220, 221